THE MOLINARI COLLECTION

Medals and Plaquettes

FROM THE

Molinari Collection at Bowdoin College

By

ANDREA S. NORRIS & INGRID WEBER

With an Introduction to the Medals Catalogue
by GRAHAM POLLARD

BRUNSWICK, MAINE

1976

This Catalogue was made possible by a matching grant from the Ford Foundation

All medals and plaquettes in the Catalogue are the gift of
Amanda Marchesa Molinari except for Number 25,
which was given in 1895 by
the Misses Harriet Sarah and Mary Sophia Walker

TYPOGRAPHIC COMPOSITION AND LETTERPRESS PRINTING BY THE ANTHOENSEN PRESS, PORTLAND, MAINE

OFFSET PRINTING BY THE MERIDEN GRAVURE COMPANY, MERIDEN, CONNECTICUT

BINDING BY CRAFTSMEN BOOKBINDERS SERVICE, PORTLAND, MAINE

DESIGN BY EDWARD BORN AND HARRY MILLIKEN

CONTENTS

FOREWORD

❧❧❧

IN 1811 James Bowdoin III gave 142 European master drawings to Bowdoin College. The collection includes the *View of Waltersburg* by Pieter Brueghel and works by Beccafumi, Zuccaro, Maratta, Moeyaert and Koninck and forms the oldest college art collection in America. In the ensuing years, important collections have been given by George Boyd, the Misses Walker, Edward Perry Warren, Susan Dwight Bliss, Sylvia Ross, William Tudor Gardiner, George Otis Hamlin, Samuel H. Kress, the Halfords, Walter Gutman and others. These collections encompass Ancient art, Oriental porcelain, European decorative arts and painting, and American painting, prints and drawings. In 1966 the distinguished Molinari collection of medals and plaquettes was added to Bowdoin's holdings.

Collections of important Renaissance and later European works of art are rare in college art museums. Great art of these periods is so costly that it is usually found only in large city museums. Works by Raphael, Da Vinci, Michelangelo are found in New York, Washington and Boston. The Molinari collection brings to Bowdoin works by their friends and companions, boasting works by Pisanello, Antico, Soldani, Dupré, Flötner, and many others. For the scholar and student the Molinari collection can reveal directly the historical currents and artistic developments in Europe 1450 to 1850.

This catalogue has been ten years in the making. During the decade three directors have played a part in its development. To me has fallen the task of final administration. I am pleased that the project has been completed in time for the rededication of the museum and inaugurate our new series of exhibition galleries.

With the help of the Ford Foundation, the Molinari collection catalogue takes its place on the shelf along side Kevin Herbert's *Ancient Art in Bowdoin College* and Marvin Sadik's *Colonial and Federal Portraits at Bowdoin College*. In the future, it is hoped that similar catalogues on the Bowdoin drawings, American art of the nineteenth and twentieth centuries, Oriental porcelain and the decorative arts will be added to that shelf of publications.

R. PETER MOOZ
Director

HISTORICAL NOTE

LATE in July of 1966, several large, heavy trunks were delivered to the Bowdoin College Museum of Art. They contained an extensive collection of medals, plaquettes and books about medals given to the College by Amanda Marchesa Molinari in memory of her husband, Cesare Molinari d'Incisa. In breadth and quality, the collection exceeded all expectations, and its arrival established the Bowdoin Museum as one of the major centers in the Americas for the study of this art form. Once assiduously collected for a variety of reasons ranging from the historical to the aesthetic, medals and plaquettes are nowadays less often the objects of attention, with major collections in private hands few and far between. That Bowdoin had become the recipient of one of the handsomest and possibly least-known of such private collections gave impetus to the desire to document properly the most significant and interesting pieces in the collection, a desire now fulfilled by the publication of this catalogue. My short account, begun *in medias res,* is an attempt to chronicle something of the history of the collection and to acknowledge the great debt owed to the people whose assistance made the gift and its subsequent documentation possible.

Fittingly enough, the story begins with the exquisite medallic collection of Mr. and Mrs. Mark Salton. In 1965, Marvin S. Sadik, then director of the museum, mounted a stunning exhibition of the Salton collection. It was accompanied by a catalogue—since become a standard reference—designed by Leonard Baskin. This catalogue came to the attention of the Marchesa Molinari and through the good offices of Bartlett Hayes, Jr. and Hanns Swarzenski the possibility of the collection coming to Bowdoin was first discussed. The Marchesa believed that the collection she and her husband had brought together during their lifetimes would be a useful study collection. Such a far-sighted and generous gesture is not without precedent at Bowdoin. Earlier in the century Edward Perry Warren presented the College with a choice collection of Greek vases and Graeco-Roman sculpture with the express purpose of giving students in the then isolated wilds of Maine firsthand acquaintance with the beauties of classical antiquity. Precedent or not, however, the Marchesa's gift was one of the most generous in recent years, not only because of the medallic objects themselves but also because the gift included a library containing practically all the important reference works—many exceedingly rare—on the subject from the seventeenth century to the fourth decade of this century.

The inventory, packing and shipping of the collection is a saga unto itself. Richard Wadleigh, former Bowdoin curator and friend of the Molinaris, gave advice and assistance. The burden of correspondence and arrangements was largely borne by the Marchesa's niece Anne Donnelly, and it was through her persistence that the collection was negotiated through the legal and bureaucratic hurdles entailed by the gift. That the collection came to Bowdoin whole and intact is a tribute to her efforts.

The inventory accompanying the gift was by necessity incomplete. As a first step toward proper documentation, a full-scale appraisal was undertaken by Michael Hall of New York, and as piece followed piece in examination, it soon became apparent that the collection contained a number of unexpected felicities as well as a full quota of fascinating, problematic pieces. Unfortunately, the Molinaris left no journal or record of the provenance of the works in the collection. A list of the dealers they visited and the many marked copies of auction catalogues included in the library show that they were familiar with most of the dealers and collections in Europe which existed in the early twentieth century, and that their tastes were eclectic and generally all-inclusive. As a result, certain areas not often represented in many collections appear here.

When I arrived at Bowdoin in 1967, I was fortunate to get Michael Hall's counsel concerning a possible editor for the proposed catalogue of the collection. I, too, was bedazzled by the collection and impressed with its possibilities. A matching grant from the Ford Foundation made it possible to implement our plans and begin the photographic documentation of the collection. Graham Pollard, Keeper of Coins and Medals at the Fitz-william Museum, Cambridge, graciously agreed to edit the proposed catalogue, and a visit to the collection was arranged.

I am not sure how Graham recalls his intense work on the medals while he was at Bowdoin, but I felt like a jailer, sealing him in with the medals every morning and only letting him out for a breath of fresh air and an occasional meal. It was also possible to invite Dr. Ulrich Middeldorf, director emeritus of the Kunsthistorisches Institut in Florence, to view the medals and consult with Mr. Pollard. Dr. Middeldorf's genuine interest and warm encouragement were deeply appreciated. As a result of many discussions, it was decided to divide the research. Dr. Ingrid Weber of the Staatlich Münzsammlung was asked to prepare the plaquette portion of the catalogue. It was again our good fortune that she agreed to do so, and a visit to Bowdoin ensued to permit firsthand evaluation and selection of the plaquettes. I stress these visits because in making judgments of medals and plaquettes, the state and condition of the piece are of critical importance and very difficult to gauge from photographs alone.

Because of Mr. Pollard's other commitments and the problems of doing research in Cambridge, Munich, and Brunswick, we decided to prepare the medal entries at Bowdoin. We were able to obtain the services of Andrea S. Norris who then and since has worked intensely to shape and refine the entries for the selected medals. David P. Becker coordinated the catalogue production and research over a long haul, and even after leaving Bowdoin for the Houghton Library at Harvard has continued to shepherd the manuscript through all the stages and permutations of its development. His personal commitment and passion for accuracy gave continuity and momentum to the perforce episodic nature of the research and photography. I would also like to thank Frederick den Broeder for his assistance in preparing a number of the initial entries for the Papal medals. To Peter Mooz, to whom the baton was passed and under whose aegis, the catalogue and exhibition has come together, I give my congratulations.

RICHARD VINCENT WEST

ACKNOWLEDGMENTS

THE administration and supervision of this large project has been carried on during the tenures of three directors of the Bowdoin College Museum of Art. The interest of Marvin S. Sadik played a major part in securing the gift of the collection. Richard V. West began the work of publishing the catalogue while he was director. Besides arranging for the initial Ford Foundation grant and selecting the authors, he did much of the preliminary cataloguing. He also translated the introduction to the plaquette section and many of the entries. Since leaving Bowdoin, he has given many useful suggestions, and his continued interest and cooperation in the work of publication has been very helpful. The administrative experience of R. Peter Mooz, the present director, has been instrumental in bringing the catalogue through the final stages of organization and production.

We are enormously indebted to Graham Pollard of the Fitzwilliam Museum, Cambridge, for his initial interest in the collection, his visit to Bowdoin in 1971, the selection of items to be published, numerous helpful suggestions along the way, the stimulating introduction to the medals, and finally his careful reading of and additions to the final medals manuscript. Mr. Pollard joins us in acknowledging the assistance of Dr. Ulrich Middeldorf, who visited the collection and supplied many ideas, attributions, and references during the course of the project.

We thank Frederick den Broeder for his research on the ecclesiastical medals. Stephen A. Cerf of the Bowdoin College Department of German translated the entries for plaquette numbers 362, 371, 373, 374, 378–384, 387, 390, 394–396, 398, 400, 401, 404, 405, 410, 411, 412B–412E, 414, 416, 421, 423, and 426. Ruth Magurn of the Fogg Art Museum translated the plaquette artists' biographies and entry numbers 418, 420, 422, and 425. The resources and personnel of the American Numismatic Society Library in New York were of inestimable value in researching the medal entries. We also wish to acknowledge the valuable iconographical help of Dr. Friedrich Kobler of Munich.

The task of producing a catalogue of a major collection of medals and plaquettes is monumental, involving the participation of a large number of people, both within and outside of the museum. For this catalogue, the efforts of these people have been coordinated admirably by David P. Becker, formerly the registrar of the Bowdoin Museum and now on the staff of the Houghton Library at Harvard. Aside from maintaining contact among the authors, Mr. Becker worked to create consistency among the various sections of the catalogue, directed a major portion of the photography, attended to the problems of conservation and storage, and successfully tackled research and editorial problems.

The photography for the illustrations was done by Abelardo Morell, Jr., William Pooley, and Michael W. Mahan, with valuable advice from John McKee of the Bowdoin College Department of Art. Writer-Photographer David B. Price of the College's Office of News Services cheerfully provided some last-minute assistance. Preliminary cataloguing was greatly assisted by Lynn Yanok and Brenda Pelletier of the museum staff. Diana Bourne, also on the staff at the time, assisted in the final stages of preparing the medals manuscript and carried out much work in preparing the bibliography. Linda Horvitz did much valuable research, especially for the artists' biographies, and carefully attended to many details related to the medals catalogue.

Finally, the college editor, Edward Born, and his assistant Arnette J. Nelson oversaw and accomplished the final design and production. To them and the manufacturers of the catalogue, The Anthoensen Press, Meriden Gravure Company, and Craftsmen Bookbinders Service, go our thanks.

A. S. N.
I. W.

CATALOGUE OF THE

EXHIBITION OF MEDALS

INTRODUCTION

IN North America, there are only three sizable public collections of medals, the Kress at the National Gallery of Art in Washington, D. C., the Morgenroth at the University Art Gallery in Santa Barbara, California, and the Molinari at the Bowdoin College Museum of Art. The Molinari collection offers a conspectus of the European medal from the Italian Renaissance to the end of the nineteenth century, and its publication should admirably supplement the resources of the Kress and Morgenroth collections (both fully published) because Molinari contains substantial groups of Italian and French medals dating after 1600—classes of medals almost unrepresented in the other two catalogues. Full publication of the three American collections is most laudable and in marked contrast with practice in Europe, where publication has been only fragmentary and no major collection has ever been fully published.

The portion of the Molinari collection catalogued here contains some 230 Italian, 80 French, and 40 other medals. All told, the collection contains more than 1,500 medals and plaquettes. Of the Italian materials, one-third are Renaissance and two-thirds are dated after 1600. There are only twenty-four fifteenth century Italian medals, but they represent the full range of types for that series. There are Pisanello and Matteo de Pasti pieces which establish the form and content of the European medal to the present day. There are humanist-antiquarian medals by Antico and Camelio, papal humanist medals in the work of Caradosso, and the portrait pieces of Pope Paul II. The development of the physiognomic likeness can be seen from the work of Enzola to culminate in the medals of Niccolò Fiorentino.

The sixteenth century Italian medals are representative of the artists at the principal schools in Florence, Rome and Milan. At Florence, the self-portrait of the artist and his wife by Sangallo continues the sculptural realism of Niccolò Fiorentino, but with Sangallo the cast medal dies and the struck medal appears as an instrument of dynastic propaganda. There are characteristic works by Domenico di Polo, Domenico Poggini and Mazzafirri for the Florentine court, and by Cesati, Bon-

zagni and Frangi for the Papal Court. The antiquarian taste of the century is represented by the highly skilled medals of Cavino: two personal portraits in antique style and a reproduction of an ancient Roman coin. The anonymous medal of Antinous is of the same class. A similar, but coarser historicism appears in the imaginary portraits of popes in the series by Paladino. The more personal portrait medal is superbly represented by the Sansovino medal and the exquisite Emilian medal by Ruspagiari. The imperial court at Milan, in the medals by Leone Leoni, set a pattern for sophistication in semiofficial medals like da Trezzo's portrait of Ippolita Gonzaga, with a typical *impresa* as reverse type. In Florence Galeotti was an original artist in the same tradition. The absence of one major medalist, Pastorino da Siena, should be noted.

For the seventeenth and eighteenth century Italian medal, the collection represents the polarization of medal making at the courts of Florence and Rome. Florence enjoyed a revival of the practice of casting medals in a school led by Soldani. The collection has nine of his medals and a representative group of the work of his rivals and followers. The taste for these medals is a recent enthusiasm which began with a pioneer publication by Kalus Lankheit and was reinforced by an exhibition at Detroit and Florence. It is pleasing to find such a group of the medals in a collection formed before the material was fashionable. In Rome the cast medal also enjoyed a revival, and the collection has a fine series of the work of Cormano, Lucenti and members of the two dynasties that dominated Roman medal making, the Travani and Hamerani. The papal medals connected with the work of Bernini (nos. 96 and 97) are of particular interest. The struck medal was produced continuously at the papal court from the fifteenth century as propaganda material, and there are typical works by Moro, Sanquirico and Morone-Mola in the collection. The struck medal at other Italian centers is represented by a group of Bolognese and Neapolitan pieces. The most pleasing is the work of the Neapolitan Gennaro, which portrays the celebrated Florentine scholar Magliabecchi.

3

The nineteenth century is represented by characteristic work by Torinese, Milanese and Roman medalists. Even in a European context, the work of Mercandetti, Girometti, Lavy and Santarelli is a worthy group in the neoclassical manner of the day. The work of Italian engravers was frequently founded on training in gem engraving and in sculpture. These medalists are worthy of further study.

The French medals form the other major portion of the Molinari collection and are equally representative of the history of the medal in France. There are a few typical sixteenth century pieces, struck medals by Bechot and Delaune, and there are four medals by the greatest of all French Renaissance medalists, Guillaume Dupré. The most typical medal of the seventeenth century in France was the formal propaganda piece in the *Histoire Métallique* of Louis XIV by artists such as Bernard and Mauger. In the eighteenth century this tradition of formal medals of the events of the reign produced, in the work of such court medalists as Duvivier, medals of uncommon elegance and refinement. The state has patronized the medal through the work of the Paris Mint from the late sixteenth century until the present. Artists like Gatteaux, Tiolier, Droz and Andrieu typify the work of the late eighteenth century and the Napoleonic era. Rococo or neoclassical refinement gave way to a dramatic form in the work of David d'Angers, who revived the casting of medals in which the effigy has more romantic vigor than verisimilitude. Toward the end of the century the finest contemporary European school of medalists developed, working in both cast and struck forms and having Ponscarme as master. The Molinari collection has a fine group of these works by Roty, Chaplain, Dupré and Yencesse. The school still awaits an adequate study and reassessment.

The medals other than Italian and French total only about forty and are miscellaneous in character. They are from the Netherlands, England, Switzerland, Germany, Scandinavia and Spain. The Netherlands pieces include the remarkable medal on the murder of the brothers De Witt. The other national groups are from the seventeenth and eighteenth century. In terms of the history of the medal, they illustrate the dominance of Paris and French absolutism as a European model. Further, they point to the international character of medal making until the end of the eighteenth century.

The court of Louis XIV was the principal center of the most lavish, if not the most interesting, European medal making. The King was a serious collector of numismatic materials. A series of medals on the history of the reign, the *Histoire Métallique,* was produced, and a catalogue was published. The work is grandiloquent in conception and pedestrian in execution, but the type was widely imitated, as for instance in Russia. Other courts imitated the *Cabinet des Médailles* at Versailles, and some of these collections have also survived, as at Vienna.

Medals were collected well beyond court circles. A remarkable series commemorating events between 1679 and 1742 was issued by Kleinert and Lauffer, and a catalogue was published. The work was based in Nuremberg, with several German medalists contributing to it, and the events recorded cover the spectrum of European history without national prejudice. Hautsch, Werner and Vestner worked for the series.

The medal was regarded by the literate as an adjunct to historical study. Collections contained Greek and Roman coins as an aid to ancient history and medals as an aid to modern history. The collector was interested in events and personalities, and the activity of medal making made the medalists themselves pan-European figures until the end of the eighteenth century. Hedlinger was the most celebrated medalist of his day, long employed in Sweden and much sought after by other courts. The papal court attracted many foreign medalists. This is reflected in the Molinari collection by the work of St. Urbain of Nancy, which has been classed as Italian, and of J. A. Dassier, classed as Swiss and whose medals portray Savoyard, Austrian and English sitters. The celebrated medal of Voltaire (no. 347) was prepared in Switzerland by a German medalist, G. C. Waechter, and struck in Munich. Waechter and his brother also worked in Russia.

The study of the medal as a source for portraiture, as a minor historical document and as a work of art in its own right retains interest. For the student who wishes to begin this study, the only general bibliography is P. Grierson, *Bibliographie Numismatique,* Brussels, 1966, pp. 159–169. The only works dealing in general terms with the medal are J. Babelon, *La médaille et les médail-*

leurs, Paris, 1927; M. Bernhart, *Medaillen und Plaketten,* (2nd edition) Berlin, 1920, (3rd edition) ed. T. Kroha, Brunswick, 1966 (the bibliographical references in the second edition are more useful); G. F. Hill, *Medals of the Renaissance,* Oxford, 1920; G. F. Hill, *Guide to the Exhibition of Medals of the Renaissance in the British Museum,* London, 1923; G. F. Hill, "The Medal: Its Place in Art," *Proceedings of the British Academy,* vol. 27 (1941), pp. 225–245.

The principal periodicals concerned with medals are *Archiv für Medaillen- und Plakettenkunde,* 5 vols., 1913–1914, 1920–1926; *Gazette numismatique française,* 1897–1914; and *Medaglia,* Milan, 1971 ff. The periodical *Numismatic Literature,* published by the American Numismatic Society, New York, has a section which reports publications on historical medals. It may be supplemented by using the appropriate portions of *Art Index, Répertoire d'Art et d'Archeologie,* and the annual bibliographical fascicule of *Zeitschrift für Kunstgeschichte.* The problem of finding illustrations of Italian sixteenth century medals is being solved by the Warburg Institute, London, which is compiling a photographic survey of that class of medal.

May one hope that the publication of the Molinari collection will be a real stimulus to the serious study and collecting of the medal in North America.

Graham Pollard

BIBLIOGRAPHY

Arm.	Alfred Armand, *Les Médailleurs Italiens,* three vols., Paris 1883–87.
Assandria	G. Assandria, "Una famiglia torinese d' artisti: I. Lavy," *Atti della Società Piemontese di Archeologia e Belle Arti* 8 (1917), pp. 209–74.
Bartolotti	E. Bartolotti, *La Medaglia Annuale dei Romani Pontifici da Paolo V a Paolo VI,* Rome 1967.
Beaupré	M. Beaupré, "Catalogue descriptif des Ouvrages de Ferdinand de Saint-Urbain et de Claude-Augustin de Saint-Urbain," *Societé d' Archeologie lorraine. Memoires* (1867), pp. 1–98.
Bernhart	M. Bernhart, "Nachträge zu Armand," *Archiv für Medaillen-und Plakettenkunde* 5 (1925–26), pp. 69–90.
Bertolotti	Bertolotti, *Artisti subalpini in Roma nei Secoli XV, XVI, e XVII,* Mantua 1884.
Bianchi	Nicomede Bianchi, *Le medaglie del Terzo Risorgimento Italiano: 1748–1848,* Bologna 1881.
Bonnani	F. Bonnani, *Numismata Pontificum Romanorum,* Rome 1699.
Bonnani-*Tempio Vaticano*	Bonnani, Philippo, *Numismata Summorum Pontificum Templi Vaticani Fabricam Indicantia,* Romae, 1696 & iterum Anno Magni Jubilaei, 1700.
Bramsen	L. Bramsen, *Les médailles de Napoléon le Grand, Consulat et Empire,* 3 vols., Copenhagen 1904–07.
Brescia	P. Rizzini, *Illustrazione dei civici musei di Brescia: Parte II Medaglie,* 2 parts, Brescia 1892, 1893.
Brettauer	E. Holzmair, *Katalog der Sammlung Dr. Josef Brettauer, Medicina in Nummis,* Vienna 1937.
Bulgari	C. G. Bulgari, *Argentieri, gemmari e orafi d'Italia, Parte Prima-Roma,* 2 vols., Rome 1958–59.
Calabi & Cornaggia	A. Calabi & G. Cornaggia, *Matteo de' Pasti,* 1926.
Charpentier	Francois Charpentier, *Médailles sur les Principaux Événements du Regne Entier de Louis Le Grande avec des Explications Historiques,* Paris 1723.
G. Chesneau	G. Chesneau and C. Metzger, *Les oeuvres de David d'Angers,* Angers (Musée des Beaux-Arts), 1934.
Cicogna	Emmanuele Cicogna, *Biografie de Dogi di Venezia,* Venice 1847.
Corpus	G. F. Hill, *A Corpus of the Italian Medals of the Renaissance before Cellini,* 2 vols., London 1930.
Crespellani	A. Crespellani, *Medaglie Estensi ed Austro-Estensi,* Modena 1893.
d'Angers	*Les Médaillons de David d'Angers réunis et publiés par son fils,* Paris 1867.
DBdI	*Dizionario Biografico degli Italiani,* vol. 1–, 1960–.
De Bildt	Le Baron De Bildt, *Les Médailles Romaines de Christine de Suède,* Rome 1908.
De Caro Balbi	S. De Caro Balbi, "Gian Lorenzo Bernini e la medaglia barocca romana," *Medaglia,* anno 4, numero 7 (1974), pp. 6–26.
De Haye	P. De Haye, *Les Graveurs d'Acier et la Médaille de l'Antiquité a nos Jours,* Paris, Musée de la Monnaie, 1971.
Detroit	Detroit Institute of Art, *The Twilight of the Medici: Late Baroque Art in Florence, 1670–1743,* 1974.
Durand	A. Durand, *Médailles et jetons des Numismates,* Geneva 1865.

Dworschak	Fritz Dworschak, "Der Medailleur Gianlorenzo Bernini," *Jahrbuch der Preussischen Kunstsammlungen*, 55 (1934), pp. 27–41.
Fabriczy	C. Fabriczy, *Italian Medals*, London 1904.
Forrer	L. Forrer, *A Biographical Dictionary of Medallists*, 8 vols., London 1904–30.
Foville	Jean de Foville, "Cristoforo Geremia," *Revue de l'Art ancien et Modern*, vol. 30 (1911).
Freeman	S. E. Freeman, *Medals relating to medicine and allied sciences in the numismatic collections of Johns Hopkins University*, Baltimore 1964.
Gruyer	G. Gruyer, *L'art Ferrarais à l'Epoque des Princes d'Este*, Paris 1897.
Habich	G. Habich, *Die Medaillen der Italienischen Renaissance*, Berlin 1924.
Heiss	Aloiss Heiss, *Les Médailleurs de la Renaissance*, 9 vols., Paris 1881–92.
Heraeus	C. G. Heraeus, *Bildnisse der regierenden Fürsten und berühmter Männer*, Vienna 1828.
Hill-*Artists*	G. F. Hill, *Portrait Medals of Italian Artists of the Renaissance*, London 1912.
Hill-*Christ*	G. F. Hill, *Medallic Portraits of Christ*, Oxford 1920.
Hill-*Historical*	G. F. Hill, *A Guide to the Exhibition of Historical Medals in the British Museum*, London 1924.
Hill, *Med. Ren.*	G. F. Hill, *Medals of the Renaissance*, Oxford 1920.
Hill, N. I. A.	G. F. Hill, "Not in Armand," *Archiv für Medaillen—und Plakettenkunde* 2 (1920–21), pp. 10–28; 45–54.
Hill-Notes	G. F. Hill, "Notes on Italian Medals XX," *Burlington Magazine* 27 (1915), p. 241, pl. IIR.
Hill-Paul II	G. F. Hill, "The Medals of Paul II," *Numismatic Chronicle* 10 (1910), pp. 340–69.
Houston	J. Fischer, *Sculpture in Miniature: The Andrew S. Ciechanowiecki Collection of Gilt and Gold Medals and Plaquettes*, The Museum of Fine Arts, Houston, Texas, 1970.
Jacquiot	J. Jacquiot, *La Médaille au Temps de Louis XIV*, Paris, Musée de la Monnaie, 1970.
Jacquiot *Médailles*	J. Jacquiot, *Médailles et jetons de Louis XIV d'après le manuscrit de Londres*, one vol. in four, Paris 1968 (1970).
Kress	G. F. Hill and Graham Pollard, *Renaissance Medals from the Samuel H. Kress Collection at the National Gallery of Art*, London 1967.
Lankheit	K. Lankheit, *Florentinische Barock Plastik*, Munich 1962.
Lanna	O. v. Falke (sale catalogue), *Sammlung des Freiherrn Adalbert von Lanna*, Berlin, Lepke 1909–11.
Lawrence	Richard Hoe Lawrence, *Medals by Giovanni Cavino, The "Paduan,"* New York 1883.
Lepage	H. Lepage, "Ferdinand de Saint Urbain," *Société d'Archeologie lorraine—Memoirs*, Nancy 1866.
Löbbecke	Arthur Löbbecke Collection, *Sale Catalogues*, Munich 1908; Halle 1925.
Louis XIV	*Médailles sur les principaux évenements du Règne de Louis le Grand avec des explications historiques*, Paris 1702.
Louis XV	N. Godonnesche, *Médailles du Regne de Louis XV*, n.p., n.d., Paris 1736(?).
Madrid	Francisco Alvarez-Ossorio, *Catálogo de las medallas de los siglos xv y xvi conservadas en el Museo Arqueológico Nacional*, Madrid 1950.
Magnaguti	Conte Alessandro Magnaguti, *Ex Nummis Historia IX, Le Medaglie dei Gonzaga*, Rome 1965.

Magnaguti-*Mant*	Conte Alessandro Magnaguti, *Le Medaglie Mantovane*, Mantova 1921.
Martinori	E. Martinori, *Annali della Zecca di Roma*, 24 fasc., Rome 1917–22.
Mazerolle	F. Mazerolle, *Les Médailleurs Français du 15ème au millieu de 17ème siecle*, 2 vols., Paris 1902–04.
Mazerolle-*Varin*	F. Mazerolle, *Jean Varin*, Paris 1932.
Mazio	F. Mazio, *Serie de' Conj di Medaglie Pontificie da Martino V a Pio VII*, Rome 1824.
Mazio (1885)	Mazio, *Supplemento al Catalogo della Serie dei Coni di Medaglie Pontificie di Martino V a Pio VII che comprende i Pontificati di Leone XII a Pio IX*, Roma 1885.
Med. Ill.	E. Hawkins (ed. A. W. Franks and H. A. Greuber), *Medallic Illustrations of the History of Great Britain and Ireland to the Death of George II*, London, British Museum, 1885; Plates, 19 fascicules, 1904–11.
MM.	P. A. Gaetani, *Museum Mazzuchellianum seu Numismata Virorum Doctrina Praestantium*, 2 vols., Venice 1761–63.
Médailles Françaises	*Médailles Françaises dont les coins sont conservés au Musée Monetaire, Paris*, Paris 1892.
Menestrier	C. F. Menestrier, *Histoire du Roy Louis le Grand par les Médailles, etc.*, Paris 1691.
Michel	André Michel, *Histoire de l'Art*, 8 vols., Paris 1905–29.
Migeon	G. Migeon, *Catalogue des Bronzes et Cuivres du Moyen Age, de la Renaissance et des Temps Modernes*, Paris 1904.
Molinier	E. Molinier, *Les Plaquettes: Catalogue Raisonné*, 2 vols., Paris 1886.
Morgenroth	Ulrich Middeldorf and Oswald Goetz, *Medals and Plaquettes from the Sigmund Morgenroth Collection*, Chicago 1944.
Naples	A. De Rinaldis, *Medaglie dei Secoli XV e XVI nel Museo Nazionale di Napoli*, Napoli 1913.
Nocq	H. Nocq, *Les Duvivier*, Paris 1911.
Patrigiani	A. Patrigiani, *Le Medaglie Pontifice da Clemente XII a Pio VI*, Bologna 1939.
Patrigiani-*Pio VII*	A. Patrigiani, *Le Medaglie di Pio VII (1800–23)*, Pescara 1930.
Pollard, *Udine*	G. Pollard, "La medaglia con ritratto di epoca barocca in Italia," *La Medaglia d'Arte. Atti del primo convegno internazionale di studio, Udine 1970*, Udine 1973, pp. 139–61.
Pyke	E. J. Pyke, *A Biographical Dictionary of Wax Modellers*, Oxford 1973.
Rasmusson	N. L. Rasmusson, "Medaillen auf Christina," *Analecta Reginensia. Queen Christina of Sweden, Documents and Studies*, ed. M. v. Platen, 1, Stockholm 1966, pp. 296–321.
Rinaldi	Alfio Rinaldi, *Catalogo delle Medaglie Papali Annuali da Pio VII a Paolo VI*, Verona 1967.
Robert	P. Charles Robert, *Événements Militaires accomplis sous le règne de Henri II de 1551 a 1553 et leurs médailles commemoratives*, Paris 1876.
Rondot	Natalis Rondot, *Les Médailleurs et les Graveurs de Monnaies*, Paris 1904.
Rosati	F. Panvini-Rosati, *Medaglie e Placchette italiane dal Rinascimento al XVIII secolo*, Rome 1968.
Salton	*The Salton Collection, Renaissance and Baroque Medals and Plaquettes* (second edition), Bowdoin College Museum of Art, Brunswick, Maine, 1969.
Siciliano	Tommaso Siciliano, *Memorie Metalliche delle Due Sicilie, 1600–1735*, Naples 1957.
Supino	I. B. Supino, *Il Medagliere Mediceo nel R. Museo Nazionale di Firenze*, Florence 1899.

Tervarent   Guy de Tervarent, *Attributs et Symboles dans l'Art Profane, 1450–1600*, Geneva 1958. *Supplément et index*, Geneva 1964.

Thieme-Becker   U. Thieme, F. Becker, F. C. Wills, H. Vollmer (editors), *Allgemeines Lexikon der bildenden Künstler*, 37 vols., Leipzig 1907–50.

Trésor   *Trésor de Numismatique et de Glyptique*, ed. P. Delaroche, H. Dupont and C. Lenormant, Paris. *Médailles Coulées et Ciselées en Italie au XVe et XVIe Siècles*, Part 1, 1834; Part 2, 1836; *Choix Historique des Médailles des Papes*, 1839. *Médailles Français depuis la Règne de Charles VII à celui de Louis XVI*, Part 1, 1834; Part 2, 1836; Part 3, 1837; *Médailles de la Revolution Française*, 1836.

van Loon   G. van Loon, *Histoire métallique des XVII Provinces des Pays Bas depuis l'Abdication de Charle-Quint jusqu'a la Paix de Bade en MDCCXVI*, 5 vols., The Hague 1732–37.

Van Mieris   Van Mieris, *Histori de Nederlandsche Vorsten*, 3 vols., The Hague 1732–35.

Venuti   R. Venuti, *Numismata Romanorum Pontificum praestantiora a Martino V ad Benedictum XIV*, Romae 1744.

Vives   A. Vives, *Medallas de la casa de Borbon, de D.Amadeo I, del Gobierno provisional y de la Republica española*, Madrid 1916.

Weiss   Roberto Weiss, *Un Umanista Veneziano, Papa Paolo II*, Civiltà Veneziana, Saggi 4, Venezia—Roma: Istituto per la Collaborazione Culturale, 1957.

Zanetti   G. A. Zanetti, *Nuova Raccolta delle Monete e Zecche d'Italia*, 5 vols., Bologna 1775–79.

CATALOGUE

ITALY
To the Sixteenth Century

PISANELLO
(1395–1455)

Antonio di Puccio Pisano, considered the founder of the modern medal, was born in Pisa and trained in Verona. He worked in most of the major courts of Italy and had become famous as a painter of frescoes, portraits and animals by the time he cast his first medal, that of John Palaeologus, in 1438.

See *Corpus*, pp. 6–13; Hill, "On some dates in the career of Pisanello," *Numismatic Chronicle* (1931), pp. 181–96; Hill, "A lost medal by Pisanello," *Pantheon* 8 (1931), pp. 487–88; Hill in Thieme-Becker 27, pp. 92–93; M. Salmi, "Appunti su Pisanello medaglista," *Annali dell'Istituto Italiano di Numismatica* 4 (1957), pp. 13–23; B. Degenhart, *DBdI* 3 (1961), pp. 571–74; idem "Pisanello," *Encyclopedia of World Art* 11 (1966), cols. 369–75. Monographs on the artist are by Hill, London 1905; B. Degenhart, Turin 1945; E. Sindona, Milan 1961; G. Paccagnini, London/New York 1973; and G. Paccagnini, *Pisanello alla corte dei Gonzaga*, Venice 1972. The monograph on the drawings by Pisanello is M. Fossi Todorow, *I disegni del Pisanello e della sua cerchia*, Florence 1966. G. F. Hill, *Drawings by Pisanello*, Paris/Brussels 1929 (reissued New York 1965), contains seventy-one drawings of which only thirty-five are accepted by Fossi Todorow.

1 JOHN VIII PALAEOLOGUS, Emperor of Constantinople, 1425–48

Obv. Bust to right, wearing hat with tall crown and upturned brim. Around, I ΩΑΝΝΗC · ΒΑCΙΛΕVC · ΚΑΙ · ΑVΤΟ · ΚΡΑ[ΤWΡ] ΡWΜΑΙWΝ · Ο · ΠΑΛΑΙΟΛΟΓΟC +, John, King and Emperor of the Romans, Palaeologus

Without reverse

Lead, 105 mm.

1966.103

Made at Ferrara, between 29 February 1438 and 10 January 1439, at the Council of the Two Churches.

Besides those noted in *Kress,* other lead specimens are T. W. Greene sale, 31 October 1932, Sotheby, no. 1; Coll. Michael Hall, Esq., New York (2 specimens). The Molinari Collection also contains a bronze late cast of this medal, with reverse (1966.106.24).

Bibl.: Corpus, no. 19; Arm. 1, p. 7,20; Rosati, no. 3; *Kress,* no. 1; *Morgenroth,* nos. 1, 2; Habich, pl. 1,1; Supino, no. 14; Brescia 1, p. 3, no. 16; *Trésor Ital.* 1, pl. 5,1; Fabriczy, p. 31 (dated 1438); R. Weiss, *Pisanello's Medallion of the Emperor John VIII Palaeologus,* London, British Museum, 1966; J. A. Fasanelli, "Some Notes on Pisanello and the Council of Florence," *Master Drawings* 3 (1965), pp. 36–47 (suggesting that the medal was made at Florence between 6 July and 26 August 1439); M. Fossi Todorow, *I Disegni del Pisanello e della sua Cerchia,* Florence, 1966, nos. 57r, 58r, 33 (drawings by Pisanello relating to the reverse of this medal); J. Babélon, "Un thème iconographique dans la peinture de la Renaissance. L'empereur Jean Paléologue et Ponce Pilate," in *Actes du XIIe congrès international d'histoire de l'art,* Brussels, 20–29 September 1930, pp. 544–52.

FRANCESCO LAURANA
(1420/5–ca. 1502)

From Dalmatia, Laurana is first noted at work on the Triumphal Arch at Naples in 1458. He was in France from about 1460–66 and again from 1477 to his death. From 1466–76 he was in Sicily and Naples. Laurana was primarily a marble sculptor; the medals attributed to him appear to date from his first sojourn in France.

See Forrer 3, pp. 339–43; *Corpus,* pp. 16–18; *Kress,* p. 11; W. Rolfs, *Francesco Laurana,* 1907.

2 JEAN D'ANJOU (1427–70), Duke of Calabria and Lorraine 1464

Obv. Bust to right, wearing tall cap. Around, ΙOHANES DVX CALABER ET LOTHORINGVS · SICVLI · REGIS PRIMOGENITVS

Rev. Figure of Saint Michael atop a circular temple. In field, · M · CCCC · LXIIII · ; around, · MARTE FEROX · RECTICVLTOR · GALLVSQ · REGALIS

Bronze, 86 mm.

1966.106.23

The medal should have Laurana's signature below the reverse design. Heiss says the medal was made when Jean, as a result of the negotiations of René with Louis XI and Pope Pius II, awaited auxiliaries at Ischia. Rolfs says it is more likely that the King had the medal made, and Laurana modeled it, when Jean returned from Ischia in 1464.

Bibl.: Corpus, no. 61; Arm. 1, p. 42,6; 3, p. 7a; *Kress,* no. 26 (also unsigned); Habich, pl. 12,3; Fabriczy, p. 41 (identifies reverse as Temple of Vesta at Tivoli); *Trésor Ital.* 1, pl. 17,3; W. Rolfs, *Francesco Laurana,* 1907, p. 251, pl. 23,2; Heiss, *Francesco Laurana,* 1882, p. 25.

JACOPO LIXIGNOLO
(active ca. 1460)

All that is known of this artist is his signature on two medals dated 1460, that of Borso d'Este below and one of Beata Maria Anna of Siena.

See Forrer 3, p. 450; *Corpus,* p. 26; *Kress,* p. 13.

3 BORSO D'ESTE (1413–71), Duke of Modena and Reggio 1460

Obv. Bust to right, wearing cap with fluted crown and rich dress. Around, BORSIVS · DVX · MVTINE · ET · REGII · MARCHIO · ESTENSIS · RODIGII ··· COMES · ET C ·

Rev. Unicorn in mountainous landscape, dipping horn into stream, sun above. Around, OPVS IACOBIS LIXIGNOLO MCCCCLX

Lead, 81 mm. Hole at top

1966.107.5

According to legend, the unicorn purified streams by dipping its horn in the water.

Bibl.: Corpus, no. 94; Arm. 1, p. 33; *Kress,* no. 35; Brescia 1, p. 8, no. 59; *Trésor Ital.* 2, pl. 55,2; Tervarent, cols. 235–36 (Unicorn as purifier), col. 240, ix (Unicorn as device of Borso); Heraeus, pl. 52,5; Gruyer 1, p. 608; Heiss, *Niccolo etc.,* p. 32, pl. 4,1.

MATTEO DE' PASTI
(active 1441–1467/8)

Born in Verona, Matteo is first recorded in Venice in 1441. After working in Verona and Ferrara he moved to Rimini in 1446 where he worked for Sigismondo

Malatesta on the architecture and sculpture of Alberti's Tempio Malatestiano and on a series of medals of Sigismondo and Isotta degli Atti. Besides being a medalist, Matteo had a reputation as an architect, sculptor, painter and illuminator.

See Forrer 4, pp. 402–08; *Corpus,* pp. 37–43; Thieme-Becker 26, pp. 287–88; *Kress,* pp. 15–17; P. Pasini, "Note su Matteo de'Pasti e la medaglistica maltestiana," *La Medaglia d'Arte. Atti del primo convegno internazionale di studio, Udine 1970,* Udine 1973, pp. 41–75 (an important account of the excavated specimens of the medals).

4 SIGISMONDO PANDOLFO MALATESTA (1417–68), Lord of Rimini and Fano, inherited Rimini, 1432 1446

Obv. Bust to left. Around, SIGISMONDVS · P · D · MALATESTIS · S · R · ECL · C · GENERALIS ·

Rev. Casque with coronet on a tilting shield with monogram SI · . Elephant-head crest and mantling. Below, · M CCCC XLVI ·

Bronze, old aftercast, 40 mm.

1966.104.2

Calabi and Cornaggia say the SI emblem stands for *Sigismundus Imperator,* but it is generally thought to be the initials of Sigismondo and Isotta. The initials are used extensively in the Tempio Malatestiano.

Bibl.: Corpus, no. 166; Arm. 1, p. 21,16; Rosati, no. 25; Calabi and Cornaggia, no. 6bis, p. 31; Naples, p. 15; Brescia 1, p. 5, no. 39; *Trésor Ital.* 2, pl. 3,2; de Jonghe sale catalog, Schulman, 24 November 1936, no. 11.

5 SIGISMONDO PANDOLFO MALATESTA 1446

Obv. Bust to left. Around, SIGISMONDVS · PANDVLFVS · DE · MALATESTIS · S · RO · ECLESIE · CAPITANEVS · G

Rev. The Castle at Rimini. Around, CASTELLVM · SISMONDVM · ARIMINENSE · M · CCCC · XLVI

Bronze, old aftercast, 81 mm. Traces of green patina

1966.106.7

Hill called the reverse of this medal "perhaps the finest architectural design to be found on a medal."

Bibl.: Corpus, no. 177; Arm. 1, p. 19,7 (obv.), 1, p. 19,8 (rev.); *Morgenroth,* no. 23; Calabi and Cornaggia, p. 93, pl. 1 (as Anonymous Riminese, 1451–56); Lanna, no. 17, pl. 3; Brescia 1, p. 4, no. 33.

6 SIGISMONDO PANDOLFO MALATESTA 1450

Obv. Bust to left, laureate. Around, · SIGISMVNDVS PANDVLFVS MALATESTA · PAN · F ·

Rev. View of facade of San Francesco, Rimini, based on Alberti's proposed reconstruction. Around, PRAECL · ARIMINI · TEMPLVM · AN · GRATIAE · V · F · M · CCCC · L ·

Bronze, 40 mm.

1966.104.1

Specimens of this, the foundation medal of the Tempio Malatestiano, have been excavated in the walls of the castle at Rimini. Hill says this medal is after Pasti's model, but that he was not responsible for the casting. The church was dedicated in 1450 but never finished.

Bibl.: Corpus, no. 183 (as after Matteo de' Pasti); Arm. 1, p. 21,17; Rosati, no. 31; *Kress,* no. 66 (as after Pasti); *Morgenroth,* no. 28; Habich, pl. 14, 2; Calabi and Cornaggia, no. 15, p. 44 (as anonymous Riminese artist); Naples, pp. 16–17; Supino, no. 33; Brescia 1, p. 5, nos. 40–41; *MM.* 1, p. 81, pl. 14,1; *Trésor Ital.* 2, pl. 3,4; Münzen und Medaillen, Basel (auction catalog), 17, 2 December 1957, lot 88 (excavated specimen); C. Ricci, *Il Tempio Malatestiano,* Milan/Rome 1924, chapter 10; C. Brandi, *Il Tempio Malatestiano,* Turin 1956, pp. 14–20 (facade).

BARTOLOMMEO MELIOLI
(1448–1514)

A goldsmith, coin engraver and medalist, Melioli spent his whole life at Mantua. His earliest dated medal is of 1474, and in 1492 he became master of the mint. Melioli's medals show the influence of Cristoforo di Geremia.

See Forrer 4, pp. 14–17; *Corpus,* pp. 47–50; *Kress,* pp. 17–18.

7 FRANCESCO II GONZAGA (1466–1519), later, fourth Marquess of Mantua 1484

Obv. Bust to right, in cap and decorated breastplate. Around, D · FRANCISCVS · GON · D · FRED · III · M · MANTVAE · F · SPES · PVB · SALVSQ · P · REDIVI ·

Rev. Health, standing between water and fire, holds a staff and a medicine basket inscribed, CAVTIVS. Around, ADOLESCENTIAE AVGVSTAE; on listel, MELIOLVS DICAVIT

Bronze, black patina, 71 mm.

1966.104.5

D'Arco and, later, Panofsky identify the reverse figure as Health, holding a basket of medicines. Thus the medal celebrates Francesco's recovery from a serious illness in 1484.

Bibl.: Corpus, no. 196 (dates medal 1481, identifies rev. figure as Pandora); Arm. 1, p. 80,4; Rosati, no. 40; *Kress,* no. 69; Brescia 1, p. 17, no. 117; Magnaguti-*Mant,* no. 19; J. de Foville, *Gazette des Beaux-Arts* 39 (1908), p. 392, no. 1; C. D'Arco, *Delle Arti e degli Artefici di Mantova* i (1857), p. 75 (unsigned); D. and E. Panofsky, *Pandora's Box,* London 1956, pp. 22–23, n. 20.

ANTICO (Pier Iacopo Alari Bonacolsi)
(ca. 1460–1528)

Antico is celebrated as a classicizing sculptor, particularly of small bronzes. He always worked for the Gonzaga family, at Mantua, Bozzolo and Gazzuolo. In 1497 he was in Rome making reduced copies of antiquities.

See *Corpus,* pp. 51–53; *Kress,* pp. 18–19; M. Chiarini in *DBdI* 1, pp. 580–82.

8 ANTONIA DEL BALZO (1441–1538), married in 1479 Gianfrancesco Gonzaga di Rodigo (1443–96)

Obv. Bust to right. Around, DIVA ANTONIA BA[V]TIA DE GONZ · MAR ·

Rev. Hope, holding broken anchor and tattered sail, stands on prow of broken-masted vessel drawn by two Pegasi over which flies a putto. Engraved on side of vessel, MAI PIV; around, SVPEREST M SPES

Bronze, old aftercast, 39 mm. Hole at top

1966.104.7

Mai più, the motto of Antonia and her husband, is found also on the bronze vase in the Modena Museum attributed to Antico.

Bibl.: Corpus, no. 212 (signed on reverse with incised ANTI in exergue); Arm. 1, p. 62,5; Rosati, no. 46 (signed); *Kress,* no. 72 (signed); *Morgenroth,* no. 33 (reverse only); Habich, pl. 63,2 (signed); Supino, no. 73 (signed); Brescia 1, p. 13, no. 90; *Trésor Ital.* 2, pl. 23,5; Pompeo Litta, *Famiglie Celebri Italiani,* Milan-Turin 1819–85, *Gonzaga,* no. 60 (signed).

GIANFRANCESCO ENZOLA
(active 1455–78)

Gianfrancesco Enzola of Parma, goldsmith, medalist and die engraver, is recorded there from 1467–71 and as master of the mint at Ferrara in 1472–73. His earlier medals, before 1471, are small in scale, but after 1473 he cast large medals, notably those for Costanzo Sforza of Pesaro and Federigo of Urbino. Plaquettes and seals are also attributed to him.

See Forrer 2, pp. 22–23; *Corpus*, pp. 70–76; *Kress*, pp. 22–23; J. Pope-Hennessy, *Renaissance Bronzes in the Samuel H. Kress Collection*, London/New York 1965, pp. 22–24.

9 FRANCESCO I (1401–66) and GALEAZZO MARIA (1444–76) SFORZA, fourth (1456) and fifth (1459) Dukes of Milan

Obv. Bust of Francesco Sforza, to right, in armor. Around, (Sforza biscione) FR SFORTIA VICE-COMES MLI DVX IIII BELLI PATER ET PACIS AVTOR MCCCCLVI; across field, ·V· ·F·

Rev. Bust of Galeazzo Maria, to left, in mail. Around, (Sforza biscione) GALEAZ MARIA SFORTIA · VICECOMES · FR · SFORTIAE · MLI · DVCIS · IIII · PRIMOGENTS; across field, ·V· ·F· | MCCCCLVIIII

Bronze, 43 mm.

1966.105.2

The original of this medal was struck from dies, but it is unlikely that any of these specimens survive.

Bibl.: *Corpus*, no. 284; Arm. 1, p. 44,7; Rosati, no. 35; *Kress*, no. 93; Naples, p. 21; Supino, no. 52; Brescia 1, p. 10, no. 72; *MM.* 1, p. 72, pl. 11,2; Heraeus, pl. 57,3 (rev. insc. variant FIL PRINCEPS for IIII PRIMOGENTS).

SPERANDIO OF MANTUA
(1425/31–1504)

The son of a goldsmith, Sperandio was the most prolific fifteenth-century medalist. Born in Mantua, he is first noted in 1445 as a goldsmith in Ferrara. Later he worked in Faenza (1477), Bologna (1478–90), and Venice, as well as in Ferrara and Mantua. He was noted as a goldsmith, architect, sculptor and cannon-founder. A strong portraitist, but sometimes a careless medalist, his oeuvre is unusually well defined.

See Forrer 5, pp. 583–97; *Corpus*, pp. 89–103; Hill in Thieme-Becker 31, pp. 359–60; *Kress*, pp. 26–28.

10 ANTONIO SARZANELLA DE' MANFREDI, of Faenza, diplomat

Obv. Bust to right, wearing robe and mortier

Without reverse

Bronze, old aftercast, 67 mm. x 46 mm.

1966.109.1

A cutout from the medal by Sperandio (*Corpus*, no. 358; *Kress*, no. 113). No plaquette version of the medal is recorded. Sarzanella, a diplomat in the Estensi service, was in Ferrara in 1463, and the original medal was probably made then.

11 LUDOVICO CARBONE (1435–82), of Ferrara, poet

Obv. Bust to right, laureate. Below, incised, OPVS · SPERANDEI; around, OR SETTV QVEL CAR-BONE QVELLA FONTE

Rev. A siren above waves holds one of her tails in each hand; rocky foreground with leafless tree at left and right. Around, CHE SPANDI DI PARLAR SI LARGO FIVME | · MVSIS GRATIISQVS VOLENTIBVS ·

Bronze, 85 mm. Hole at top

1966.106.22

The medal probably dates from 1464, when Carbone received a wreath from Pius II at Bologna, although he was crowned a second time in 1469, by Frederick III.

For the obverse inscription, see Dante's *Inferno* i, 79–80.

Bibl.: *Corpus*, no. 360; Arm. 1, p. 66,14; Brescia 1, p. 14, no. 96; *MM.* 1, p. 99, pl. 21,1; *Trésor Ital.* 2, pl. 11,1; Gruyer, p. 646 (dated 1477).

CAMELIO (Vettor di Antonio Gambello)
(ca. 1455/60–1537)

Sculptor, medalist, die engraver, jeweler, armorer. He is noted as a master of dies at the Venetian mint in 1484 and worked there until 1510. From 1513–16 he was engraver at the papal mint, but earlier papal medals have been attributed to him. From 1516–37 he was again in Venice, but probably did little work during the last decade of his life. Camelio was one of the earlier artists to experiment with striking medals from dies.

See Forrer 1, pp. 331–33; *Corpus,* pp. 115–21; *Kress,* pp. 31–32.

12 CORNELIO CASTALDO (1480–1537), Jurisconsult, poet and orator 1505–10

Obv. Bust to left. Around, CORNELIVS CASTA-LIDVS FELTRIEN IVRIS CON ·

Without reverse

Lead, late cast, 63 mm.

1966.106.18

Bibl.: Corpus, no. 441 (with rev., dated 1505–10); Arm. 1, p. 115,5 (with rev.); Habich, pl. 65,6 (with rev.); Forrer 1, p. 332; Brescia 1, p. 24, no. 156; *MM.* 1, p. 204, pl. 45,4; Jean de Foville, *Revue de l'Art Ancien et Modern* 32 (1912), p. 279 (dates medal 1508–10).

GIOVANNI MARIA POMEDELLI
(1478/9–1537 or later)

Born at Villafranca and active in Verona, Pomedelli was a goldsmith, painter and engraver as well as a medalist. His mark consists of an apple overlaid with his first name, ZVAN, and flanked by a punch and graver. His earliest dated medal is of 1519.

See Forrer 4, pp. 643–47; *Corpus,* pp. 148–53; *Kress,* pp. 35–37.

13 ISABELLA SESSO

Obv. Bust to left, hair swathed in drapery. Around, · ISABELLA · SESSA · MICHAEL · VENETA

Rev. Fortune seated to left, semi-nude, holds out a bridle in left hand and three nails in right. Her right foot rests on a skull; behind her a dry tree and a helmet with a sphinx crest. Around, EK ΠΑΛΑΙΜΟΙ ΜΗΝΙΖ ΟΜΕΝΗ; in exergue, the artist's mark, made from the letters ZUAN

Bronze, old aftercast, 44 mm. Hole at top

1966.106.26

The reverse seems to refer to Isabella's distresses resulting from her support as governess of Vicenza of the Imperialists against Venice in 1511. The Venetians confiscated her property and Maximilian did not reward her.

Bibl.: Corpus, no. 597; Arm. 1, p. 127,8; *Kress,* no. 182; Supino, no. 238; Brescia 1, p. 26, no. 165; Morsolin, "Isabella Sesso," *Rivista Italiana di Numismatica* 3 (1890), pp. 250–58 (for the career of Isabella); Ter-

varent, col. 267ii (bridle as symbol of Fortune or Occasion—this reverse called Fortune), col. 278 (Death with a bridle).

CARADOSSO
(ca. 1452–1526/7)

Cristoforo Caradosso Foppa is first noted in 1475 working in Milan as a goldsmith and medalist. He remained there after the fall of Ludovico Il Moro, then went to Rome via Mantua in 1505. Although there is no documentation of him at the papal mint, Caradosso made several medals of Julius II and helped found in 1509 the Guild of Roman Goldsmiths. None of his medals are signed, and attributions to him are based on the word of Vasari and Lomazzo.

See Forrer 1, pp. 345–50; *Corpus,* pp. 168–73; *Kress,* pp. 38–39.

14 JULIUS II della Rovere, Pope 1503–13 1506

Obv. Bust to right, wearing cope. Around, IVLIVS · LIGVR · PAPA · SECVNDVS · MCCCCCVI

Rev. The elevation of Saint Peter's following Bramante's design. Around, TEMPLI · PETRI · INSTAVRACIO; below, · VATICANVS · M ·

Bronze, 56 mm.

1966.113.55

Another version exists with Julius wearing the papal cap and cape (*Corpus,* no. 660). Gold and silver versions of these medals were placed in the foundation of Saint Peter's on 18 April 1506, when the pope laid the first stone. The medal is attributed to Caradosso by Vasari.

Bibl.: Corpus, no. 659; Arm. 1, p. 108,2; Rosati, no. 98; *Kress,* no. 194; Roberto Weiss, "The Medals of Julius II," *Journal of the Warburg and Courtauld Institutes* 28 (1965), pp. 163–82 (this medal pp. 169–72); *Morgenroth,* no. 69; Forrer 1, p. 346; Habich, pl. 66; Fabriczy, pl. 34,2; Martinori, fasc. vi, p. 65; Bonnani, pp. 148–49, no. 8; *Trésor Ital.* 1, pl. 26,4.

MEDALIST OF THE ROMAN EMPERORS

A medalist of the third quarter of the fifteenth century, active probably in Lombardy, whom Charles Seymour has identified as Filarete on the basis of comparisons with the bronze doors of Saint Peter's in Rome.

See *Corpus,* pp. 186–87; *Kress,* p. 40; Charles Seymour, "Some Reflections on Filarete's Use of Antique Visual

Sources," *Arte Lombarda* 38/39 (1973), *Il Filarete*, pp. 36–47.

15 FAUSTINA I and ANTONINUS PIUS

Obv. Bust of Faustina to right. Around, DIVA AVGVSTA DIVAE FAVSTINA

Rev. Faustina and Antoninus Pius, seated facing each other with hands joined. Around, ·DIVA·FAVSTINA DIVS ANTONINVS · ; in exergue, S. C

Bronze, 110 mm.

1966.105.1

Bibl.: Corpus, no. 735; Arm. 1, p. 100,3; *Kress,* no. 204; Brescia 1, p. 20, nos. 131–32.

ANDREA GUACIALOTI (or Guazzalotti) (1435–95)

Son of a Florentine family living in Prato, he was a clerk in the papal curia until 1467, when he became canon of Prato. He was a widely known bronze founder, and executed most of his medals in Rome.

See Forrer 2, pp. 330–33; *Corpus,* pp. 191–95; *Kress,* p. 41.

16 PIUS II Piccolomini, Pope 1458–64

Obv. Bust to left. Around, ΕΝΛΕΛS PIVS SENEN-SIS PΛPΛ SECVNDVS ·

Rev. Pelican in her piety. Around, ΛLESVTHEC-CORDISPΛVI · DESΛNGVINENΛTOS

Bronze, 53 mm.

1966.107.6

Generally dated 1460–64. Patrigiani reproduces an example with the date 1458 incised in the field. The reverse of the pelican in her piety is copied from the medal of Vittorino da Feltre by Pisanello, and denotes Charity.

Bibl.: Corpus, no. 749; Arm. 1, p. 50,8; Rosati, no. 82; Habich, pl. 33,3; Naples, p. 24; Supino, no. 60; Brescia 2, p. 2, no. 12; *Trésor Ital.* 1, pl. 22, 3–4; A. Patrigiani, "La data di una rara medaglia di Papa Pio II," *Numismatica* (1948), p. 39; Venuti, p. 21, no. 5; Martinori, fasc. iii, p. 54; Bonnani, p. 68, no. 4.

CRISTOFORO DI GEREMIA (active 1456–76)

Mantuan, goldsmith, medalist and metal worker. He

arrived in Rome in 1456 and by 1461 was in the service of Cardinal Scarampi. In 1465 he entered the service of Pope Paul II, of whom he made many medals. In 1468 he restored the bronze statue of Marcus Aurelius.

See Forrer 2, pp. 246–48; *Corpus,* pp. 195–201; *Kress,* pp. 41–42.

17 ALFONSO V OF ARAGON (1394–1458), King of Naples and Sicily

Obv. Bust to right, over crown. Around, ALFONSVS · REX · REGIBVS · IMPERANS · ET · BELLORVM · VICTOR

Rev. Alfonso seated, crowned by Mars and Bellona. Around, VICTOREM REGNI MARS ET BELLONA CORONANT; on listel, CHRISTOPHORVS HIERIMIA

Lead, two holes at top, 75 mm. Very worn

1966.107.4

The medal is generally dated shortly, if at all, after the death of Alfonso in 1458. Rosati suggests that it refers to the victory of Alfonso over the Angevins in 1442 but proposes no date for the making of the medal. The placing of the crown below the bust is borrowed from one of Pisanello's medals of Alfonso.

Bibl.: Corpus, no. 754; Arm. 1, p. 31,1; Rosati, no. 84; *Kress,* no. 210; *Morgenroth,* no. 77; Habich, pl. 18,2; Naples, p. 13; Supino, no. 44; Brescia 1, p. 7, no. 56; *Trésor Ital.* 2, pl. 17,1; Foville, p. 441ff; Heraeus, pl. 31,3.

18 PAUL II Barbo, Pope 1464–71

Obv. Bust to left, tonsured, wearing cope. Around, PAVLVS · II · VENETVS · · PONT · MAX ·

Rev. The pope, with cardinals, seated at left on a dais, blesses the faithful, who kneel to kiss his toe. In exergue, · AVDIENTIA · PVBLICA · | · PONT · MAX ·

Bronze, 39 mm.

1966.113.74

Medals of this type were found in the walls of the Palazzetto of San Marco. Paul II commissioned a large number of medals of himself for the foundations of buildings, for which his enemies took him to task.

With Paul II begins the official series of commemorative medals of the popes.

Bibl.: Corpus, no. 766; Arm. 2, p. 33,13; Supino, no. 182; Brescia 2, p. 2, no. 17; Bonnani, pp. 75–76, no. 6; *Trésor Ital.* 1, pl. 23,1; Foville, pp. 447–48 (dates the reverse

1466–70); Hill-Paul 2, no. 24, pl. 12; Weiss, p. 61 (suggests the date 1466–67 for the reverse).

ROMAN SCHOOL UNDER PAUL II

19 PAUL II Barbo 1465

Obv. Bust to left, wearing cope. Around, PAVLVS · II · VENETVS · PONT · MAX

Rev. Barbo coat of arms surmounted by papal tiara. Around, HAS AEDES CONDIDIT ANNO CHRISTI · M · CCCCLXV ·

Bronze, 34 mm. Hole at top

1966.113.73

Foundation medal for Palazzo Venezia. Modeled after Roman *sestertii*.

Bibl.: Corpus, no. 782; Arm. 2, p. 32,9; Naples, p. 25; Supino, no. 179; Hill-Paul 2, no. 9, pl. 11; Weiss, pp. 51–52.

20 PAUL II Barbo 1465

Obv. Bust to left, wearing cope. Around, PAVLVS · II · VENETVS · PONT · MAX

Rev. Facade of the Palazzo Venezia in Rome. Around, HAS · AEDES · CONDIDIT · ANNO CHRISTI · M · CCCCLXV ·

Bronze, 34 mm.

1966.113.72

Foundation medal. Specimens of this version have been found in the foundations of the Palazzo Venezia, and the reverse inscription appears on the facade. From the obverse it appears that the Palazzo was originally planned with Gothic-style windows.

Bibl.: Corpus, no. 783; *Kress,* no. 216; Naples, p. 26; Supino, no. 176; Brescia 2, p. 23, no. 25; Bonnani, pp. 85–86, no. 13; Venuti, p. 24, no. 6; Weiss, pp. 51–52; Hill-Paul II, no. 10.

GIOVANNI CANDIDA
(Giovanni di Salvatore Filangieri)
(before 1450–after 1495)

Of a noble Neapolitan family, Candida went to Flanders and became secretary to Charles the Bold in 1472, traveling to Venice, Rome, Naples and Milan in his service. At Charles' death he became secretary to Maximilian I and Mary of Burgundy in 1477. After several changes

in fortune, he settled at the Court of France in 1480 where he eventually became royal councillor. He was with Charles VIII in Italy in 1494 but disappears from the documents after 1495. Candida signed a number of medals, and many others showing a wide variety of styles have been attributed to him.

See Forrer 1, pp. 334–38; *Corpus,* pp. 211–14; *Kress,* pp. 43–45.

21 MAXIMILIAN OF AUSTRIA (1459–1519) and MARIA OF BURGUNDY (1457–82) ca. 1477

Obv. Bust to right. Around, · MAXIMILIANVS · FR · CAES · F · DVX · AVSTR · BVRGVND ·

Rev. Bust to right of Maria. At left, interlaced MM surmounted by crown. Around, MARIA · KAROLI · F · DVX · BVRGVNDIAE · AVSTRIAE · BRAB · C · FLAN:

Bronze, old aftercast, 49 mm.

1966.107.3

Probably made in 1477 for the marriage of the couple, this medal exists in great numbers.

Bibl.: Corpus, no. 831; Arm. 2, p. 80,1; *Salton,* no. 27; *Kress,* no. 225 (attributed to Candida); *Morgenroth,* no. 85; Habich, pl. 62,7; Brescia 1, p. 75, no. 505; *Trésor German,* pl. 4,3; L. Baldass, "Die Bildnisse Maximilians I," *Jahrbuch der kunsthistorischen Sammlungen in Wien* 31 (1913/14), p. 249; Heraeus, pls. 14,7, 18,7; Van Mieris 1, p. 141; Forrer 1, p. 336.

SCHOOL OF CANDIDA
Early Sixteenth Century

22 FRANÇOIS, Duke of Valois (1494–1547), afterwards King Francis I 1504

Obv. Bust to right. Around, · FRANCOIS · DVC · DE · VALOIS · COMTE · DANGOLESME · AV · X · AN · D · S · EA

Rev. Salamander amid flames. Around, · NOTRISCO · ALBVONO · STINGO · EL REO · MCCCCCIIII

Bronze, 65 mm.

1966.107.9

The salamander has the power to extinguish fire without burning. It first appears here as the device of Francis I. The device was inherited from Francis' father, Charles de Valois, duc d'Angoulême, who died in 1496. The medal has a pendant piece of Louise de Savoie and her daughter Marguerite de Valois-Angoulême (*Corpus,* no.

852). Bought at auction, Hotel Drouet, Paris, 15 June 1923, Lot 2, pl. 1.

Bibl.: Corpus, no. 848; Arm. 2, p. 187,1 (as French); *Kress,* no. 232; Habich, pl. 62,10; Fabriczy, p. 165, pl. 33,5; Mazerolle, no. 68; Supino, no. 814; *Trésor Fr.* 1, pl. 6,4; Van Mieris 1, p. 378; Tervarent, cols. 333–34 (for the salamander device).

NICCOLÒ FIORENTINO
(1430–1514)

Niccolò di Forzore Spinelli, born in Florence of a family of goldsmiths. He signed five medals, but a much larger number, many of higher quality than the signed ones, have been attributed to him. His medallic portraits are strongly modeled with reverses often dependent on the antique. In 1468 he is noted in Burgundy as a seal engraver to Charles the Bold.

See Forrer 2, pp. 93–97; *Corpus,* pp. 243–80; Hill in Thieme-Becker 31, pp. 387–88; *Kress,* pp. 49–51.

ATTRIBUTED TO NICCOLÒ FIORENTINO

23 MARSILIO FICINO (1433–99) of Florence, humanist

Obv. Bust to left. Around, · MARSILIVS · FICINVS · FLORENTINVS ·

Rev. Inscription, PLATONE

Bronze, old aftercast, 55 mm.

1966.104.6

Generally dated shortly before 1499.

Bibl.: Corpus, no. 974 (as a medal more or less in the style of and attributed to Niccolò Fiorentino); Arm. 2, p. 49,8; *Kress,* no. 268 (in the manner of); *Morgenroth,* no. 101; Naples, p. 168 (anonymous); Brescia 1, p. 71, no. 475; Habich, pl. 51,3; Supino, no. 143; Fabriczy, p. 130; T. W. Greene sale catalog, Sotheby, 31 October 1932, no. 75 (as after Niccolò Fiorentino).

24 STEFANO TAVERNA (d. 1499), Secretary to the Duke of Milan

Obv. Bust to left. Around, STEPHANVS · TABERNA · SECRETARIVS · ET ORATOR · ILLVSTRISS · DVCIS · MEDIOLANI ·

Rev. Virtus in armor, holding Love to left and Fortune to right, by the hair. Around, · VIRTVTI · OMNIA · PARENT ·

Bronze, 79 mm.

1966.104.9

Stefano Taverna is noted in Florence in 1486–87 and in Rome in 1489, 1491–92, and 1496–99. In 1497 he became Archbishop of Parma. His title on the medal indicates that it was made before he became archbishop. Hill and Middeldorf suggest a date about 1495–97.

Bibl.: Corpus, no. 1019; Arm. 2, p. 56,13; *Morgenroth,* no. 104; Habich, pl. 39,3.

Sixteenth Century, Florence

FRANCESCO DA SANGALLO
(1494–1576)

Florentine sculptor and medalist, son of the architect Giuliano da Sangallo. He went to Rome with his family in 1504 and is said to have been trained by Andrea Sansovino, whom he resembles little. Sangallo's medals are large and heavily modeled in high relief.

See Forrer 5, pp. 324–31; U. Middeldorf in Thieme-Becker 29, pp. 404–06; U. Middeldorf, "Portraits by Francesco da Sangallo," *Art Quarterly* 1 (1938), pp. 109–38; *Kress,* p. 59.

25 FRANCESCO DA SANGALLO | HELENA MARSUPINA   1551

Obv. Bust to left. Around, FRANCESCO DA SANGALLO SCVLTORE ARCHIETTO FIOREN; on truncation, FACIEB (incised)

Rev. Bust of Helena Marsupina to left. Around, HELENA MARSVPINI CONSORTE · FIOREN · A · M · D · L · I ·

Bronze, 94 mm.

1895.35

Bibl.: Arm. 1, p. 158,7; Fabriczy, p. 142, pl. 29,4; Forrer 5, p. 330, no. 7 (ill. pp. 324–25); Hill-*Artists,* p. 37, pl. 25; *Morgenroth,* no. 136; G. Clausse, *Les Sangallo,* 3 vols., Paris 1900–02, 3, pp. 235–37.

DOMENICO DE' VETRI
(Domenico di Polo di Angelo de' Vetri)
(after 1480–1547)

Domenico, a Florentine, was apprenticed to the gem engraver Pier Maria Serbaldi da Pescia. Vasari reports that he was a follower of Giovanni delle Corniole and that he made medals of Cosimo I and Alessandro I de' Medici.

See Forrer 4, pp. 639–41; Hill in Thieme-Becker 9, p. 408; *Kress,* pp. 59–60.

26 ALESSANDRO I DE' MEDICI (1510–37), Duke of Florence 1532   1534

Obv. Bust to right, in cuirass. Around, ALEX · M · FLORENTIAE · DVX · PRIMVS · ·

Rev. Peace setting fire to the weapons of war. Around, · FVNDATOR · QVIETIS · M · D · XXX · IIII · ; in exergue, symbol of Mars

Bronze, struck, 36 mm.

1966.104.15

Bibl.: Arm. 1, p. 151,3; 3, p. 58; *Morgenroth,* no. 137; Supino, no. 251; Brescia 1, p. 30, no. 198; *MM.* 1, p. 199, pl. 44,3; H. de la Tour, "Domenico di Polo, Médailleur et Graveur de Pierres Fines du Duc Alexandre de Médicis," *Congrès International de Numismatique,* Paris 1900, pp. 382–99, no. 1; Heraeus, pl. 61, no. 10 (insc. variant ALEX · MED · FLORENTINE).

DOMENICO POGGINI
(1520–90)

Florentine goldsmith, sculptor, coin engraver and medalist, Domenico served with his brother Giampaolo at the Florentine court from 1554–62, making both cast and struck medals of Cosimo I, Francesco I and their families. From 1585 to his death he was master of the papal mint for Sixtus IV. His medals are some of the best examples of later sixteenth-century academicism.

See Forrer 4, pp. 628–32; P. Grotemeyer in Thieme-Becker 27, pp. 187–88; P. Grotemeyer, "Domenico Poggini als Münzstempelschneider," *Numismatik* 1 (1932), pp. 42–44; *Kress,* pp. 63–64.

27 COSIMO I DE' MEDICI (1519–74), Duke of Florence 1537, first Grand Duke of Tuscany 1569, and FRANCESCO DE' MEDICI (1541–87), second Grand Duke of Tuscany 1574   1567

Obv. Bust of Cosimo to right in armor. Around, COSMVS MED · FLOREN · ET SENAR · DVX · II · ; below, 1567

Rev. Bust of Francesco to right in armor. Around, FRANCIS · MEDICES FLOREN · ET SENAR · PRINCEPS ·

Bronze, struck, 42 mm.

1966.104.13

Bibl.: Arm. 1, p. 261,39 (attributed to Poggini); Supino, no. 400 (as Pietro Paolo Galeotti, called Pietro Paolo Romano); Forrer 4, pp. 629 (ill. of Francesco), 630; *Salton,* no. 40 (obv.); Fabriczy, pl. 35,4 (rev.).

28 COSIMO I DE' MEDICI 1561

Obv. Bust to right, in cuirass. Around, COSMVS MED · FLOREN · ET SENAR · DVX II · ; below, 1561

Rev. View of the Uffizi, with Palazzo Vecchio in background; in front, Equity with scales and cornucopia. Around, PVBLICAE COMMODITATI

Bronze, struck, with traces of gilt, 41 mm. Very worn

1966.104.14

The building of the Uffizi was ordered by decree in 1560.

Bibl.: Arm. 1, p. 256,13; Rosati, no. 195; *Kress,* no. 341; Fabriczy, pl. 35,2 (obv. only); Supino, no. 448; Brescia 1, p. 55, no. 260 (rev. only); Forrer 4, p. 629(e); *Trésor Ital.* 2, pl. 44,5; *MM.* 1, p. 355, pl. 78,5; Heiss, *Florence* 2, p. 52, no. 5, pl. 4,6; Madrid, p. 189, no. 254; Heraeus, pl. 63,6 (without reverse).

STYLE OF DOMENICO POGGINI

29 HELEN OF TROY

Obv. Bust to left. Around, ΕΛΕΝΗ ΛΗΔΑΙΑ ΣΓΑΡΤΗΣ ΒΑΣΙΛΙΣΣΑ

Rev. The Judgment of Paris. Around, ΑΚΑΘΑΡΤΟΣ ΓΑΡΙΔΟΣ ΚΓΙΣΙΣ

Bronze, struck, 48 mm.

1966.104.12

Hill attributes the medal to Domenico Poggini, and points out its stylistic similarity to the medals of Sibilla Lippi (Supino, no. 443, pl. 43; Rosati, no. 193) and Lucrezia de' Medici, wife of Alfonso II d'Este (Arm. 1, p. 260,36; 3, p. 123G). Hill associates with this group a medal inscribed "Vincentia Arm. na Veneta" (*Gall. Naz. Ital.* 4 (1899), pl. 11, no. 150).

Bibl.: G. F. Hill, "Notes on Italian Medals XXIII," *Burlington Magazine* 30 (1917), pp. 197–98, pl. 1,D.

MICHELE MAZZAFIRRI
(ca. 1530–97)

Florentine medalist and goldsmith at the court of Francesco I and Ferdinand I de' Medici. Mazzafirri was better known as a goldsmith and his medals show the delicate workmanship of that art.

See Forrer 3, pp. 647–49; Thieme-Becker 24, p. 305; Supino, pp. 181–84; Hill, "Notes on Italian Medals XVI," *Burlington Magazine* 24 (1913–14), pp. 211–17 (at 217); S. J. A. Churchill, "Michele Mazzafirri, Goldsmith and Medalist," *ibid.*, pp. 348–49; Hill, N. I. A., nos. 191, 198, 200, 205; Habich, p. 119; Pyke, p. 90, fig. 188.

30 FERDINAND I DE' MEDICI (1549–1609), third Grand Duke of Tuscany, 1587 1588

Obv. Bust to right, in armor. Around, FERD MED MAGN DVX ETRVRIÆ III; below, MICHE · M · · 1588

Rev. Plan of the fortress at Livorno. Around, PVBLI-CÆ · SECVRITATE; below, [A · S · CIƆ · IƆ · XC]

Bronze, struck, 47 mm.

1966.104.10

Ferdinand created the port of Livorno.

Bibl.: Arm. 1, p. 284,7; 3, p. 136,a; Forrer 3, p. 648; Supino, no. 588; Fabriczy, p. 182, pl. 36,3 (obv. only); Habich, pl. 82,5 (obv. only).

31 FERDINAND I DE' MEDICI 1588

Obv. Bust to right, in armor. Around, FERDINAN-DVS · M · MAGN · DVX · ETRVRIAE · III · ; below, [MICHELE · MAZA · F · 1588]

Rev. Grand ducal crown and scepter with Medici *palle*. Around, VIRTVTIS PREMIA

Bronze, 43 mm.

1966.104.11

Bibl.: Arm. 1, p. 284,8 (obv.); 1, p. 284,5 (rev.).

PIER PAOLO GALEOTTI
(called Pier Paolo Romano)
(ca. 1520–84)

Goldsmith and medalist, born in Rome. He was brought to Florence by Cellini as his pupil and accompanied him to Ferrara and Paris. Galeotti worked as a medalist in Florence after 1550, but executed commissions from Milan, Genoa and Turin. He produced at least seventy-two medals and was highly praised by Vasari. His reverse types are often elaborate decorative scenes.

See Forrer 2, pp. 190–94; 7, pp. 336–37; Thieme-Becker 13, pp. 91–92; Habich, p. 136; *Kress,* pp. 65–67.

32 GIOVANNI BATTISTA GRIMALDI, Genoese nobleman, poet and philosopher

Obv. Bust to left. Around, IOANNES BAPTISTA GRIMALDVS | PPR

Rev. Prometheus chained to rocks with eagle feeding on his liver. Around, COR EXEST NVNQVAM EXCORDIS REGINA VOLANTVM

Lead, 56 mm.

1966.108.12

Forrer dates the medal ca. 1565.

Bibl.: Arm. 1, p. 230,11; Forrer 2, p. 191; Fabriczy, pl. 36,2; *MM.* 1, p. 349, pl. 76,5; Brescia 1, p. 48, no. 317.

33 GIANFRANCESCO TRIVULZIO (1509–73), Marquess of Vigevano, Count of Mesocco (1519–49), Rheinwald and Stoss

Obv. Bust to right, in armor and cloak. Around, IO · FRAN · TRI · MAR · VIG · CO · MVSO · AC · VAL · REN · Έ · STOSA · D; on truncation, AET 39

Rev. Fortune on a dolphin on a sea full of swimmers and drowning people, four zephyrs around. Around, FVI SVM ET ERO

Bronze, aftercast, 57 mm.

1966.108.11

The medal has been attributed to Galeotti. The sitter's age dates the medal to about 1548.

Bibl.: Arm. 2, p. 302,13*bis*; Rosati, no. 212; *Kress,* no. 360a; *Salton,* no. 42; Habich, pl. 96,5 (as Milanese); Supino, no. 673 (as Milanese); Forrer 2, p. 192 (ill.); Brescia 1, p. 50, no. 329; Madrid, p. 232, no. 447; Tervarent, col. 145, 5 (Fortune and dolphin); G. F. Hill, *A Guide to the Exhibition of Medals of the Renaissance in the British Museum,* London 1923, p. 39 (as hardly in the style of Galeotti).

Sixteenth Century, Rome

ALESSANDRO CESATI
(called Il Grechetto)
(active 1538–64)

Born in Cyprus about 1500, Cesati was in Rome in 1538 in the service of Alessandro Farnese. He was engraver at the papal mint from 1540 and worked also for the Farnese family. In 1561 he became mint master for the

Duke of Savoy, but he returned to Cyprus in 1564. Cesati often used classical models and was highly praised by Vasari.

See Hill in Thieme-Becker 6, pp. 313–14; Forrer 1, pp. 389–92; *Kress*, pp. 68–69; Hill, *Med. Ren.*, pp. 93–94.

34 JULIUS III Del Monte, Pope 1550–55   1553

Obv. Bust to right, wearing tiara and cope. Around, IVLIVS · III · PONT · MAX · A · III

Rev. Prudence, with snake and mirror at right, reaches for Fortune on a dolphin at left. Around, KPATOY-MAI ·

Silver, 34 mm.

1966.113.54

The reverse alludes to the conduct which raised Julius to the papacy.

Bibl.: Arm. 1, p. 173,12; Forrer 1, p. 390; Naples, p. 214 (obv. as not Cesati, rev. as Cesati); Supino, no. 309; Brescia 2, p. 7, no. 87; Mazio, no. 66; Venuti, p. 93, no. 13; Bonnani, p. 249,14; *Trésor Papes*, pl. 9,1.

GIOVANNI PALADINO
(active to ca. 1572)

Roman medalist, known for a series of medals of the popes from Martin V to Pius V. His medals of the earlier popes are reproductions of fifteenth-century medals.

See Grotemeyer in Thieme-Becker 26, p. 154; Forrer 4, pp. 366–67; *Kress*, p. 71; Supino, pp. 170–76; Hill, *Med. Ren.*, p. 95.

35 MARTIN V Colonna, Pope 1417–31

Obv. Bust to right, wearing cope. Around, MAR-TINVS · V · COLVMNA · PONT · MAX ·

Rev. Colonna shield surmounted by papal tiara and keys. Around, ANNO PRIMO MCDXVII PONT; below shield, ROMA

Bronze, struck, 41 mm.

1966.113.56

One of the series of restitutions by Paladino. This specimen is a modern restrike issued by the vatican mint from the original dies.

Bibl.: Arm. 1, p. 295,1; Forrer 4, p. 366; Supino, no. 533; Mazio, no. 1; Venuti, p. 2, no. 1; Bonnani, pp. 6–9, no. 2.

36 PIUS II Piccolomini, Pope 1458–64

Obv. Bust to left, wearing mozzetta and cap. Around, · PIVS · II · · PONT · MAX ·

Rev. A table with books on it, one inscribed, IMP | ROBA | TVR | CAR | VM | LEX; around, VELO-CITER · SCRIBENTIS · SOBOLES; in exergue, · NE · TANTI · ECCLESIÆ · | · PACISQ · AMAN-TIS · | · DELEATVR · | · MEMORIA ·

Bronze, struck, 44 mm.

1966.113.57

Restitution, refers to Pius' numerous writings.

Bibl.: Arm. 1, p. 297,14; Forrer 4, p. 366; Naples, p. 148; Supino, no. 546; Brescia 2, p. 2, no. 14; Mazio, no. 15 (inscription on book read as IMPOSITA TURCARUM LEX); Venuti, p. 21, no. 6 (also IMPOSITA TUR-CARUM LEX); Bonnani, p. 67, no. 3; *Trésor Papes*, pl. 2,2.

37 CLEMENT VII dé Medici, Pope 1523–34

Obv. Bust to right, wearing cope. Around, CLEMENS · VII · PONT · MAX · ; below, MDXXV · AN · II ·

Rev. Medici coat of arms surmounted by papal tiara and keys. Around, GLORIA ET HONORE CORO-NASTI EVM; below, ROMA

Bronze, 41 mm.

1966.113.69

Restitution.

Clement is represented erroneously with a beard, which he did not have before the Sack of Rome in 1527. The reverse appears earlier on a medal of Leo X (Bonnani, p. 164, no. 2).

Bibl.: Arm. 3, p. 144P; Forrer 4, p. 367; Naples, p. 144; Supino, no. 561; Brescia 2, p. 5, no. 62; Mazio, no. 45; Venuti, p. 66, no. 1; *Trésor Papes*, pl. 5,7; Martinori, fasc. viii, p. 177.

GIAN FEDERIGO BONZAGNI
(called Federigo Parmense)
(after 1507–88)

Born in Parma, Bonzagni made medals of the popes from Paul III to Gregory XIII, and of the Dukes of Parma. In 1554 he came to Rome as an assistant to his brother Gian Giacomo and Alessandro Cesati. His more than fifty medals date from 1547–75.

See G. Pollard in *DBdI* 12, pp. 480–81; *Kress,* p. 70; Lottici in Thieme-Becker 4, p. 329; Forrer 1, pp. 214–15; 7, pp. 95–96.

38 PIERLUIGI FARNESE (1503–47), Duke of Parma and Piacenza 1545

Obv. Bust to right, in cuirass. Around, P · LOYSIVS · F · PARM · ET · PLAC · DVX · I · ; below, I · F · PARM ·

Rev. Bird's-eye view of citadel of Parma, with gate opening into a river with snakes. Around, AD · CIVI-TAT · DITIONISQ · TVTEL · MVNIM · EX-TRVCTVM

Bronze, struck, 37 mm.

1966.108.16

Three variations of this medal exist: Madrid, p. 147, no. 220; Hill, N. I. A., no. 103; Arm. 1, p. 222,7.

Bibl.: Arm. 1, p. 222,6 (signature incomplete); Rosati, no. 110 (signature not noted); *Kress,* no. 375; *Salton,* no. 47 (signature incomplete); Forrer 1, p. 214 (notes four variations); Supino, no. 358 (obv.), 359 (rev.).

39 FEDERICO CESI (1500–65), Cardinal, 1544, Bishop of Palestrina, 1557 1561

Obv. Bust to left, wearing mozzetta. Around, · FEDER-ICVS · EPS · PRENESTIN · S · R · E CARDIN · CÆSIVS · ; on truncation, · F P ·

Rev. Facade of Santa Caterina de' Funari, Rome. Around, DIVE · CATHERINE · TEMPLVM · ANNO · CHRISTI; in exergue, · MDLXI ·

Silvered bronze, struck, 36 mm.

1966.114.43

In 1560 Cardinal Cesi undertook the complete reconstruction of the Church of Santa Caterina de' Funari. This was finished in 1564. The facade is signed by Guido Guidetti.

Bibl.: Arm. 1, p. 221,1; Rosati, no. 131; Forrer 1, p. 214; Naples, no. 184; *MM.* 1, p. 334, pl. 72,8.

40 PIUS V Ghislieri, Pope 1566–72

Obv. Bust to right, wearing cope. Around, · PIVS · V · PONTIFEX · MAX · ; below, · F · P ·

Rev. Christ driving the money changers from the temple. In exergue, DOMVS · MEA · DOM | VS · ORA-TIONIS | · VOC

Gilt bronze, 32 mm.

1966.113.51

The reverse is noted also on medals of Pius IV (Arm. 1, p. 224,21), Gregory XIII (Naples, p. 67), and Paul IV (Venuti, p. 104, no. 6).

Bibl.: Arm. 1, p. 226,30; Rosati, no. 124; Naples, p. 74; Supino, no. 374; Mazio, no. 104; Venuti, p. 129, no. 18; Bonnani, pp. 293–94, no. 6; Martinori, fasc. xi, p. 22.

41 PIUS V Ghislieri 1571

Obv. Bust to left, wearing mozzetta and cap. Around, PIVS · V · PONT · OPT · MAX · ANNO · VI · ; below, F · P ·

Rev. Naval battle. God hurls lightning above; on one of the boats, an angel holding cross and chalice. Around, DEXTERA · TVA · DOM · PERCVSSIT · INI-MICVM · 1571

Gilt copper (original fire gilding), 37 mm.

1966.113.49

The reverse inscription is from Exodus 15:6. Commemorates the Battle of Lepanto.

Bibl.: Arm. 1, p. 226,33; Houston, no. 239; Rosati, no. 126; *Salton,* no. 48; *Kress,* no. 373; Naples, p. 78; Supino, no. 375; Brescia 2, p. 8, nos. 109–11; Mazio, no. 96; Venuti, p. 125, no. 7; Bonnani, p. 297, no. 11; *Trésor Papes,* pl. 15,4; Martinori, fasc. xi, p. 23.

BARTOLOMMEO ARGENTARIO AND BERNARDINO PASSERO

On 30 March 1582, Passero was paid for three medals of Gregory XIII and Argentario for two. These were made to be placed in the foundations of the colleges of the Jesuits. (*Libro della fabrica del Collegio della Compagnia di Gesù di Roma,* 1581–92, fol. 9a 35, quoted in Bertolotti, pp. 124–25.)

See also Forrer 1, p. 69; 7, p. 25; Thieme-Becker 2, p. 92 (Argentario); Forrer 4, p. 401; Grotemeyer in Thieme-Becker 26, p. 284 (Passero).

42 GREGORY XIII Buoncompagni, Pope 1572–85

Obv. Bust to left, wearing cap and cope. Around, COL-LEG · SOC · IESV · OMNIVM · NATIONV[M] GRATIA · FVNDATO · DE · RELIG · ET · LIT · OPT[MER]; below, GREGORIVS · XIII · AN · PON · X

Rev. Abraham with four soldiers. Around, VT · ERVAT · PRAEDAM CAPTIVORVM · FRATRVM; in exergue, ABRAHAM · TRECENTOS | VERNA-CVLOS | EXPEDITOS · NVMERAT

Bronze, 48 mm.

1966.113.66

The reverse alludes to the large number of Jesuit missionaries sent out by the pope in 1583.

Bibl.: Arm. 3, p. 134A; Forrer 4, p. 401; Brescia 2, p. 11, no. 146; Venuti, p. 148, no. 49; Bonnani, p. 362, no. 57; *Trésor Papes,* pl. 17,4.

LORENZO FRAGNI
(called Lorenzo Parmense)
(1548–1618)

Medalist, goldsmith, gem engraver, Lorenzo was called to Rome in 1568 by his uncle, Gian Federigo Bonzagni. He is recorded as working at the papal mint from 1572–86.

See Thieme-Becker 12, pp. 274–75; Forrer 2, pp. 133–35; *Kress,* p. 71.

43 GREGORY XIII Buoncompagni 1583

Obv. Bust to left, wearing cope. Around, GREGORIVS · XIII · PONTIFEX · MAX · A · 1583; below truncation, · LAV · P ·

Rev. Roma, seated on a shield, holds a dragon in her right hand. Around, TVTVM · REGIMEN · ; in exergue, · ROMA ·

Bronze, 33 mm.

1966.113.3

For precautions against pirates and restoration of the fortifications at Ancona.

This medal exists with several dates. The dragon is the device of the Buoncompagni family.

Bibl.: Arm, 1, p. 280,11; Forrer 2, p. 134; Supino, nos. 485, 486 (dated 1577, 1578); Rosati, no. 146 (dated 1577, variant signature); *Trésor Papes,* pl. 17,6; Brescia 2, p. 11, no. 143; Naples, p. 114,10; Mazio, no. 24; Bonnani, p. 329, no. 15; Martinori, fasc. xi, p. 79.

NICOLÒ DE BONIS
(active 1580–92)

Medalist of the popes from Gregory XIII to Clement VIII, Nicolò came from Venice and is recorded as engraver at the papal mint in 1591. De Bonis also worked as a master goldsmith.

See Supino, pp. 165–67; Forrer 1, p. 212; Thieme-Becker

4, p. 301; Martinori, fasc. xi, pp. 69, 82; fasc. xii, pp. 8, 33, 34, 41, 68, 69, 76; Bulgari, Roma 1, p. 188.

44 SIXTUS V Peretti, Pope 1585–90 1589

Obv. Bust to right, tonsured, wearing cope. Around, * SYXTVS * V * PONT * MAX * ; below, AN * V * ; on truncation, · NI · BONIS ·

Rev. A bridge with five arches. Around, PONS * FELIX; in exergue, · AN · DOM · M · D · | LXXXIX ·

Bronze, 43 mm.

1966.113.15

In 1589 Sixtus V commissioned Domenico Fontana to construct the Ponte Felice over the Tiber in the Borghetto. The medal shows an early project for the bridge, which was completed in 1603. As completed, the bridge has only four arches with large eyes in the pylons.

Bibl.: Arm. 1, p. 288,2; Rosati, no. 140; Houston, no. 246 (with variant signature); *Trésor Papes,* pl. 19,9; Brescia 2, p. 11, no. 153; Supino, no. 513; Martinori, fasc. xii, p. 33; Venuti, p. 168, no. 36; Bonnani, p. 422, no. 34.

45 SIXTUS V Peretti 1589

Obv. Bust to left, wearing cope. Around, · SIXTVS · V · PONT · MAX · ; below, · AN · V · ; on truncation, · NI · BONIS

Rev. In center, obelisk. Behind, the Porta del Popolo and to right the Church of Santa Maria del Popolo. Around, · B · MARIE · D · POP · QVARTVM AN · IIII · EREXIT ·

Bronze, struck, 37 mm.

1966.113.16

In 1589 Sixtus V had Domenico Fontana move the obelisk from the Circus Maximus to the Piazza del Popolo.

Bibl.: Arm. 1, p. 288,4; Rosati, no. 139; Supino, no. 514; *Trésor Papes,* pl. 20,3; Venuti, p. 164, no. 21; Bonnani, p. 419, no. 31; Martinori, fasc. xii, p. 34.

ROMAN SCHOOL—UNATTRIBUTED

46 SAINT PAUL

Obv. Bust to right, nimbate. Around, · VAS ELEC-TIONIS · PAVLVS · APOSTOLVS

Rev. In wreath, inscription, BENEDICIE | IN EX-CELSIS DEO | DOMINO DE FONT-I | BVS ISRAEL IBI BENI | AMIM ADOLESCENTV | LVS IN MENTIS | EXCESSV

Bronze, black patina, 91 mm. Large chip at bottom

1966.107.7

The medal is the companion piece of a medal of Christ in a group dated by *Corpus* to ca. 1492–1500. The reverse inscription is from Psalm 67:27–28. For *vas electionis* see Acts 9:15.

Bibl.: *Corpus,* no. 902; Arm. 2, p. 7,4; *Kress,* no. 244; Hill-*Christ,* p. 22e, fig. 11; Lanna, no. 354 (with head of Christ on rev.); *Trésor Ital.* 2, pl. 26,1; de Jonghe sale catalog, Schulman, 24 November 1936, no. 84.

47 JULIUS II della Rovere, Pope 1503–13

Obv. Bust to right, wearing cope. Around, IVLIVS LIGVR PAPA SECVNDVS

Rev. Figure of Abundance, carrying cornucopia and stalks of grain. Around, · ANNONA · PVBLICA ·

Bronze, struck, black patina, 35 mm.

1966.114.5

The obverse belongs to a medal ascribed in the *Corpus* to Serbaldi, and is one of a group reattributed to Giancristoforo Romano by Weiss. Both Weiss and Hill attribute a number of struck medals to Giancristoforo on the basis of documents published by Paolo Giordani ("Studii sulla scultura romana del Rinascimento: Gian Cristoforo Romano a Roma," *L'arte* 10 (1907), pp. 197–208). These documents were found to be spurious (see Enrico Brunelli, "Jacopo d'Andrea Scultore Fiorentino del Secolo XV," *L'arte* 11 [1908], pp. 373–77, and G. de Nicola, "Falsificazione di documenti per la statua dell'arte romana," *Repertorium für Kunstwissenschaft* 32 [1909], pp. 55–60); thus the attributions cannot be supported, especially since, as Weiss notes, there is no stylistic similarity to the known cast medals by Giancristoforo. There is no documentation to support any attributions of struck medals of Julius II to Giancristoforo Romano. The reverse design is slightly smaller than the obverse, and is also known as the reverse for a medal of Clement VIII by Giorgio di Antonio Rancetti (Arm. 3, p. 148,A, 32 mm.).

Late restrike.

Bibl.: *Corpus,* no. 869 (obv.); cp. Arm. 2, p. 110,7; Naples, p. 225; Mazio, no. 34; R. Weiss, "The Medals of Pope Julius II (1503–1513)," *Journal of the Warburg and Courtauld Institutes* 28 (1965), pp. 163–82 (at p. 172, n. 86, for the reattribution); Martinori, fasc. vi, p. 67.

48 GIULIANO II DE' MEDICI (1478–1516), Duke of Nemours

Obv. Head to left. Around, MAG IVLIANVS MEDICES

Rev. Roma seated on shields, holding Victory. In field, C P; below, ROMA

Bronze, old aftercast, 33 mm.

1966.104.8

This and other medals were made for distribution to the crowds at the festivities celebrating the adoption of Giuliano as citizen and baron of Rome, 1513. A contemporary authority explains CP as *consenso pubblico*.

Bibl.: *Corpus,* no. 889; *Morgenroth,* no. 90; *Kress,* no. 241; Supino, no. 631; *MM.* 1, p. 158, no. 35,1.

49 PIUS V Ghislieri, Pope 1566–72

Obv. Bust to left, wearing cope and tiara with right hand raised in blessing. Around, · PIVS · V · GHISLERIVS · BOSCHEN · PONT · M ·

Rev. The Madonna and Child enthroned in clouds, flanked by two saints with four saints below. Around, · S · DOMIN · S · CAT · ERIN · S · THOM · AQ · | · S · HIACIN · S · RAIMVN · ; in exergue, · B · MARG · SAVO | IA

Bronze, struck, 41 mm.

1966.113.1

The Blessed Margaret of Savoy was a Dominican nun who died in 1464. The population of Alba gave her a cult immediately. It was first officially recognized by Pius V (who had been prior of the convent of Alba and vicar of the monastery) in 1566 and finally confirmed by Clement X in 1670.

Bibl.: Arm. 3, p. 264FFF; *Trésor Papes,* pl. 14,2; Venuti, p. 132, no. 32 (variant insc.); Bonnani, p. 309, no. 26 (variant insc.); Martinori, fasc. xi, p. 26.

Sixteenth Century, Padua

GIOVANNI DEL CAVINO
(1500–70)

Cavino, who worked all his life in Padua, is known for his imitations, today still called Paduans, of Roman coins, which were passed off as originals in the sixteenth century. One hundred twenty-two of Cavino's dies are preserved in the Bibliothèque Nationale in Paris.

For extensive bibliography on Cavino, see *Kress*, p. 73, to which may be added F. Cessi, *Giovanni da Cavino medaglista del Cinquecento*, Padua 1969; G. Gorini, "Appunti su Giovanni da Cavino," *La Medaglia d'Arte. Atti del primo convegno internazionale di studio*, *Udine 1970*, Udine 1973, pp. 111–20.

50 NERO, Emperor 54–68 A.D.

Obv. Head to right, laureate. Around, NERO CLAVD CAESAR AVG GER P M TR P IMP PP

Rev. Nero on horseback with spear, followed by another horseman holding banner. In field, S · C; in exergue, DECVRSIO

Bronze, struck, "Sestertius," 37 mm.

1966.108.9

Bibl.: Kress, no. 403 (obv.); Forrer 1, p. 368; Lawrence, no. 17 (imitation of a genuine coin).

51 COSIMO SCAPTI

Obv. Head to right. Around, COSMVS SCAPTIVS

Rev. Salus seated facing left, facing statue of Bacchus on a column; she gives drink from a patera to a serpent entwined on a vine branch. Around, · PM · TR · P · X IMP VI · COS · III · P · P ·; in exergue, SALVS

Bronze, struck, 38 mm.

1966.108.8

The reverse is from Cavino's "sestertius" of Commodus (Lawrence, no. 64).

Bibl.: Arm. 1, p. 184,33; *Kress*, no. 398; Forrer 1, p. 372 (ill.); Lawrence, no. 108 (says statue is Aesculapius).

52 BALDUINO DEL MONTE (d. 1556), Count of Montesansavino 1550, brother of Pope Julius III

Obv. Bust to left, wearing fur trimmed robe. Around, · BALDVINVS DE MONTE · COMES ·

Rev. Combat between two horsemen. Around, MAGIS · VICI · SED · TIBI

Lead, old aftercast, light brown patina, 40 mm.

1966.108.7

The reverse, which is larger than the obverse, belongs to a medal of Antinous by Cavino.

Bibl.: Arm. 1, p. 182,22; Rosati, no. 164; *Kress*, no. 394; Forrer 1, p. 372 (one of two reverses); Supino, no. 322; Brescia 1, p. 42, no. 272; *MM.* 1, p. 277, pl. 60,6; Lawrence, no. 99; Madrid, p. 199, no. 191.

PADUAN SCHOOL

53 GIOVANNI BATTAGLINI

Obv. Bust to left. Around, IO · BATTAGLINVS PATR · PISA ·

Rev. A stork in her nest. Around, HAEC MERVIT PIETAS PRAEMIA

Bronze, 39 mm.

1966.108.5

The stork is a symbol of filial piety, because it is said to feed its parents when they grow old. Also, by extension, it is a symbol of recognition for services rendered.

Bibl.: Forrer 1, p. 370 (as Cavino); Brescia, 1, p. 39, no. 256 (as Cavino); Supino, no. 701; Hill, N. I. A., no. 25; Tervarent, col. 97 (for the stork); F. Cessi, *Giovanni da Cavino*, Padua 1969, p. 73, no. 50 (one of five different medals of the sitter, none of which is securely attributed to Cavino).

54 CHURCH OF SANTA GIUSTINA, PADUA 1515

Obv. Busts to right, jugate, of SS. Prosdocimus and Giustina. Around, S · PROSDOCIMVS · S · IVS-TINA ·; below, C · C

Rev. Inscription, DEO | OPTIMO | ET · B · IVSTIĒ · V · | ET · M · HOC · T · D | ICA · E · ANNO | · DNI · MDXV ·

Bronze, 41 mm.

1966.104.3

The Church of Santa Giustina at Padua was begun in 1505 and soon given up; after the rejection of new designs in 1515 and 1516 it was begun again in 1521 and finished in 1532. Santa Giustina, virgin and martyr, is the patron saint of Padua; San Prosdocimus was its first bishop.

Bibl.: Corpus, no. 547; Arm. 3, p. 150G (as by Coreto Cagnoli, Paduan goldsmith active in early sixteenth century); Lanna, no. 357; Brescia 1, p. 32, no. 202 (Coreto Cagnoli?).

Sixteenth Century, Venice

JACOPO TATTI (called Sansovino) (1486–1570)

A major sculptor and architect of the sixteenth century, Jacopo took the name of his master Andrea Sansovino.

He was active in Rome until the Sack in 1527, when he moved to Venice, becoming the major sculptor there in the middle of the century.

See *Kress,* p. 78; Forrer 5, pp. 332–34. For Sansovino as a sculptor see Weihrauch in Thieme-Becker 32, pp. 465–70 and John Pope-Hennessy, *Italian High Renaissance and Baroque Sculpture,* revised ed., London/New York 1970, pp. 78–85, 350–53, 404–10.

55 TOMMASO RANGONE of Ravenna (1493–1577), known as Philologus; doctor, philosopher and astronomer

Obv. Bust to right, bearded, in gown. Around, · THOMAS · PHILOLOGVS · RAVENNAS ·

Rev. Jupiter, disguised as an eagle, brings the infant Hercules to Juno, who reclines in a circle of stars; below, lilies and birds. Around, · A · IOVE · ET · SORORE · GENITA

Bronze, 38 mm. Hole at top

1966.108.13

The reverse illustrates the mythological creation of the Milky Way and probably refers to Rangone's own adoption. Jupiter, wishing to gain immortality for his son Hercules, brings him to Juno to nurse. Her milk falling in heaven creates the Milky Way; on Earth it creates lilies.

Tommaso Rangone was a patron of both Jacopo Sansovino and Alessandro Vittoria. Sansovino is not known as a medalist, while Vittoria is. However, the handling of this medal is unlike that of Vittoria's known medals, and since Sansovino is the author of the monumental portrait of Rangone on the facade of S. Giuliano in Venice, the medal has been attributed to him.

Pasi suggests that, as the will of Rangone mentions only medals by Matteo della Fede and Vittoria, the attribution of this medal to Sansovino should be rejected. Middeldorf (private communication) maintains the attribution to Sansovino on stylistic grounds.

Bibl.: Arm. 2, p. 196,20; *Kress,* no. 417b; Habich, p. 129, pl. 86,6; Fabriczy, pp. 82–83, pl. 16,6 (as Vittoria); Supino, no. 675 (as Modenese); Brescia 1, p. 91, no. 635; *MM.* 1, p. 301, pl. 65,5 (incised in field, 1562), 6; Forrer 6, p. 288 (as Vittoria); Francesco Cessi, *Alessandro Vittoria, medaglista (1525–1608),* Trento 1960, pp. 76–77, pl. 15 (as Vittoria, ca. 1560?); E. Mandowsky, "'The Origin of the Milky Way' in the National Gallery," *Burlington Magazine* 72 (1938), pp. 88, 89, 93 (where Tintoretto's painting of the same subject is first connected to Rangone); R. Pasi, "Le medaglie del ravennate Tommaso Rangoni detto il Filologo," *Medaglia* 3, no. 6 (1973), pp. 6–24.

ANDREA SPINELLI
(1508–72)

A pupil of Gian Francesco Bonzagni, Spinelli was born in Parma, but was active principally in Venice, where he was made assistant engraver at the mint in 1535, and chief engraver in 1540.

See N. Pellicelli in Thieme-Becker 31, p. 385; Forrer 5, pp. 611–12; *Kress,* pp. 77–78.

56 ANDREA GRITTI (1454–1538), Doge of Venice 1523–38

Obv. Bust to left, in robe and cap. Around, ANDREAS · GRITI · DVX VENETIAR

Rev. Facade of the church of San Francesco della Vigna. Around, FRANCISCI DIVI

Bronze, 37 mm.

1966.108.14

Another version, with a reverse showing a view of San Francesco, signed AN. SP. F and dated 1524, is more common (Arm. 1, p. 155,4).

Bibl.: Arm. 3, p. 233A; *Trésor Ital.* 1, pl. 28,3.

VENETIAN SCHOOL

57 MARINO GRIMANI, Doge of Venice 1595–1605 1595

Obv. Bust to right, wearing doge's hat and brocaded robe. Around, MARIN · GRIMANVS DVX · VENETIAR

Rev. Lion of Saint Mark rampant to left, holding cross. Around, · SYDERA · · CORDIS · ; in exergue, · 1595

Bronze, 38 mm.

1966.119.2

Bibl.: Arm. 2, p. 273,1; *Salton,* no. 74; Vogel sale, Frankfort, 4 November 1924, no. 56, p. 10, pl. 9; Lanna, no. 295; Löbbecke, no. 39 (gilded); Supino, no. 797; Brescia 1, p. 106, no. 752; *Trésor Ital.* 2, pl. 27,3; Cicogna, vol. 2, pt. 2.

Sixteenth Century, Lombardy

JACOPO NIZOLLA DA TREZZO
(1515/19–89)

Jacopo Nizolla was born in Milan, first distinguished himself as a gem engraver, and worked for Cosimo III de'Medici. He entered the service of Philip II of Spain in 1550, and worked for him as sculptor, architect, gem engraver and medalist both in Spain and the Netherlands. His first medal is that of Gianello della Torre of ca. 1550.

See Thieme-Becker 33, pp. 392–93; Forrer 6, pp. 132–39; *Kress,* pp. 83–84; Hill, *Med. Ren.,* p. 101; Supino, pp. 140–42.

58 GIANELLO DELLA TORRE (1500–85), Cremonese military architect in the service of Charles V

Without obverse

Rev. The Fountain of the Sciences. Around, VIRTVS; in exergue, NVNQ : DEFICIT

Bronze, hollow cast, 80 mm.

1966.108.10

The reverse is an allusion to a hydraulic machine which della Torre made to raise water from the Tagus to Toledo. Armand notes that the same design appears on a cameo in the Cabinet de France. The reverse type also appears on an unsigned medal of Philip II (Arm. 1, p. 168,27). Since the medal of Philip derives from one by Leone Leoni, the medal of della Torre has been given to him also. However, since Jacopo is known to have copied Leoni's types on at least one other occasion, the medal of Ippolita di Ferdinando Gonzaga (see no. 59), and since Jacopo and della Torre both worked in Spain for long periods, the medal is probably by Jacopo. It is normally dated about 1550.

Bibl.: Arm. 1, p. 170,38; 3, p. 74nn; 3, p. 115C; *Kress,* no. 441a (rev.); *Salton,* no. 67 (as Leone Leoni); Habich, pl. 93,8; Lanna, no. 227, pl. 15; Supino, no. 417, pl. 40; Forrer 6, pp. 133, 134 (ill.); Fabriczy, pl. 39,4; *MM.* 1, p. 215, pl. 49,1; E. Plon, *Leone Leoni et Pompeo Leoni,* Paris 1887, pp. 273–74, pl. 34,8,9; Hill, *N. I. A.,* no. 330 (for a different medal of della Torre describing him as architect to Philip II); Rosenheim sale catalog, Sotheby, 30 April 1923, no. 133 (as Leoni); Molinier 2, no. 353 (example in the Louvre as reverse of medal of Philip II, attributed to Leoni); Madrid, p. 231, no. 270.

59 IPPOLITA DI FERDINANDO GONZAGA (1535–63) 1552

Obv. Bust to left, wearing double necklace and loose drapery. Around, HIPPOLYTA · GONZAGA · FERDINANDI · FIL · AN · XVII; below, IAC TREZ

Rev. Aurora, in a chariot drawn by a winged horse, holds a torch and scatters flowers. Around, VIRTVTIS FORMÆQ PRAEVIA

Bronze, 67 mm. Hole at top

1966.106.16

The obverse portrait derives from a Leone Leoni prototype of the year before. Ippolita married Fabrizio Colonna (died 1551) in 1548 and Antonio Caraffa in 1554.

Bibl.: Arm. 1, p. 241,1; *Salton,* no. 68; Rosati, no. 181; *Kress,* no. 438; Habich, p. 134, pl. 94,4; Naples, p. 92; Supino, no. 412; Brescia 1, p. 51, no. 336; *MM.* 1, pp. 327–28, pl. 70,5; Madrid, p. 169, no. 276; Magnaguti, no. 138, pl. 22; Tervarent, cols. 78 (Car of Aurora), 79 (ref. to medal, 1552); 182, 191 (attributes of Aurora).

GIOVANNI V. MELON

The medalist was thought by Milanesi (*apud* Armand 3,125) to have been from Cremona, a nephew of Altobello Melone, which Hill accepted with reservation. The medals date between 1571–89.

See Forrer 4, pp. 17–19; Supino, pp. 156–57; Martinori fasc. xi, pp. 70–71, 82–83; fasc. xii, pp. 8, 38; Hill in Thieme-Becker 24, p. 368; *Kress,* pp. 121–22.

60 ALESSANDRO FARNESE (1520–89), Cardinal, 1534 1575

Obv. Bust to right, in cape. Around, ALEXANDER CARD · FARN · S · R · E · VICECAN; on truncation, · IO · V · MILON · F ·

Rev. Facade of the Gesù. Around, FECIT ANNO · · DOM · MDLXXV; below, ROMAE

Bronze, struck, 48 mm.

1966.108.1

Farnese was the founder of the Church of Il Gesù and had laid the cornerstone in 1568. This medal commemorates the completion of Giacomo Della Porta's facade in 1575. The building was consecrated in 1584.

Bibl.: Arm. 1, p. 264,3; 3, p. 126,a.

61 ALESSANDRO FARNESE 1575

Obv. Same as no. 60

Rev. Facade of the Gesù in Rome. Around, FECIT ANNO SAL · MDLXXV; below, ROMAE

Gilt bronze, struck, 46 mm.

1966.108.2

See no. 60.

Bibl.: Arm. 1, p. 264,3; Forrer 4, p. 18; Naples, p. 110; Lanna, no. 248; Supino, no. 475; Brescia 1, p. 57, no. 376; *MM.* 1, p. 407, pl. 91,7.

Sixteenth Century, Emilia

ALFONSO DA TOMASO RUSPAGIARI
(1521–76)

Active in Reggio Emilia, Ruspagiari became superintendent of the mint there in 1571. Very little is known of his career. Ruspagiari leads a group of artists whose medals are finely modeled in low relief and who tend to portray romantic women and heroic men in informal poses.

See Thieme-Becker 29, pp. 225–26; Forrer 5, pp. 272–75; *Kress,* pp. 85–86; Hill, *Med. Ren.,* p. 102; Habich, pp. 138–39; Hill, N. I. A., nos. 278, 358; Bernhart, pp. 75, 85, 88.

62 ERCOLE II D'ESTE (1508–59), fourth Duke of Ferrara, 1534

Obv. Bust seen frontally with head to right, wearing lionskin robe of Hercules. Around, DVX FERRARIAE IIII

Without reverse

Lead, 65 mm.

1966.108.3

Bibl.: Arm. 1, p. 218,14; Forrer 5, p. 275; Heraeus, pl. 55,5 (with reverse of river god with lamb in landscape, FELICITATI · TEMPORVM · S · P · Q · F ·).

63 UNKNOWN LADIES

Obv. Bust seen partly from behind, head to left, wearing veil which falls behind and joins drapery, covering back and breast and leaving left shoulder bare

Rev. Bust to left, wearing veil which falls over right shoulder; thin bodice and sleeves of dress held up by a loose band over shoulders

Bronze, 62 mm.

1966.104.16

Bibl.: Arm. 1, p. 216,4 (obv. only, oval); *Kress,* no. 449 (obv. only, oval); Hill-*Notes,* p. 241, pl. 2R.

AGOSTINO ARDENTI
(active ca. 1563)

An artist who signs himself AA and works in a free, sometimes rough style related to that of Ruspagiari.

See Rosenheim and Hill, "Notes on Some Italian Medals," *Burlington Magazine* 12 (1907–08), pp. 141–54 (at 141–47); R. F. Burckhardt, "Über die Medaillensammlung des Ludovic Demoulin de Rochefort im Historischen Museum zu Basel," *Anzeiger für Schweizerischer Altertumskunde,* NF. 20 (1918), pp. 36–53 (at pp. 42–49); Hill, *Med. Ren.,* p. 103; Hill, N. I. A., nos. 10, 11, 78, 113, 215; Staatliche Museen zu Berlin, *Die italienischen Bronzen der Renaissance und des Barock,* bearbeitet von E. F. Bange, Berlin/Leipzig 1922, nos. 256–59; Bernhart, p. 77 (Lucretia Grilinciona?); G. F. Hill, "Some Italian Medals of the Sixteenth Century," *Georg Habich zum 60. Geburtstag,* Munich 1928, pp. 11–12.

64 TITIAN

Obv. Half-length portrait to right, holding a framed picture. Around, TITIANI PICTORIS EXIMII . EFFIGIESI . A . ; below, on scroll, HORATIVS FIL

Without reverse

Lead, bronzed and painted, 103 mm.

1966.106.21

The medal represents Titian holding a portrait of his son Orazio. Hill dates it, with the rest of Ardenti's medals, about 1563, when Orazio would have been about forty.

Other medals of Titian are noted in Arm. 1, pp. 166, 208; Brescia 1, p. 37, no. 241; p. 121, no. 854; *Trésor Ital.* 2, pl. 38,1; and Hill-*Artists,* p. 57.

Bibl.: G. F. Hill, "Some Italian Medals of the Sixteenth Century," *Georg Habich zum 60. Geburtstag,* Munich 1928, p. 11.

Sixteenth Century, Italian School

MEDALIST M. B.

An unknown medal engraver, whose works are dated 1586–90 and signed M., M. B. or Mo. B.

See Forrer 4, p. 2; Arm. 1, pp. 293–94.

65 SIXTUS V Peretti, Pope 1585–90   1588

Obv. Bust to right, wearing cope. Around, SIXTVS · V · PONT · MAX · ANO · IIII; on truncation, M · B ·

Rev. Obelisk in front of cityscape of Rome. Around, QVARTVM · ANNO* * QVARTO · EREXIT; below, *1588

Bronze, struck, 46 mm.

1966.113.17

Commemorates erection of obelisk in Piazza del Popolo. See no. 45.

Bibl.: Arm. 1, p. 294,1 (as M. D.); Forrer 4, p. 2; Brescia 2, p. 12, no. 155; Venuti, p. 163, no. 20; Bonnani, p. 419, no. 32; Martinori, fasc. xii, p. 37; *Trésor Papes,* pl. 19,7 (rev.).

ATTRIBUTED TO MEDALIST M. B.

66 URBAN VII Castagna, Pope 1590   1590

Obv. Bust to left, wearing cope. Around, · VRBANVS · VII · PONT · MAX · ANNO · I · ; below, M · D · L · XXXX

Rev. Seven-branched candelabrum. Around, SIC · LVCEAT · LVX · VESTRA ·

Bronze, 39 mm. Hole near top

1966.113.62

Bibl.: Arm. 3, p. 141D; Forrer 4, p. 2 (signed variant); Naples, p. 133; Supino, no. 530; Brescia 2, p. 12, no. 160; Mazio, no. 147; Venuti, p. 176, no. 2; Bonnani, pp. 433–37, no. 3; Martinori, fasc. xii, p. 60.

ITALIAN—UNATTRIBUTED

67 ANTINOUS

Obv. Nude bust to left. Around, ANTINOOC HPωC

Rev. Antinous reclining on a flying griffin. Around, ΚΑΛΧΑΔΟΝΙΟΙC; below, ΙΠΠΩΝ

Bronze, 39 mm.

1966.108.18

The type is based on a Greek imperial coin of Calchedon, Bithynia.

Bibl.: Kress, no. 516; Gustave Blum, "Numismatique d' Antinoos," *Journal International d'Archéologie Numismatique* 16 (1914), pp. 33–70 (coin prototype at p. 47, no. 1).

68 ANTONIO AGOSTINO DI SARAGOSSA (1516–86), celebrated antiquarian and numismatist, Bishop of Lerida, 1561, and of Tarragona, 1576

Obv. Bust to left. Around, ΑΝΤ ΑΥΓΟΥCΤΙΝ ΕΡICΚΙΛΕΡΔ

Rev. Monogram of Christ. Around, ΓΝΩΘΙ CΑΥΤΟΝ ΚΑΙ ΘΕΟΝ; in field, ΑΩ; below, seven stars

Bronze, struck, 43 mm.

1966.119.3

Bibl.: Arm. 2, p. 244,1; *MM.* 1, p. 386, pl. 86,7; Brescia 1, p. 101, no. 711 (obv. insc. adds EY · NE); Supino, no. 835; Durand, p. 244.

69 PIERIO VALERIANO BOLZANIO (1475–1558)

Obv. Bust to right. Around, · PIERIVS · VALERIANVS · BELLVNENSIS

Rev. Mercury, holding caduceus and resting left hand on obelisk inscribed with hieroglyphics. Between, INSTAVRATOR

Bronze, 60 mm.

1966.106.12

Made about 1545–50, probably at Padua; other medals by the same hand represent Fra Urbano Bolzanio and Florio Maresio. The reverse alludes to Piero's work *Hieroglyphica* (published at Basel in 1556). In 1545 Piero had marble medallion portraits of himself and Fra Urbano put outside the door of the Frari Church towards S. Rocco. These portraits seem to be dependent on the medals of the two men, which would mean the medals must date from 1545 or earlier.

Bibl.: Arm. 2, p. 176,14; *Kress,* no. 507 *bis; MM.* 1, p. 296, pl. 64,4; Brescia 1, p. 89, no. 622; G. F. Hill, "Medals of the Bolzanio Family," *Archiv für Medaillen- und Plakettenkunde* 1 (October 1913), pp. 1–6.

70 CHRIST

Obv. Bust to left, nimbate. Around, EGO SVM VIA VERITAS ET VITA

Rev. Crucifixion with Mary, Saint John and Mary Magdalene. Around, · ECCE · MATER · TVA · · MVLIER · ECCE · FILIVS · TVVS ·

Bronze, 89 mm.

1966.107.11

North Italian.

The detailed handling and sharply rounded surfaces indicate that the medal may be the work of a gem engraver. Hill suggests Giovanni Antonio de' Rossi.

Bibl.: Arm. 2, p. 7,2 (obv. only; as before fifteenth c.); Hill-*Christ,* p. 62, no. 5; p. 61, fig. 32 (obv. only); Lanna, no. 355 (obv. only); Supino, no. 608 (obv. only).

71 CHRIST

Obv. Christ wearing loincloth and holding cross stands in landscape with castle in background. Around, SINE IPSO FACTVM EST NICHIL

Without reverse

Bronze, 46 mm.

1966.116.1

This is the reverse of a medal of Christ illustrated in Hill, *Medallic Portraits of Christ.*

Bibl.: Arm. 2, p. 7,3; Hill-*Christ,* p. 65, no. 12; p. 66, fig. 38.

72 LIVIA COLONNA (d. 1552), wife of Marzio Colonna, married 1540

Obv. Bust to left. Around, LIVIA COLVMNA

Rev. A cupid leads a bacchante to right

Bronze, 39 mm. Hole at top

1966.106.5

Armand says the same reverse is found on several other medals, including one of Titian by Leone Leoni (vol. 1, p. 166,21).

This specimen from auction at Hotel Drouet, Paris, 15 June 1923, no. 49.

Bibl.: Arm. 2, p. 170,29; *Trésor Ital.* 2, pl. 43,2.

73 VITTORIA COLONNA (1490–1547), married, 1507, to Fernando Francesco I d'Avalos (ca. 1490–1525), Marquis of Pescara

Obv. Bust to left, with floating hair. Around, VICTORIA · COLVMNIA · DAVALA ·

Without reverse

Gilt bronze, 47 mm.

1966.106.6

Bibl.: Arm. 2, p. 107,7; *Kress,* no. 485.

74 ERCOLE II D' ESTE (1508–59), fourth Duke of Ferrara

Obv. Bust to right, wearing armor. Around, HER · II · DVX · FERRARIAE · IIII

Rev. Female draped figure, half seated to right, holding cornucopia in left hand. In exergue, FERRARIA

Gilt bronze, 41 mm. Hole at top. Worn

1966.106.4

Bibl.: Arm. 2, p. 147,3.

75 INNOCENZO FRANCUCCI, called INNOCENZO DA IMOLA, painter (1494–1549)

Obv. Bust to right. Around, INNOCENTIVS · FRANCHVTIVS

Rev. Scratched on, 1877 | In Firenze | Memoria | Ma pia casa | di Lavoro | Visitata il | 28 giugno | 1877

Lead, 71 mm. Hole at top

1966.107.10

Bibl.: Arm. 3, p. 230P (as Imolese; Armand mentions reverses of this medal); Hill-*Artists,* p. 51, no. 27, pl. 23 (medal has something of the Venetian style, but may have been produced in Bologna).

76 GIAN BATTISTA MALVEZZI

Obv. Bust to left, wearing cuirass. Around, IO : BAP · MALVETIVS · EQVES · A [C ·] COMES · BON · ETATIS · AN · XX7 ·

Rev. A palm tree flanked by two hanging boxes. Around, ACCEDO · SED · NON · SVCEDO · ONERI

Bronze, 59 mm. Hole at top

1966.106.15

Bolognese. Malvezzi was one of the Anziani in 1534.

Our medal has a reverse unsigned, but with legend ending in a leaf.

Bibl.: Arm. 3, p. 56A (as IO. F., signed on reverse).

77 PAOLO PELLICANI (b. 1528)   1556

Obv. Bust to left. Around, PAVL - S PELLICANVS AE -- T ---- · XXX · A · M · D · LVI ·

Rev. Pelican with wings outspread, nursing her young on her blood. Around, AMORIS MAXIMA

Bronze, 48 mm. Hole at top

1966.106.13

Bibl.: Arm. 2, p. 303,16*bis* (with different reverse inscription); *Trésor Ital.* 2, pl. 39,4 (with different reverse inscription); Bernhart, p. 82 (reverse insc. as * MAXIMA * – + VIS + – * AMORIS * below P * P; Munich, bronze, 49 mm.).

78 GIACOMO SAVELLI (d. 1587), Cardinal, 1539 1576

Obv. Bust to right, wearing mozzetta. Around, IACOBVS · S · R · E · PRESB · CARD · SABELLVS · ; on truncation, · 1576 ·

Rev. A ship at sea with personifications of winds blowing the sails. Around, AGOR · NON · OBRVOR

Bronze, 46 mm.

1966.114.61

Bibl.: Arm. 2, p. 219,26; *MM.* 1, p. 405, pl. 91,3 (dated in field).

79 GABRIELE SERBELLONI (1508–80), Italian General

Obv. Pallas Athena seated on military trophies, facing right, holding Victory in left hand. Around, GABRIELI · SERBELLONO · S · P · Q · R ·

Rev. View of fortified city of Rome. In exergue, VRBE COMMVNITA

Bronze, 74 mm. Hole at top

1966.119.6

Serbelloni fought for Charles V and Philip II, distinguishing himself at the Battle of Lepanto. In 1560–65 he fought for Pius IV, and fortified the Vatican and Castel S. Angelo.

Bibl.: Arm. 3, p. 251,1; Supino, no. 672; Brescia 1, p. 94, no. 656.

80 SUBJECT UNKNOWN

Obv. Bust to right, wearing cuirass and ruff

Rev. Inscription, OPTI | MO | PRINCI | PI

Bronze, 44 mm. Hole at top

1966.119.5

Probably North Italian.

Bibl.: Sammlung von Renaissance-Kunstwerken gestiftet von Herrn James Simon zum 18 Oktober 1904

(Kaiser Friedrich-Museum), Berlin 1904, no. 371; Hill, N. I. A., no. 367.

81 MEDAL OF CHRIST

Obv. Bust to left. In field, א ישו

Rev. Inscription, עשוי | לום ואדמא | מלך באבש | משיה | חי | דם

Bronze, 35 mm.

1966.116.3

Sixteenth century or later.

This is the most common of all medals of Christ, which originated in sixteenth-century Italy and were used as talismen.

Bibl.: Hill-*Christ,* p. 50, no. 2a.

Seventeenth-Eighteenth Century, Rome

GIACOMO ANTONIO MORO (d. 1624)

Medalist and coin engraver from Milan, master of the papal mint from 1610–24 under Paul V and Gregory XV.

See Forrer 4, pp. 152–53; Thieme-Becker 25, p. 162.

82 PAUL V Borghese, Pope 1605–21 1614

Obv. Bust to left, in cope. Around, PAVLVS · V · PONT · MAX · AN · VIIII · ; below, I · AMORI ·

Rev. The facade of Saint Peter's with bell towers. Around, · IN · HONOREM · PRINCIPIS · APOST · ; in exergue, · ET · PORTÆ · INFI · NŌ · | · P̄VⱢEBV̄T ·

Bronze, struck, 38 mm.

1966.113.11

Paul V commissioned Carlo Maderno to add towers to his facade of Saint Peter's in 1612. This medal shows the basilica as projected with towers. They were not completed, but were built as far as the substructure which forms the two end bays of the facade. See no. 83 for a medal of 1608 showing the facade without these substructures. The reverse inscription is from Matthew 16:18.

Bibl.: Forrer 4, p. 153; Brescia 2, p. 14, no. 185; Mazio, no. 172; Venuti, p. 209, no. 10; Bonnani, p. 507, no. 7; Bonnani, *Tempio Vaticano,* p. 145; Martinori, fasc. xiii, p. 112.

PAOLO SANQUIRICO
(1565–1630)

Sculptor, architect and medalist, born at Villa di San Quirico near Parma. He came to Rome as a young man and was a pupil of the sculptor Camillo Mariani and the mint master G. A. Moro. The majority of Sanquirico's medals are of Pope Paul V. He stopped making medals long before his death and worked primarily as a monumental sculptor (for example carving the statue of Paul V in S. Maria Maggiore) and portraitist in wax.

See Forrer 5, pp. 331–32; N. Pelicelli in Thieme-Becker 29, p. 416; Bernhart, p. 74 (medal of G. B. Deti); Bulgari 2, p. 374; Pyke, p. 127.

83 PAUL V Borghese, Pope 1605–21   1608

Obv. Bust to right, wearing cope. Around, PAVLVS · V · BVRGHESIVS ROM · PONT · MAX · A · S · MDC · VIII PONT · III · ; below truncation, P · SANQVIRIC ·

Rev. The Basilica of Saint Peter's. Around, TEM · D · PETRI · IN · VATICANO; in exergue, ET · POR-TAE · INFIRI · NON | PRAEVALEBVNT

Bronze, struck, 57 mm.

1966.113.14

Under Paul V, Carlo Maderno added the nave, portico and facade to Saint Peter's, beginning in 1607. This medal depicts the facade of the church as planned in 1608. Four years later Paul V commissioned bell towers, which were never completed and which exist as substructures today. See no. 82 for a medal showing the later projected facade.

The reverse inscription is from Matthew 16:18.

Bibl.: Forrer 5, p. 332; Brescia 2, p. 15, no. 199; Venuti, p. 209, no. 11; Bonnani, p. 507, no. 6; Bonnani, *Tempio Vaticano,* p. 145; Martinori, fasc. xiii, p. 112; *Trésor Papes,* pl. 25,5.

84 PAUL V Borghese   1613

Obv. Bust to right, in biretta, mozzetta and stole. Around, PAVLVS · V · BVRGHESIVS · RO · PONT · MAX · A · D · MDCXIII · P · IX · ; below truncation, PAVL · SANQVIR ·

Rev. View of port and castle. In field, COL · IVL · |

FANESTRIS; around, + PORTV · BVRGHESIO · A · FVNDAMEN · EXTRVCTO

Bronze, struck, 59 mm. Hole at top

1966.113.13

The port of Fano was fortified by Paul V in 1614. The reverse inscription refers to the fact that Fano was a Roman colony under Julius Caesar.

Bibl.: Venuti, p. 213, no. 23; Bonnani, p. 539, no. 32; Martinori, fasc. xiii, p. 116; *Trésor Papes,* pl. 26,7; Brescia 2, p. 14, no. 191.

GASPARE MOLA
(ca. 1580–1640)

Goldsmith, medalist and coin engraver, born in Coldrè near Como, trained as a goldsmith in Milan. From 1609–11 Mola was chief engraver at the Florentine mint, making Medici medals and probably coins. In 1613–14 he was at the mints at Guastalla and Mantua, working for the Gonzaga. He settled finally in Rome where he succeeded Giacomo Antonio Moro as mint master from 1625–39. Mola was also a skilled armorer and executed a helm and shield now in the Bargello which were once attributed to Cellini.

See Forrer 4, pp. 111–17; 8, p. 68; Fr. Noack and G. F. Hill in Thieme-Becker 25, pp. 27–28; *Kress,* p. 68; Rosati, pp. 54–55; Bulgari 2, p. 160; Pyke, p. 93.

85 MARIA MAGDALENA OF AUSTRIA (1591–1631), Grand Duchess of Tuscany, married Cosimo II de' Medici, 1608

Obv. Bust to left, in cape and hood. Around, MARIA · MAGD · ARCHID · AVSTR · MAGN · DVX · ETR

Without reverse

Lead, 40 mm. Hole at top

1966.108.15

Executed after 1621, when the Grand Duchess was widowed.

Several specimens of this medal exist with the inscription reading MAG instead of MAGN (Forrer 4, p. 114; Fabriczy, pl. 36,7; with reverse of flying pea-hen; Heraeus, no. 62,26; and Supino, no. 604, with signature).

86 URBAN VIII Barberini, Pope 1623–44   1638

Obv. Bust to right, wearing cope. Around, VRBANVS · VIII · PON · MAX · A · XV · ; below, GASP . MOL .

Rev. View of the summer palace at Castel Gandolfo. Around, SVBVRBANO RECESSV CONSTRVCTO; in exergue, ROMAE

Gilt bronze, struck, 41 mm. Hole at top

1966.113.35

The palace at Castel Gandolfo was built by Urban VIII.

Bibl.: Forrer 4, p. 116; Brescia 2, p. 18, no. 230; Mazio, no. 206; Venuti, p. 237, no. 41; Bonnani, pp. 594–95, no. 31; Martinori, fasc. xiv, p. 75; Bartolotti, no. E. 638.

ATTRIBUTED TO GASPARE MOLA

87 NICHOLAS, Duke of Asinaglossi

Obv. Bust to right. Around, D · NICCOLO · DVCA · D'ASINAGLOSSI; on truncation, [INITIALS?] · 16–2

Without reverse

Lead, oval, 65 x 53 mm. Hole at top

1966.130.3

ALESSANDRO ASTESANO
(Born 1604, active at papal mint 1622–33)

From Turin, the son of Orazio Astesano. In 1622 Alessandro was appointed to replace Gaspare Mola as engraver at the papal mint. He took office in 1623 and prepared gold and silver medals for distribution at the Washing of the Feet on Holy Thursday. After May there is no official notice of him again except for payments of 1632 and 1633; regular payments are again to Mola.

See Bertolotti, pp. 221,222; Forrer 8, p. 309; Bulgari 1, p. 79.

88 URBAN VIII Barberini, Pope 1623–44   1632

Obv. Bust to right, wearing cope. Around, VRBANVS* VIII* PONT* MAX * A * VIIII; on truncation, M · DC · XXXII · ; below truncation, A · ASTESSANO · F ·

Rev. Aerial view of the port of Civitavecchia flanked by two bees. Around, NVNC RE PERFECTO

Gilt bronze, struck, 43 mm.

1966.113.2

New fortifications of the port of Civitavecchia.

Bibl.: Mazio, no. 193; Venuti, p. 232, no. 25; Bonnani,

p. 586, no. 24; Forrer 8, p. 309; Bertolotti, pp. 221, 222; Martinori, fasc. xiv, p. 90 (records paying six *scudi* to A. Astesano for expenses of trip to Civitavecchia to take the plan for the reverse of the medal, made for the festival of Saints Peter and Paul); p. 60 (obverse designed by G. Mola); Bulgari 1, p. 79 (record of the assay of the medal in gold, 12 July 1632); Bartolotti, no. E.632; Houston, no. 248 (very similar medal with obverse by Mola, dated 1634).

GASPARE MORONI (or Moroni-Mola)
(d. 1669)

From Milan, Moroni was the nephew of Gaspare Mola. Although he is first noted in 1633 as engraver at the Mantuan mint, the medal of Vincenzo II Gonzaga (d. 1627) is signed by him. Moroni later went to Rome where he had joined his uncle in partnership by 1637. He succeeded Mola as engraver to the papal mint and from 1640–65 executed the annual pontifical medals and most of the coins for Popes Urban VIII, Innocent X, Alexander VII and Clement IX. Girolamo Lucenti, who eventually succeeded him, became his assistant in 1668.

See Forrer 4, pp. 153–57; Fr. Noack in Thieme-Becker 25, p. 165; Magnaguti, *Mant.,* pp. 60, 102–03, 168–69 (documents); Bulgari 2, p. 182, fig. 15; Rosati, pp. 55–56.

89 VINCENZO II GONZAGA (1595–1627), seventh Duke of Mantua, 1626

Obv. Bust to left, in ruff and cuirass. Around, VINCEN II · D · G · DVX · MANT · VII · ET · M · F · V · ; below, G · MORON

Rev. Hound standing three-quarters to left. Around, · FERIS · TANTVM · INFENSVS ·

Bronze, 45 mm.

1966.108.4

Vincenzo was the last of the main branch of Gonzaga Dukes.

Bibl.: Salton, no. 49; Rosati, no. 220; Forrer 4, p. 156; Brescia 1, p. 116, nos. 820–21; Magnaguti-*Mant.,* nos. 73, 74.

90 INNOCENT X Pamphili, Pope 1644–55   1655

Obv. Bust to left, wearing cap and mozzetta. Around, INNOCEN · X · PONT · MAX · A · XI; below, · GM ·

Rev. In a wreath, the dove of the Holy Spirit above inscription, REPLEVIT | ORBEM | TERRARVM

Bronze, struck, 38 mm. Restrike

1966.113.24

The dove is also the device of the Pamphili family.

Bibl.: Forrer 4, p. 156; Mazio, no. 247; Venuti, p. 256, no. 37 (as Gaspare Mola); Bonnani, pp. 627–28, no. 19; Martinori, fasc. xv, p. 37.

91 ALEXANDER VII Chigi, Pope 1655–67 1658

Obv. Bust to right, wearing cap and mozzetta. Around, ALEXAN · VII · PONT · MAX · A · IIII · ; below, MDCLVIII · GM ·

Rev. Facade of church. Around, DILEXI · DOMINE · DECOREM · DOMVS · TVÆ; in exergue * S : NI-COLAO · *

Gilt bronze, 63 mm.

1966.113.38

The reverse shows the facade of Bernini's church at Castel Gandolfo which Alexander commissioned in 1658. Initially dedicated to Saint Nicholas, it was later rededicated to the newly canonized Saint Thomas of Villanova, in 1659. The reverse inscription is from Psalms 25:8.

Bibl.: Forrer 4, p. 156; Brescia 2, p. 20, cp. no. 253; Mazio, no. 258; Venuti, p. 262, no. 16; Bonnani, p. 651, no. 13; *Trésor Papes,* pl. 33,4 (rev.).

JOHANN JAKOB KORNMANN
(also known as Giovanni Jacopo Cormano)
(mid-seventeenth century)

Goldsmith, medalist, wax modeler, born in Augsburg. In 1630 he was active as a wax modeler in Venice and he became medalist to Urban VIII, Innocent X and many cardinals. He made many enemies in Rome and is believed to have been a professional rival of both Mola and Morone-Mola. Known for his licentious speaking, he reportedly represented Pope Innocent X on a medal with his mistress, Olimpia Maldalchini, as a result of which he was tried before the Inquisition and put in prison. Martinori (fasc. xiv, pp. 69–70, n. 2) denies that a feud with Mola could have caused Cormano's fall from favor and subsequent suicide, since Mola died in 1640 and Cormano was active in making medals of Pope Innocent X in 1644–45. The artist may have remained active until 1672 for a medal of Flavio Orsini, Duke of Bracciano, bearing that date and signed by Cormano is recorded (Pollard, *Udine,* p. 159, n. 10).

See Forrer 3, pp. 206–08; Thieme-Becker 21, p. 319; *Kress,* p. 92; Pyke, p. 74, fig. 155.

92 PAOLO GIORDANO II ORSINI (1591–1656), Count of Anglaria, Duke of Bracciano, Prince of the Holy Roman Empire 1621

Obv. Head to right. Around, PAVL · IORD · II · DG · ANG · C · BRACC · DVX · SRI · P · ; on truncation, 1621

Rev. Minerva, holding shield and spear, stands by flowering bush. Behind, Neptune, drawn by two horses, on the sea. Around, VT · VTRVNQVE · TEMPVS ·

Bronze, struck, 32 mm.

1966.130.9

The medals of the Duke of Bracciano have been used to identify and date busts of the duke attributed to Bernini (see Wittkower, *Gian Lorenzo Bernini,* London 1966, cat. nos. 36a,b).

Bibl.: Kress, p. 92; Brescia 1, p. 115, nos. 807–08; *MM.* 2, p. 51, pl. 111,1; Forrer 3, pp. 207, 208.

93 FILIPPO PIROVANI, jurisconsult 1641

Obv. Bust to right. Around, PHILIPPVS · PIROVA-NVS · S · ROTÆ · ROMANÆ · DECANVS; below, [OPVS CORMANI 1641]

Rev. A ship at sea. Around, SALVS · NOSTRA · A · DOMINO

Bronze, aftercast, 90 mm.

1966.106.19

Bibl.: Houston, no. 251 (without rev.); *Kress,* p. 92; Forrer 3, pp. 206–07 (ill.); Brescia 1, p. 118, no. 829; *MM.* 2, p. 25, pl. 106,1.

94 CHRISTOPH WIDMAN (1615–60), Cardinal, 1647 1648

Obv. Bust to right. Around, CHRISTOPHORVS · S · R · E · CARD · VIDMAN · ; on truncation, OPVS · CORMANI

Rev. Two chamois. Around, ODIT · TAMEN · OTIA · VICTOR · ; in exergue, [MDC?] XXXX [VIII?]

Bronze, struck, 38 mm. (irregular)

1966.130.25

Bibl.: Kress, p. 92 (other specimens in the British Museum and Cambridge); Forrer 3, p. 207; Pyke, p. 74, fig. 155 (a wax model of Widman).

ATTRIBUTED TO KORNMANN

95 HENRI DE FOIX (1591–1639), Duke of Candalle, soldier

Obv. Bust to left. Around, HENR · FOX · VALETTÆ · DVX · CANDALLÆ · PAR · FR ·

Rev. Stemma, draped and crowned, surmounted by eagle

Bronze, 42 mm.

1966.130.32

A medal of Henri de Foix by Cormano is noted in Forrer (3, p. 208) and *Kress* (p. 92). The portrait and style of lettering of our medal are very close to Cormano's illustrated in Rondot.

Henri was in the service of the Venetian army from 1624–33 and commander of the Italian army in 1638–39 (he died at the siege of Casal). The medal could have been cast during either of these periods.

Bibl.: Rondot, p. 408, pl. 29,1 (with similar obverse signed I. I. Koremano and different reverse).

GIOACCHINO FRANCESCO TRAVANI (d. 1675)

Master goldsmith, engraver of seals and medalist, active in Rome 1634–74. In 1655 Travani was consul of the Roman guild of goldsmiths, and from 1655(?) to 1674 was employed as an engraver at the mint. The sitters for his medals include Pope Alexander VII, Queen Christina of Sweden, and Medici dukes.

See Forrer 6, pp. 129–30; 8, p. 238; Thieme-Becker 33, p. 360; Martinori, fasc. xv, pp. 35, 66, 67, 71, 77; Bulgari 2, p. 482; Bartolotti, pp. 77–81, 415 (document no. 44); Dworschak (for the medals of Alexander VII).

96 ALEXANDER VII Chigi 1659

Obv. Bust to left, wearing cap, mozzetta and stole. Around, ALEXANDER · VII · P · M · PIVS · IVST · OPT · SENEN · PATR · GENTE · CHISIVS · MDCLIX

Rev. Androcles and the lion in the arena. Around, MVNIFICO · PRINCIPI · DOMINICVS · IACOBATIVS; below, on scroll, ET · FERA · MEMOR · BENEFICII ·

Bronze, 94 mm.

1966.113.39

The medal was commissioned by Domenico Iacobacci, a Roman noble, to commemorate the Pope's refusal to have a statue of himself erected on the capitol. Dworschak states that it was designed by Bernini and executed by Travani, an attribution supported by Pollard. De Caro Balbi suggests that the medal was designed by Gianfrancesco Romanelli.

Bibl.: Houston, no. 255; Brescia 2, p. 20, no. 260; Venuti, p. 264, no. 20; Bonnani, pp. 697–99, no. 40; *Trésor Papes,* pl. 30,2; Dworschak, pp. 27–41; Pollard, *Udine,* pp. 148–49, fig. 13; De Caro Balbi, pp. 9–11.

97 ALEXANDER VII Chigi 1659

Obv. Bust to left, wearing cap, mozzetta and stole. Around, ALEXANDER * VII * P * M * PIVS * IVST * OPT * SENEN * PATR * GENTE * CHISIVS * MDCLIX * ; on truncation, FT · F

Rev. Fortified port at Civitavecchia. Above, on scroll, NAVALE CENTVMCELL

Bronze, 66 mm.

1966.113.40

In 1659 and 1660 Alexander enlarged and fortified the port of Civitavecchia. The effigy is after a design by Bernini.

Bibl.: Brescia 2, p. 20, no. 261; Venuti, p. 265, no. 3; Bonnani, pp. 658–59, no. 20; *Trésor Papes,* pl. 31,4; Pollard, *Udine,* pp. 148–49; De Caro Balbi, p. 13 and fig. 1.

98 ALEXANDER VII Chigi 1662

Obv. Bust to left, wearing cope decorated with Christ carrying the cross and tiara. Around, ALEX · VII · PONT · MAX · A · VII · ; below truncation, 1662

Rev. Church of Santa Maria dell'Assunzione, Ariccia. Around, * BENE · FVNDATA · DOMVS · DOMINI * ; below, on scroll, B · VIRGINI ARICINORVM PATRONAE ·

Bronze, old aftercast, 65 mm. Diagonal casting crack on reverse

1966.114.73

See no. 99 for a different reverse.

Foundation medal. Alexander VII commissioned Bernini to design the Chiesa dell' Assunta in Ariccia. The first stone was laid in 1662 and the church was completed in 1665.

Bibl.: Venuti, p. 267, no. 34; Bonnani, pp. 694–95, no. 36; *Trésor Papes,* pl. 33,6; Dworschak, pl. 3, no. 4.

99 ALEXANDER VII Chigi 1662

Obv. Bust to left, wearing cope decorated with the Annunciation and tiara. Around, ALEX · VII · PONT · MAX · A · VII · ; in exergue, · 1662 ·

Rev. Facade of church. Below, on scroll, ARICIAE; around, OSTENDIT · DOMINVS · MISERICOR-DIAM · IN · DOMO · MATRIS · SVAE

Bronze, 64 mm.

1966.114.58

See also no. 98. The reverse may represent a second project for the church at Ariccia.

Bibl.: Venuti, p. 267, no. 33; Bonnani, p. 694,35; *Trésor Papes,* pl. 33,3.

100 FERDINAND II DE' MEDICI (1610–70), Grand Duke of Tuscany, 1620 1666

Obv. Bust to left, in armor. Around, FERDINANDVS · II · MAG · DVX · ETRVRIÆ; below, · I · F · T · · 1666 ·

Rev. Rose branch with three blooms. Around, GRATIA · OBVIA · VLTIO · QVESITA; below, TRAVANVS

Bronze, struck, with mounts, 47 mm.

1966.124.6

Bibl.: Forrer 6, p. 130; Brescia 1, p. 119, no. 835; *MM.* 2, p. 95, pl. 122,1 (reverse unsigned); Heraeus, pl. 63,3.

101 COSIMO III DE' MEDICI (1642–1723), Grand Duke of Tuscany, 1670 1666

Obv. Bust to left, in armor. Around, COSMVS · III · PRINC · ÆTRVR; below, · I · F · T · ; on truncation, 1666

Rev. Three-masted ship on sea, cipher surrounded by four stars and blazon in sky. Around, CERTA · FVL-GENT · SIDERA; below, TRAVANVS

Bronze, struck, with mount, 50 mm.

1966.124.3

Bibl.: Brescia 1, p. 119, no. 836; *MM.* 2, pp. 115–16, pl. 126,7 (unsigned).

102 CLEMENT IX Rospigliosi, Pope 1667–69 1669

Obv. Bust to left, wearing cap, mozzetta and stole. Around, AMPLIATA · BASILICA · LIBERIANA; below, CLEMENS · IX · PONT · MAX · AN · SAL · MDCLXIX

Rev. The apse of Santa Maria Maggiore. Around, DILI-

GIT · DOMINVS · DECOREM · DOMVS · GENI-TRICIS · SVÆ +

Bronze, 73 mm.

1966.113.67

Clement IX commissioned Bernini to design the new apse facade of Santa Maria Maggiore, which is represented here. In 1673 Clement X, abandoning Bernini's project, had a new design executed by Carlo Rainaldi. Bernini's project adds a colonnade encircling the apse; Rainaldi omitted this.

Bibl.: Dworschak, pl. 4, no. 2, p. 37 (designed by Bernini and executed by Travani); Venuti, p. 281, no. 15 (DOMVS omitted in insc.); Bonnani, p. 716, no. 15; *Trésor Papes,* pl. 34,1.

103 FRANCESCO BARBERINI (1597–1679), Cardinal, 1623 1675

Obv. Bust to right, wearing skullcap and mozzetta. Around, F · EPIS · VELITER · CARD · BARBERI-NVS · S · R · E · VICECAᴺ; below, I · F · TRA-VANVS; on truncation, 1675

Rev. In wreath, sunrise over sea. Around, ALIVSQVE ET IDEM

Bronze, struck, 45 mm. Hole at top

1966.114.60

The nephew of Pope Urban VIII, Barberini was named vice chancellor in 1632.

Bibl.: Forrer 6, p. 130; Brescia 1, p. 119, no. 838 (dated 1661); *MM.* 2, pp. 123–24, pl. 128,2.

ANTONIO TRAVANI
(b. 1661)

Forrer records only one medalist named Antonio Travani, as the son of Gioacchino Francesco, b. 1674, d. 1741. Martinori observes that the date of birth must be wrong, because there are coins of 1689 with his signature. Thieme-Becker proposes two such medalists, the other being born in 1627. The problem may have been resolved by Bulgari, who gives one artist, born in Rome in 1661 and son of Francesco, not Gioacchino Francesco. This Antonio worked with his father from 1682, and the last payment recorded to him is in 1712. Besides the medal below, there are coins and medals of Pope Alexander VIII (1689–91), and two cast medals of Bernini's equestrian statue of Louis XIV of France (Dworschak) ascribed to the artist. These works are, chronologically, possible for an artist born in 1661, and it is also possible that an elder Antonio Travani is a mythical figure.

See Forrer 6, pp. 128–30; Thieme-Becker 33, p. 360; Martinori, fasc. xvii, pp. 9, 14, 19–20, no. 6; Dworschak, pp. 34–36, figs. 4, 5; Bulgari 2, pp. 481–82.

104 IPPOLITO FORNASARI (1627–97)   1692

Obv. Bust to right. Around, HIPP . ABB . FORNASA-RIVS BON . ARCHIGY . I . C . DEMANEPR . EM; below, Æ . AN . 65; on truncation, A . TRAVANVS . F .

Rev. A horse's head facing right, flanked by two laurel branches, holds in its mouth the center portion of a drape which serves as a backdrop. In center, a burst of rays above a small structure supported by an arch of rocks. Under the arch a radiating rock. Above, NOMEN IN ORE SEDET; around, APOLLINI IVRIS VTRIVSQ · VNIVERSITAS A · D · 1692

Bronze, struck, 54 mm. Hole at top

1966.124.1

Fornasari was abbot of San Michele del Poggio and professor of law at the University of Bologna.

Bibl.: Rosati, no. 246 (as Trovano); Forrer 6, p. 128; Brescia 1, p. 165, no. 1102; *MM.* 2, p. 171, pl. 142,4.

GIROLAMO LUCENTI
(1627–98)

A pupil of Alessandro Algardi, Lucenti was active as a sculptor and a bronze caster. He became an engraver at the papal mint in 1668 under Morone-Mola and worked there until 1679 in competition with Giovanni Hamerani.

See Forrer 3, pp. 487–88; Thieme-Becker 23, p. 436; Bulgari 2, p. 59; R. Wittkower, *Art and Architecture in Italy, 1600–1750*, London 1958, p. 210 (for Lucenti's monumental sculpture).

105 INNOCENT XI Odescalchi, Pope 1676–89

Obv. Bust to right. Around, INNOCENTIVS · XI · PONT · MAX · ; below, LVCENTI

Without reverse

Bronze, 90 mm.

1966.113.21

Bibl.: Forrer 3, p. 488.

GIOVANNI BATTISTA GUGLIELMADA
(active 1665–88, d. 1689)

Medalist active in Rome for Popes Clement IX, Clement X, and Innocent XI and for the Dukes of Mantua and Modena and King John Sobieski of Poland. He collaborated with Lucenti on the Jubilee medal of 1675.

See Forrer 2, p. 339; Thieme-Becker 15, p. 253.

106 QUEEN CHRISTINA OF SWEDEN (1626–89)

Obv. Bust to right. Around, REGINA CHRISTINA; in hair, G F

Rev. Sun with face, streaming rays. Around, NEC FALSO NEC ALIENO

Bronze, struck, 40 mm.

1966.127.7

Bibl.: De Bildt, pp. 61–63, figs. 33–34, p. 139, no. 23; Rasmusson, p. 314; Pollard, *Udine*, p. 153.

107 QUEEN CHRISTINA OF SWEDEN

Obv. Same as no. 106

Rev. Celestial globe with seven stars and band. Above, SVFFICIT

Bronze, struck, 40 mm.

1966.127.8

This medal is one of a pair, the other of which has as its reverse the globe showing the Eastern Hemisphere with a band and the inscription NON SVFFICIT.

Bibl.: De Bildt, pp. 65–68, figs. 37, 39; Rasmusson, p. 315.

Queen Christina proposed in 1679 to commission a series of 118 medals in a suite which would record her life and rival the Histoire Métallique of Louis XIV of France. The sun was used by both Christina and Louis XIV as a personal symbol, and on the medal the queen attempts to outdo the emblematic sun used by the king (see De Bildt, pp. 112–13 for Christina's comment on her medal type). The type and the legend on no. 106 appear in the list of subjects chosen by the queen for her series of medals (De Bildt, p. 139, no. 23) but no. 107 is not recorded in the list. De Bildt suggests however (pp. 65–68) that the reverse of no. 107 represents the queen's comment on her relationship with the Cardinal Azzolino. The series of medals was begun by Soldani who modeled and cast some work in 1680. Guglielmada and other engravers reproduced medals for the series in struck versions and in two diameters.

108 CESARE IGNAZIO D' ESTE (1674–1713), Duke of Modena 1687

Obv. Bust to left, in peruke. Around, CÆSAR IGNAT · PRIN · ÆSTENSIS; on truncation, [I B G F] 1687

Rev. Heraldic eagle of the Este, crowned, facing left. Around, CANDORE ET CONSTANTIA

Bronze, 42 mm.

1966.130.11

Bibl.: Forrer 2, p. 339; Crespellani, pp. 21 (ill.), 22.

GIOVANNI HAMERANI
(1646–1705)

The most important of a family of goldsmiths, medalists, and seal engravers, Giovanni worked first with his father Alberto at the mint of Massa Carrara. He completed the coinage of Innocent XI in 1676, and worked for the papal court from 1677. In 1679 he replaced Girolamo Lucenti as engraver at the papal mint. After 1681 he was the only medalist at the papal court, serving the popes from Clement X to Clement XI.

See Forrer 2, pp. 399–403; Fred. Noack in Thieme-Becker 15, p. 549; Bulgari 2, p. 10.

109 FRANCESCO NERLI (1636–1708), Cardinal, 1673

Obv. Bust to right, wearing biretta and mozzetta. Around, FRANC · S · R · E · PRESB · CARD · NER-LIVS · ; on truncation, IO : HAMERANVS · F :

Rev. Club and slain animal on altar. At right, slain Hydra; at left, two slain dragons. Fourteen stars above. Around, HINC AVCTVS FVLGORIBVS AETHER; in exergue, coat of arms

Bronze, struck, 43 mm.

1966.114.47

Bibl.: Brescia 1, p. 136, no. 941.

110 LODOVICO PORTOCARRERO (1629–1709), Cardinal 1669, Primate of Spain, Archbishop of Toledo and Viceroy of Sicily 1678

Obv. Bust to left, wearing biretta. Around, LVDOV · CARD · PORTOCARRERO · PROT · HISP · ARCH · TOLET · HISP · PRIMAS · A · CONS · STAT · | PROREX · ET · CAP · GEN · SICIL · TEN · GEN ·

MARIS · ORATOR · EXTR · AD · INNOC · XI · ; below, · MDCLXXVIII · ; on truncation, · IO · HAME-RANVS · F · A

Rev. Fame atop a tall pedestal, above figures of four virtues at corners. Pedestal inscribed, HAC | DVCE | CVNCTA | PLA | CENT. At left, angels with symbols of cardinal and bishop, landscape, soldier with cannon. At right, castle, ship, cannon

Bronze, struck, 45 mm.

1966.114.53

Portocarrero served as provisional viceroy of Sicily for less than a year, during which he was made archbishop of Toledo.

Bibl.: Brescia 1, p. 137, no. 951; Siciliano, no. 56.

111 QUEEN CHRISTINA OF SWEDEN (1626–89) 1680

Obv. Bust to right. Around, REGINA · CHRISTINA; on truncation, · I · H · F ·

Rev. Globe showing Eastern Hemisphere. Around, NE · MI · BISOGNA · NE · MI · BASTA; below, 1680

Bronze, struck, 36 mm.

1966.127.6

See the note to nos. 106, 107 for the series of medals of Queen Christina.

Bibl.: Forrer 2, p. 403; De Bildt, pp. 73–74, figs. 43–44; Brescia 1, p. 137, no. 949; *MM.* 2, pp. 145–46, pl. 134,7.

112 FRANCESCO I FARNESE (1678–1727), Duke of Parma and Piacenza, 1694 1696

Obv. Bust to right. Around, FRANC · I · · PAR · ET · PLAC · DVX; on truncation, HAMERANVS

Rev. Faith and Justice seated facing each other. Behind, circular temple with inscription, DOMINI MDCIIIIC; around, IVNGVNTVR · VT · IMPERENT

Bronze, struck, 52 mm. Hole at top

1966.130.4

Bibl.: Forrer 2, p. 403.

GIUSEPPE ORTOLANI
(ca. 1674–1734)

Medalist and die engraver, born in Venice. He was in Rome from 1689 and worked under Popes Alexander VIII, Innocent XII and Clement XI.

See Forrer 4, pp. 332–33; Grotemeyer in Thieme-Becker 26, p. 67.

113 NICOLAS DUODO, Venetian Ambassador at Rome

Obv. Bust to left, in peruke. Around, NICOLAVS · DVODO · COMES · ET · EQ · ; on truncation, IO · ORTOL · F ·

Rev. Stairway, flanked by chapels, leads from town below to church at left, to church and other buildings at upper right; in background, town on a hill. Around, ROMANIS · BASILICIS · PARES ·

Bronze, struck, 51 mm.

1966.130.12

Rizzini (Brescia 1, p. 164, no. 1100) mentions that a specimen of this medal is noted by Wesener in the catalogue of the Carlo Morbio Collection, sold at Munich, 16 October 1882.

For the Ermenegildo Hamerani version of this medal, see no. 122.

Bibl.: Thieme-Becker 26, p. 67 (specimen in Padua).

FERDINAND DE SAINT-URBAIN
(1658–1738)

Born in Nancy, Saint-Urbain learned die engraving in Germany (he was in Munich in 1671) and Italy. He was appointed director of the papal mint at Bologna in 1673 and was chief engraver to the papal mint in Rome from 1683 to 1703, when he returned to Nancy. He became engraver to the mint there in 1707 and executed most of the coinage for Duke Leopold of Lorraine as well as a series of medals of the Dukes and Duchesses of Lorraine.

See Thieme-Becker 29, p. 329; Forrer 5, pp. 305–13.

114 LIVIO ODESCALCHI (1652–1713), Duke of Cera, Bracciano and Sirmia 1699

Obv. Bust to right. Around, LIVIVS · ODESC · D · G · SIRM · BRAC · D; on truncation, SV; below, 16[99]

Rev. Seaport. Around, TVETVR · ET · ARCET ·

Silvered bronze, struck, 60 mm.

1966.107.15

Livio Odescalchi was the nephew of Pope Innocent XI. Beaupré suggests that the reverse depicts Odescalchi's castle at Lake Bracciano.

Bibl.: Forrer 2, p. 312, no. 93; Brescia 1, p. 131, no. 906;

MM. 2, p. 223, pl. 155,6; Beaupré, p. 50 (obv. insc. SIRM · ET · BRAC).

115 ALEXANDER VIII Ottoboni, Pope 1689–91 1700

Obv. Bust to left, wearing mozzetta and stole. Around, ALEXANDER · VIII · OTTHOBONVS · VENE-TVS · PONT · MAX *

Rev. Tomb of Alexander. At right, Cardinal Ottoboni and the architect, Carlo di San Martino. Inscribed on tomb, ALEX · VIII | PONT · MAX; around, PETRVS · CARD · OTTHOBONVS · S · R · E · VICECAN PATRVO · MAG · BENEMERENTI · POSVIT · MDCC; on listel, COM . CAROLVS . H . S . MARTIN . INVEN . ; in exergue, Ottoboni arms flanked by S and V

Bronze, struck, 64 mm.

1966.113.41

The tomb of Alexander VIII was commissioned by his nephew Pietro Ottoboni. Begun in 1691, it was completed in 1725 from a design by Count Carlo Enrico di San Martino. The marble statues of Religion and Prudence and relief are by Angelo de' Rossi; the bronze effigy is by Giuseppe Bertosi.

Bibl.: Houston, no. 264; Brescia 2, p. 26, nos. 333, 334; Mazio, no. 358; Venuti, p. 314, no. 21; Martinori, fasc. xvii, p. 24; Renzo N. Montini, *Le Tombe dei Papi,* Rome 1957, no. 242 (for the history of the tomb); *Trésor Papes,* pl. 37, 10.

116 JACQUES DE SAINTE MARIE, CARDINAL SANT 'ANGELO and JEAN PHILIPPE, PRIOR OF SAINT ÉTIENNE 1701

Obv. Bust of Jacques to right. Around, IAC · T · S · MARIAE · DE · ARA · COELI · PRESB · CAR · DE · ANGELIS · ; below, S . V .

Rev. Bust of Jean Philippe to left. Around, MARCH · IO · PHIL · EQV · ET · PRIOR · S · STEPH · PATRVO · RES; below, MDCCI

Bronze, struck, 40 mm.

1966.130.7

Bibl.: Forrer 5, p. 312, no. 86; Beaupré, p. 51, no. 17 (reports a description, noting that he has not seen an example and that it is very rare).

117 ULISSE GIUSEPPE GOZZADINI (1650–1728), Cardinal, 1709

Obv. Bust to right, wearing skullcap and mozzetta.

Around, VLYSSES . I . S . R . E . PRESB . CARD . GOZZADINVS . PRAEF . RAVEN . LEG . A

Rev. Minerva with dove of the Holy Spirit on her head. Around, MINERVA SACRA; on base, S . V

Bronze, struck, 56 mm.

1966.114.65

Bibl.: Brescia 1, p. 131, no. 908; *MM.* 2, p. 276, pl. 164,1; Giovanni Fantuzzi, *Notizie degli Scrittori Bolognesi,* Bologna 1789, 4, p. 226.

118 JEAN II OF ANJOU (1427–70) and MARIE OF BOURBON, Duke and Duchess of Lorraine

Obv. Bust to right, in cap and royal robes. Around, IOAN · II · ANDEG · D . G . DVX · LOTHARIN-GIAE; on truncation, S · V

Rev. Marie of Bourbon, bust to left. Around, MARIA · DE · BORBONIA · DVCISSA · LOTHARINGIAE; below, · S · V ·

Bronze, struck, 47 mm.

1966.131.91

Part of Saint Urbain's series of the dukes and duchesses of Lorraine. The entire series was executed between 1727 and 1731.

Bibl.: Forrer 5, p. 310, no. 39; Lepage, p. 353, no. 39; Beaupré, p. 16, no. 22.

119 LEOPOLD I (1679–1729), Duke of Lorraine, 1697 1705

Obv. Bust to right, in peruke. Around, LEOP . I . D . G . LOT . BAR . D . REX . IER . P . P . ET . DELI-TIVM . ; on truncation, S . V .

Rev. In right foreground Hercules with his club breaks rocks from a cliff to open a passage for Mercury, seen striding in left background. Around, VITAE · CON-SVLIT · ATQVE · VIAE · ; in exergue, S · V · · MDCCV ·

Bronze, struck, 58 mm. Hole at top

1966.131.92

Commemorates opening of the road from Nancy to Toul.

Bibl.: Forrer 5, p. 309; Lepage, p. 347; Beaupré, p. 24, no. 2.

120 LEOPOLD I 1727

Obv. Bust to right, in peruke, wearing armor and the Order of the Golden Fleece. Around, LEOPOLDVS ·

I · D · G · DVX · LOT · BAR · REX · IER; on truncation, S V

Rev. A horseman crossing a bridge to right. In landscape a herm of Mercury; in right foreground Abundance. Around, PROVIDENTIA · PRINCIPIS; in exergue, VIAE · MVNITAE · | MDCCXXVII

Bronze, struck, 65 mm.

1966.131.89

For reconstruction of the bridge in the forest of Haye.

Bibl.: Houston, no. 328; Forrer 5, p. 309; Lepage, p. 348, no. 6; Beaupré, p. 29, no. 8 (silver examples also known).

121 PHILIP V (1683–1746), King of Spain, 1700

Obv. Bust to right, in peruke. Around, PHILIPPVS · V · HISPANIARVM · REX · ; below, F . | S . VRBANI

Rev. Neptune standing on a shell on the sea with aerial view of Sicily and southern Italy in right background. Around, SIC · CVNCTVS · PELAGI · CECIDIT · FRAGOR · VIR · AE · I ·

Bronze, struck, 50 mm.

1966.130.6

The reverse inscription is from the *Aeneid,* book 1, line 154. Probably celebrates Philip's accession.

Bibl.: Forrer 5, p. 310, no. 10; Lepage, p. 349, no. 10; Beaupré, pp. 40–41, no. 10; Siciliano, no. 68.

ERMENEGILDO HAMERANI
(1683–1756)

Roman medalist. With his brother Ottone he succeeded their father Giovanni as engraver to the papal mint in 1705. Beginning in 1734 he and Ottone held a monopoly of coinage for the states of the Church. Ermenegildo worked also for the King of Sardinia and at the imperial mint at Palermo.

See Fréd. Noack in Thieme-Becker 15, pp. 547–49; Forrer 2, pp. 394–98; Bulgari 2, pp. 8–9.

122 NICOLAS DUODO, Venetian Ambassador at Rome 1720

Obv. Bust to left, in long peruke. Around, NICOLAVS · DVODO · S · R · I · COMES · ET · EQ · ; on truncation, · E · HAMERANI ·

Rev. Stairway, flanked by chapels, leads from town below to church at left, to church and other buildings at upper right; in background, town on a hill. Around,

ROMANIS · BASILICIS · PARES · ; in exergue, · MDCCXX ·

Gilt bronze, struck, 50 mm.

1966.107.17

For a bronze version signed by Giuseppe Ortolani, see no. 113.

Bibl.: Houston, no. 305; Rosati, no. 229; Forrer 2, p. 398; Brescia 1, p. 164, no. 1100.

123 INNOCENT XIII de' Conti, Pope 1721–24   1721

Obv. Bust to right, wearing cap, mozzetta and stole. Around, INNOCENT · XIII · P · M · A · I; on truncation, HAMERANI

Rev. Saint Michael the Archangel trampling the devil. Around, CONSTITVI TE PRINCIPEM

Bronze, struck, 30 mm.

1966.113.45

The archangel Michael is a reference to the pope's first name, Michelangelo. Election medal.

Bibl.: Forrer 2, p. 396; Mazio, no. 412; Venuti, p. 344, no. 5; *Trésor Papes,* pl. 40,9; Martinori, fasc. xviii–xix, p. 114; Bartolotti, no. E. 721.

OTTONE HAMERANI
(1694–1761)

Ottone worked with his brother Ermenegildo as medalist (1730–57) and master of the mint at Rome from 1734 to his death, under Popes Clement XII, Benedict XIV and Clement XIII.

See Thieme-Becker 15, p. 549; Forrer 2, pp. 404–09; Bulgari 2, pp. 10–11.

124 JAMES III STUART (1688–1766), The Old Pretender 1721

Obv. Bust to right, in peruke and armor with sun insignia. Around, VNICA SALVS

Rev. Britannia seated on left with Thames and London behind. In foreground, the horse of Hanover tramples the Unicorn and Lion of England. To right, three fleeing figures. Around, QVID · GRAVIVS · CAPTA; in exergue, MDCCXXI

Copper, struck, 50 mm.

1966.131.55

Appeal against the House of Hanover.

Hamerani was a favorite of James III.

Bibl.: Forrer 2, p. 407; *Med. Ill.* 2, p. 454, no. 63; pl. 145, no. 3.

125 ANGELO MARIA QUIRINI (1680–1755), Archbishop of Brescia, 1726, Cardinal, 1727   1750

Obv. Bust to left, wearing skullcap and mozzetta. Around, ANG · M · S · R · E · BIBL · CARD · QVIRINVS · EP · BRIX; on truncation, OTHO . HAMERANI .

Rev. Inscription, BIBLIOTHECÆ | A SE ERECTÆ | DOTATAEQVE | COMMODO VRB . BRIX . | PRIMARIO HVIVS | MAGISTRATVI | POSSESSIONEM | CONTRADIDIT | ANNO IVBIL . | MDCCL .

Bronze, struck, 48 mm.

1966.114.48

Cardinal Quirini founded the Biblioteca Queriniana in Brescia in 1745. In 1750 it was opened to the public.

Bibl.: Brescia 1, p. 184, no. 1197; *MM.* 2, pp. 373–76, pl. 191,2 (illustrates later restrikes by Peter Paul Werner).

GIOVANNI BATTISTA POZZO
(ca. 1670–1752)

Born in Bergamo, Pozzo was in Rome from 1697, when he was probably a student of Ottone Hamerani. An ivory carver and medalist, he imitated the style of contemporary Florentine portraits.

See Forrer 4, pp. 681–82; G. F. Hill in Thieme-Becker 27, p. 338; Pyke, p. 115, fig. 228.

126 PIETRO LEONE GHEZZI (1674–1755), painter

Obv. Head to right. Around, EQVES · PETRVS · LEO · GHEZZIVS ·

Rev. Winged caduceus. Around, ARTES CVI MILLE

Lead, 74 mm. Hole at top

1966.130.23

FILIPPO CROPANESE
(active 1756–73)

Medalist and coin engraver. He made medals of members of the court of Parma and in Rome worked for Pope Clement XIV.

See Forrer 1, p. 480; 7, p. 198; Thieme-Becker 8, p. 164.

127 FERDINAND (1751–1812), INFANTE OF SPAIN, Duke of Parma, Piacenza and Guastalla, 1765   1771

Obv. Head to left, with hair tied back. Around, FER-DINANDVS · HISP · INF · PARM · PLAC · VAST · DVX * ; on truncation, FIL · CROPANE SE · F

Rev. Comedy and Tragedy receive laurel wreaths from a winged Genius. Around, NOVVM · VTRIQVE · COLLATVM · DECVS · ; on listel, FILIPPO · CRO-PANESE · F · ; in exergue, TRAGOED · ET · CO-MOED · | CORONA […] CRETA | CIƆIƆCCLXXI

Bronze, struck, 71 mm. Reverse struck from cracked die

1966.130.30

Son of Philip, infante of Spain, Duke of Parma; grand-son of Philip V, King of Spain.

Bibl.: Forrer 1, p. 480.

128 CLEMENT XIV Ganganelli, Pope 1769–74   1772

Obv. Bust to right, wearing cope and tiara. Around, CLEMENS XIV · PONT · M · A · IV; on truncation, F · CROPANESE ·

Rev. Crowned personification of Spain with columns and stemma at right holds infant being blessed by pope. Baptismal font surmounted by figure of Purity at left. Around, DEVS · NOVA · FÆDERA · SANCIT; in exergue, HISPAN · INFANS · A · S · | FONTE · SVSCEPTVS | 1772

Bronze, struck, 37 mm.

1966.113.27

Commemorates the baptism of the Infante of Spain, Carlo Clemente. The fact that this event would be repre-sented on the pope's Annual Medal indicates how im-portant good relations with Spain were to the papacy.

Bibl.: Brescia 2, p. 37, no. 475; Mazio, no. 506; Bar-tolotti, no. E. 772; Patrignani, p. 116, no. 11.

FRANCESCO CORRAZZINI
(b. ca. 1750)

Medalist, active in Rome during the late eighteenth and early nineteenth centuries, an imitator of the Hamer-anis. He executed a number of medals of distinguished citizens of Bergamo.

See Forrer 1, pp. 458–59; Thieme-Becker 7, p. 389; Bul-gari 1, p. 320 (as Corazzini).

129 ALESSANDRO ANTONIO BARZIZA, Governor of Bergamo 1779

Obv. Bust to left. Around, ALEX * ANT * BARZIZA * PRÆT * PROPRÆF; below, F · CORAZZINI · F

Rev. In wreath of oak and laurel leaves, inscription, OB | CIVES SERVATOS | ARMORVM | INTERDICTO | BERGOMATES | 1779

Bronze, struck, 43 mm.

1966.131.69

Bibl.: Brescia 1, p. 205, no. 1303.

130 PIETRO SERASI (1721–91), Cardinal 1786

Obv. Bust to right, wearing skullcap and cape. Around, PETRVS * ANTONIVS SERASSIVS * BERGO-MAS; below, F · CORAZZINI · F ·

Rev. Woman, holding in left hand a book inscribed VITA | DEL | TASSO, sits at right on bench with crowned stemma on it. She points to a laureate bust of Serasi at left on an altar with garlands and crowned stemma. Around, PROPAGATORI · PATRIÆ · LAVDIS; in exergue, II · VIRI · BERGOM · | AN · MDCCLXXXVI

Bronze, struck, 45 mm.

1966.114.52

The medal was ordered by the town of Bergamo to commemorate this biographer of Torquato Tasso.

Bibl.: Forrer 1, p. 458; Brescia 1, p. 205, nos. 1304, 1305.

131 GIACOMO CARRARA (1714–96) and his wife MARIA ANNA PASSI

Obv. Jugate busts to right. Around, IAC · COMES CARRARA MARIA ANNA PASSI VXOR; on trun-cation, F · CORAZZINI

Rev. Palace facade. Around, PRO BONIS ARTIBVS BERGOMI COLENDIS | PINACOTHECAM ET LYCEVM EREXERE

Bronze, struck, 45 mm.

1966.131.75

Count Giacomo Carrara in his will of 3 March 1796 be-queathed to the city of Bergamo his entire art collection and a school of design. These are housed in a building designed by Simone Elia and completed in 1810. (G. Frizzoni, *Le gallerie dell' Accademia Carrara in Ber-gamo,* Bergamo 1907, p. 13).

Bibl.: Forrer 1, p. 458.

ROMAN SCHOOL—UNATTRIBUTED

132 PAUL V Borghese, Pope 1605–21   1605

Obv. Bust to right, wearing cope. Around, PAVLVS · V · BVRGHESIVS · ROMANVS · PONT · MAX · A · S · M · DC · V · PONT · I

Rev. Exterior of Pauline Chapel of Santa Maria Maggiore. Around, BEATISS · MARIÆ · SEMP · VIRGINI · SACELLVM · AFVNDAMENTIS · EREXIT

Bronze, 55 mm.

1966.114.1

The version noted in Venuti is signed AMB. B, suggesting that the medal may be by Ambrosius Bosio, a medalist noted in Rome to 1610, who may be the Bosio whom Forrer (1, p. 227) dates in the second half of the sixteenth century. Bulgari (1, p. 200) records a Giovanni Bosio active as silversmith in Rome from 1622 until his death in 1628.

Bibl.: Venuti, p. 207, no. 3 (obv. insc. below AMB. B.); Bonnani, pp. 513–17, no. 14; *Trésor Papes,* pl. 26,5; Martinori, fasc. xiii, p. 114.

133 GIUSEPPE FERRERI (d. 1610), Vicelegate of Avignon 1609

Obv. Bust to right, wearing cape. Around, IOSEPH · FERRERIVS · VICELEG · AVENION · ADMDC · IX ·

Rev. View of Avignon. Around, ROMA · DABIT · QVONDAM · QVAS · DAT · AVEN · CLAVES *

Bronze, 58 mm. Round indentation at top
1966.114.66

Bibl.: Brescia 1, p. 148, no. 1001.

134 LUDOVICO LUDOVISI (1595–1632), Cardinal, 1621 1626

Obv. Facade of Church of Saint Ignazio, Rome, as projected in 1626. Around, LVDOVICVS CARD · LVDOVISIVS · S · R · E · VICECANCELL · FVNDAVIT * ; in exergue, AN · MDCXXVI

Rev. Inscription, LVDOVICVS | CARD · LVDOVISIVS | S · R · E · VICECANCELL | IGNATIO | CVI GREGORIVS XV P M | PATRVVS SANCTORVM | CVLTVM DECREVIT | COLENDO | TEMPLVM EXTRVXIT | AN · MDCXXVI

Bronze, struck, 62 mm.

1966.114.40

Foundation medal. Cardinal Ludovisi laid the first

stone of the Church of Saint Ignazio in 1626. The church was designed and executed by the Jesuit Orazio Grassi from 1626–50.

Bibl.: MM. 2, p. 21, pl. 105,2; Brescia 1, p. 149, no. 1013.

135 LUDOVICO LUDOVISI   1626

Obv. Bust of Saint Ignatius to right, holding a book, nimbate. Around, VT SAPIENS ARCHITECTVS FVNDAMENTVM POSVI QVOD EST XPS IESVS *

Rev. Inscription, LVDOVICVS | CARD · LVDOVISIVS | S · R · E · VICECANCELL | IGNATIO | CVI GREGORIVS · XV · P · M | PATRVVS SANCTORVM | CVLTVM DECREVIT | COLENDO | TEMPLVM EXTRVXIT | AN · MDCXXVI

Bronze, struck, obverse gilt, 64 mm. Hole at top

1966.114.41

See no. 134.

Bibl.: Brescia 1, p. 149, no. 1014.

136 THE CHURCH OF SAINT GREGORIO IN ROME, ARMS OF PRINCE GIOVANNI BATTISTA BORGHESE 1666

Obv. Facade of Church of Saint Gregorio. Around, S · P · GREG · VIGILA · TVTELÆ · NOSTRÆ · ; in exergue, MDCLXVI

Rev. Arms of Prince Giovanni Battista Borghese. Around, IOANNES · BAPTISTA · · PRINC · BVRGHESIVS

Bronze, traces of gilt, 57 mm.

1966.130.24

Bibl.: Houston, no. 260.

137 ALEXANDER VIII Ottoboni, Pope 1689–91   1689

Obv. Bust to right. Around, ALEXANDER · VIII · P · O · M · CREATVS DIE 6 OCTO; below, 1689

Without reverse

Bronze, 163 mm.

1966.121

Medallion on the election of the pope, 1689. The large portrait plaques in bronze of popes of the seventeenth century have not been studied as a group, although one has been reasonably attributed to Bernini (L. Opdycke, "A portrait medallion of Clement IX," *Fogg Art Museum Acquisitions, 1959–1962,* Cambridge, Mass. 1963, pp. 13–19). The plaque of Pope Alexander VIII is at a much humbler level. A piece of similar quality of Pope

Pius V, on his beatification in 1672, is also known (published by S. De Caro Balbi in *Medaglia,* anno. 4, no. 7 [1974], at p. 21, fig. 18).

138 GIOVANNI ANSANO, celebrated Roman tenor 1792

Obv. Bust to right. Around, IOH · ANSANVS · ROM · FAMA · ET · INVIDIA · MAIOR ·

Rev. In laurel wreath, inscription, VIRTVTI | LIBVRNI | CIVITAS | 1792; stamped under wreath, W

Bronze, 56 mm.

1966.130.47

Bibl.: Brescia 1, p. 221, no. 1391.

139 PIUS VI Braschi, Pope 1774–99

Obv. Bust to right, wearing skullcap, mozzetta and stole, blessing. Around, PIVS * SEXTVS * PONTIFEX * MAXIMVS *

Rev. Christ carrying the cross. Around, FACTVS · EST · PRINCIPATVS · SVPER · HVMERVM · EIVS ·

Bronze, struck, 50 mm.

1966.113.28

The inscription on the reverse alludes to the burdens borne by Pius during his pontificate. The medal may predate his final and losing struggle with France (1798) but it may also have been issued shortly after the restoration of the papacy in 1814 by his successor, Pius VII.

Not listed among the medals of Gioacchino Hamerani, medalist to Pius VI. Thus it may postdate his reign.

Bibl.: Mazio, no. 520; Patrignani, p. 174, no. 91.

Seventeenth-Eighteenth Century, Florence

MASSIMILIANO SOLDANI-BENZI (1656–1740)

Soldani recreated for a short time the tradition of the Italian cast medal. From a noble Florentine family, he began studying drawing with Baldassare Franceschini at age nineteen. In 1678 Cosimo III decided that Soldani should be trained to take the position of master of the grand ducal mint. Cosimo sent him for training first to the Grand Ducal Academy in Rome from 1678–81. In Rome he studied with the painter Ciro Ferri, the sculptor Ercole Ferrata and the medalist Pietro Travani. Soldani then went to the court of Louis XIV where he worked under François Chéron and Joseph Roettiers. He returned to Florence in 1682, reorganized the mint there, became professor at the *Accademia del Disegno* in 1684 and master of the mint in 1688. As well as being a medalist to Cosimo III and Christina of Sweden, Soldani was a sculptor in bronze. His medals are large and always cast; when struck medals were called for, they were engraved by other artists, such as G. B. Guglielmada or Peter Paul Borner (see the note to nos. 106, 107).

See Forrer 5, pp. 565–68; 8, p. 211; Mario Labo in Thieme-Becker 31, p. 235; Lankheit, pp. 110–53 (medals and coins on pp. 114–23), 191–97, 283–84; H. R. Weihrauch, *Europäische Bronzestatuetten,* Brunswick 1967, pp. 423–29; Detroit, pp. 102–43; Pollard, *Udine,* pp. 154–57; Pyke, pp. 139–40.

140 VALENTINO FARINOLA (d. 1683) 1677

Obv. Bust to right. Around, VALENTINVS · FARINOLA · SEREN · M · D · HETR · AVDIT · ; below, 1677

Rev. A bridle. Around, SVAVIS IN · VTROQ :

Bronze, 68 mm.

1966.126.7

Bibl.: Lankheit, docs. 349, 350.

141 LUDOVICO CAPRARA, *Generale di Battaglia* of the Tuscan Army ca. 1679

Obv. Bust to right, in peruke and cuirass. Around, LVDOVICVS · CAPRARA · ; below, SOLDANVS ·

Rev. Peace and Mars in a landscape. In exergue, NON · DEFICIT · ALTER

Bronze, 64 mm.

1966.127.3

Bibl.: Lankheit, docs. 349–50; p. 117; fig. 152.

142 FLAVIO CHIGI (1631–93), Cardinal, 1657 1680

Obv. Bust to right, wearing cape. Around, FLAVIVS · S · R · E CARD · CHISIVS; below, M · SOLDANVS · F

Rev. Figures of Justice and Truth seated together. Around, IVSTITIÆ · ET VERITATI; in exergue, M · SOLDANVS · F | ANNMDCLXXX

Lead, partially gilt, 60 mm. Hole at top

1966.127.9

Bibl.: Lankheit, docs. 349, 350; Forrer 5, p. 567; Brescia 1, p. 134, no. 929; *MM.* 2, p. 155, pl. 138,6.

143 PIETRO MATTEO MAGGI (d. 1681)

Obv. Bust to right. Around, PETRVS · MATTH · MAGIVS · SEREN · M · D · HETR · AVDIT ·

Rev. Justice and Peace embracing on clouds

Bronze, 85 mm.

1966.126.5

Bibl.: Lankheit, docs. 349, 350.

144 ERCOLE FERRATA (1610–86), sculptor 1681

Obv. Bust to right. Around, HERCVLES · FERRATA · SCVLPTOR · EXIMIVS · ; below, 1681

Without reverse

Bronze, 58 mm. Hole at top

1966.126.6

Soldani made medals of both his teachers, Ercole Ferrata and Ciro Ferri.

On reverse, remains of a figure and part of inscription, PVBLICA · legible.

Bibl.: Lankheit, docs. 349, 350; Forrer 5, p. 565.

145 FRANCESCO REDI (1626–98), doctor, poet, philosopher 1684

Obv. Bust to right. Around, FRANCISCVS · REDI · PATRITIVS · ARETINVS · ; below, M · SOLD · 1684

Rev. Bacchus and Silenus with maenads and satyrs. In exergue, CANEBAM, flanked by small M and S

Bronze, 87 mm.

1966.126.2

Redi was the chief physician to Ferdinand II and Cosimo III de' Medici. This is one of three medals of Redi commissioned by Cosimo; each has a reverse illustrating a different facet of Redi's activity. Here, the reverse of a bacchanal refers to the dithyramb by Soldani, *Bacco in Toscana,* published in 1685. The inscription means "I have sung."

Bibl.: Rosati, no. 241; Lankheit, docs. 349, 350, figs. 153, 154; Forrer 5, pp. 565, 566 (ill.); Brescia 1, p. 135, no. 932; Detroit, no. 88; *MM.* 2, p. 167, pl. 141,3.

146 COSIMO III DE' MEDICI (1642–1723), Grand Duke of Tuscany, 1670   ca. 1684–85

Obv. Bust to right. Around, COSMVS · III · D · G · MAGNVS · DVX · ETRVRIÆ · VI; below, M · SOLD · F ·

Without reverse

Bronze, 97 mm.

1966.126.3

Bibl.: Detroit, no. 89 (based on a silver coin made by Soldani in 1684).

147 VITTORIA DELLA ROVERE (1622–94), married Ferdinand II de' Medici, 1634   ca. 1685

Obv. Bust to right, in hood. Around, VICTORIA FERDINANDI · II

Rev. Winged figure of Fame running to left. Around, FAMAM QVAE TERMINET ASTRIS

Bronze, 83 mm. Hole at top

1966.126.1

Bibl.: Lankheit, docs. 349–50.

CIRCLE OF SOLDANI

148 COSIMO III DE' MEDICI (1642–1723), Grand Duke of Tuscany, 1670   1675 (1678?)

Obv. Bust to right, wearing armor. Around, COSMVS · III · D · G · MAGN · DVX · ETRVRIÆ ·

Rev. Plan of church and monastery on scroll. Around, DEO IN HONOREM SANCTI PETRI DE ALCANTARA; below, · 1678 ·

Gilt bronze, struck, 58 mm.

1966.124.7

Cosimo III invited the Alcantarines, a Spanish Reform Order of Minorites founded by Saint Peter of Alcantara (Franciscan, canonized 1669), to Tuscany, where he built a monastery for them near his villa, L'Ambrogiana. (Cp. Detroit, no. 141.)

ANTONIO MONTAUTI
(d. after 1740)

Florentine sculptor, architect, medalist, a student of Giuseppe Piamontini. He began as a medalist and bronze caster, and most of his medals date from 1709–16. In 1733 Montauti was called to Rome by Cardinal

Alamanno Salviati. He soon obtained the favor of Pope Clement XII, who made him architect of Saint Peter's in 1735 and commissioned a marble Pietà for the crypt of his family chapel.

See Forrer 4, pp. 131–32; Thieme-Becker 25, p. 83; Lankheit, pp. 186–88, 228–29 (documents); Detroit, pp. 86–89.

149 LORENZO MAGALOTTI (1637–1711), Florentine scholar, philosopher, theologian, poet 1712

Obv. Bust to left, in peruke. Around, COMES LAV-RENTIVS MAGALOTTI; below, ANT · MON-TAVTI · F ·

Rev. Apollo in radiance, holding a lyre, stands in landscape. Globe, compass, book at lower right. Around, OMNIA LVSTRAT; in exergue, CIƆ · IƆCC · XII

Bronze, 92 mm.

1966.125.5

Bibl.: Lankheit, pp. 192, 219, n. 151; Forrer 4, p. 132; Brescia 1, p. 167, no. 1111; *MM.* 2, pp. 217–18, pl. 153,2.

GIOVACCHINO FORTINI
(1671/2–1736)

A sculptor, architect and medalist, born in Settignano. Fortini was a student of Carlo Marcellini and Guiseppe Piamontini. His earliest works in sculpture were executed under the direction of Giovanni Battista Foggini and he succeeded Foggini as architect of the Royal Gallery and of the Rich Chapel of S. Lorenzo. In 1701 he signed the tomb of General Philipp Bertram Degenhard Joseph von Hochkirchen in Cologne. He executed marble portraits and medals of the grand ducal family.

See Thieme-Becker 12, pp. 228–29; Lankheit, pp. 175–78, 192–93, 226 (documents); Detroit, pp. 80–85.

150 FRANCESCO RICCARDI (1648–1719) 1715

Obv. Bust to right, in peruke. Around, F · MARCHIO · RICCARDI · R · C · COS · M · D · ETR · A · CONS · ET · SVM · AVLE · PREF · ; on truncation, G : F : F : MDCCXV

Rev. View of the Medici-Riccardi palace, with angel holding crown and key above; Charity and Abundance below. Around, EGENTIVM · VOTIS ·

Bronze, 88 mm.

1966.125.1

The Riccardi family purchased the Medici Palace in 1659. This medal probably commemorates the comple-tion of remodeling and enlarging of the palace under Francesco Riccardi.

Bibl.: Houston, no. 303; Lankheit, p. 219, n. 154; Detroit, no. 46.

151 COSIMO III DE' MEDICI (1642–1723), Grand Duke of Tuscany, 1670

Obv. Bust to right, in cuirass and cloak. Around, COS-MVS · III · ETRVSCORVM · REX; on truncation, [FORTINI . . .]

Rev. Saint Joseph on right offering lily to Christ Child, center. Above, six putti hold golden balls of Medici arms. Around, DELICIÆ POPVLI DELICIÆ DOM-INI

Bronze, 83 mm. Ring attached at top

1966.131.60

The inscription on the obverse is explained by Cosimo's having received from the emperor the title "Altezza Reale" in 1699. Cosimo had himself painted in the guise of Saint Joseph with a lily, to which perhaps the reverse of the medal makes a reference. The budded staff is the attribute of Saint Joseph, and the lily a symbol of religion and of the city of Florence.

Bibl.: Forrer 2, p. 126; Pollard, *Udine,* p. 158, figs. 20a,b.

FRANCESCO PIERI
(ca. 1698–1793)

A student and long-time associate of Giovacchino Fortini, Pieri was born in Prato. He specialized in wax sculpture, most of which is lost. Gian Gastone de' Medici promised Pieri Fortini's position as head of the grand-ducal tapestry works, but when Gian Gastone died, Pieri lost all and moved to the Neapolitan court. Pieri's five signed medals are dated 1718–26.

See Forrer 4, p. 533; Lankheit, pp. 193, 229 (document); Pyke, pp. 106–07, fig. 218.

152 GIAN GASTONE DE' MEDICI (1671–1737), seventh Grand Duke of Tuscany, 1723

Obv. Bust to right, in peruke and cuirass. Around, JO GASTO · D · G · M · DVX · ETRVRIAE · VII ·

Rev. Gian Gastone accepting crown and scepter from kneeling female figure accompanied by lion couchant. Around, CRESCAM · LAVDE · RECENS ·

Bronze, 82 mm.

1966.125.2

Bibl.: Lankheit, p. 219, n. 158.

GIOVANNI BATTISTA LAPI
(d. 1772)

Born in Rome, Giovanni Lapi was a painter, engraver, architect, sculptor, goldsmith, medalist and gem engraver. He went to Livorno in 1732, where he practiced painting, sculpture and architecture until his death. He was also noted in Florence in 1732, where he was a student of C. Gregori at the academy, and again in 1736.

See Thieme-Becker 22, p. 369.

153 GIOVANNI LAMI (1697–1770), theologian and historian, President of the Biblioteca Riccardiana

Obv. Bust to right. Around, V · C · IOH · LAMIO · ACAD · APATH · PRAEF · B · M · ; below truncation, IO · LAPI

Rev. Pedestal with bust, books, papers, and an inkstand and pen, flanked by Minerva standing at left and tyche of Florence seated at right; both pointing towards bust. Around, PRAESIDIVM · ET · DVLCE · DECVS · MEVM; in exergue, IO · LAPI F ·

Bronze, black patina, 88 mm. Brass rim

1966.131.59

The obverse inscription refers to Lami's office as prefect of the *Accademia degli Apatisti.*

See also no. 158.

Bibl.: Brescia 1, p. 194, no. 1254.

ANTONIO SELVI
(1679–1753)

Little is known of Selvi's early life. Probably from Venice, he came to Florence and became a close follower of Massimiliano Soldani. He was active in Florence and, beginning in 1740, executed with Bartolommeo Vaggelli a series of seventy-six medals of the House of Medici. There are several medals of Englishmen among his works. Selvi is documented as a sculptor but only his medals are known. As a medalist he is strongly dependent on the work of Soldani, often reworking Soldani's reverses for his own.

See Forrer 5, pp. 472–74; Grotemeyer in Thieme-Becker 30, p. 483; *Kress,* p. 92; Lankheit, pp. 195–97; Detroit, pp. 96–101.

154 BERNARDINO PERFETTI, Sienese poet (1681–1747) 1725

Obv. Bust to right, laureate. Around, EQVES · BER-

NARDINVS · PERFETTI · SENENSIS · ; below, 1725

Rev. In rocky landscape, sibyl gesturing to left toward rays of light. Around, DEVS · ECCE · DEVS

Bronze, 89 mm. Hole at top

1966.128.2

At the order of Pope Benedict XIII, Perfetti was crowned poet laureate on the Campidoglio on 13 May 1725. The medal was issued for that occasion.

Bibl.: Brescia 1, p. 210, no. 1328 (as anonymous, eighteenth c.); *MM.* 2, pp. 352–53, pl. 187,1.

155 FRANCESCO DEL TEGLIA (1671–1731), Florentine jurisconsult, moral philosopher 1729

Obv. Bust to right. Around, FRANCISCUS DEL-TEGLIA · FLOREN · ; below, S · MDCCXXIX ·

Rev. Female draped figure (Philosophy) seated with book. At left, putto with lyre and horn; at right, Pegasus and swans. In exergue, ET IUCUNDA ET | IDONEA VITÆ ·

Bronze, 88 mm.

1966.128.3

Bibl.: MM. 2, p. 292, pl. 170,3.

156 FERDINAND II DE' MEDICI (1610–70) Grand Duke of Tuscany, 1620

Obv. Bust to right. Around, FERDINANDVS · II · MAG · DVX · ETR · V

Rev. A rosebush with three blossoms. Around, GRATIA · OBVIA · VLTIO · QVÆSITA

Bronze, 88 mm.

1966.130.48

One of Selvi's series of the Medici. For a possible prototype by Travani, see no. 100.

157 FRANCIS I (1708–65), Duke of Lorraine 1729–37, Grand Duke of Tuscany 1737–65, Holy Roman Emperor 1745–65 1745

Obv. Bust to right, laureate, wearing the Order of the Golden Fleece. Around, IMP . CAES . FRANCISCVS . PIVS . FELIX . AVG; below, A · S [F]; on truncation, 1745

Rev. Jupiter, on clouds, holding lightning rods, under circular band of zodiac signs. Below, crown and swords rest on altar surrounded by weapons and armor. Landscape behind with ship at left and volcano at right. Around, TANTÆ MOLIS ERAT ·

Bronze, 86 mm. Hole at top

1966.128.16

Coronation medal. Heir to Leopold I, he married (1736) Maria Theresa of Austria and founded the house of Hapsburg—Lorraine.

Bibl.: Forrer 5, p. 472.

158 GIOVANNI LAMI (1697–1770), theologian and historian 1747

Obv. Bust to right. Around, ΙΩΑΝΝΗC Ο ΛΑΜΙΟC·

Rev. Minerva, helmeted and seated with a snake at her feet, writes on a scroll on table at left with lamp on it and owl beneath. At right, tree, table with two books on it, and shield with Victory. In exergue, ΛΥΜΖ (1747)

Bronze, 84 mm.

1966.128.4

For another medal of Lami, see no. 153.

Bibl.: Brescia 1, p. 178, no. 1168 (reverse), 1169 (obverse); *MM.* 2, pp. 406–08, pl. 200,2 (obverse signed).

BARTOLOMMEO GIOVANNI VAGGELLI
(first half of eighteenth century)

Probably of Swiss extraction, Vaggelli was a follower of Massimiliano Soldani. He executed few medals and never achieved artistic independence; he was the partner of Selvi for the series of medals on the House of Medici, of 1740.

See Forrer 6, p. 183; Thieme-Becker 34, p. 38; Lankheit, p. 195; Pyke, p. 152.

159 PIETRO OTTOBONI (1667–1740), Cardinal, 1689 1719

Obv. Bust to right. Around, · PETRVS · CARD · OTHOBONVS · S · R · E · V · CANCELL · ; below truncation, · BART · VAGGELLIVS · F ·

Rev. On right, figure kneeling, creating fire from the sun with a reflecting glass. To left, a genius with laurel wreath and cornucopia. Around, · COELESTIS · ORIGO · ; in exergue, MDCC[IX]

Bronze, dark brown patina, 80 mm.

1966.131.61

Pietro Ottoboni was the nephew of Pope Alexander VIII.

Bibl.: Forrer 5, p. 183 (as General Pietro Ottoboni,

1720); Brescia 1, p. 170, no. 1129; *MM.* 2, pp. 316–17, pl. 177,4.

LORENZO MARIA WEBER
(1697–1764)

The grandson of a German soldier in the service of Ferdinand II de' Medici, Lorenzo was a follower first of Foggini, then of Soldani in 1720. Three years later, in 1723, he became heir to the office of *Maestro de' Coni e Custode della Zecca Vecchia*. He worked primarily for the Medici and the later dukes of Tuscany. To the style of Soldani, Weber added a rococo elegance.

See Forrer 6, pp. 404–06; Thieme-Becker 35, p. 224; Lankheit, pp. 193–95, 243–44 (Weber's autobiography of 1753); Detroit, pp. 150–53; Pyke, p. 155, fig. 297.

160 FRANCIS III (1708–65), Duke of Lorraine 1729–37, Grand Duke of Tuscany 1737–45

Obv. Bust to right, in long peruke, laureate. Around, FRANCISCVS · III · D · G · LOTH · BAR · ET · M · ETR · D · REX · HIER ·

Rev. Duke on horseback received by tyche kneeling in front of triumphal arch at right. Around, SPES · PVBLICA · ; below, L · M · WEBER; in exergue, ADVEN · OPT · PRINC | MDCCXXXIX ·

Bronze, 87 mm.

1966.125.3

Later became Emperor Francis I (see also no. 157). In 1735, in the War of the Polish Succession, he ceded his duchy to Stanislaus I of Poland in exchange for the right of succession to Tuscany.

Bibl.: Lankheit, p. 195; Forrer 6, pp. 404–05 (ill.); Detroit, no. 104.

GIOVANNI ZANOBIO WEBER
(active 1761–1806)

The nephew of Lorenzo Maria Weber, Giovanni appears to have signed a pattern Taler for Emperor Francis I of Austria in 1763. From this it has been suggested that he studied in Vienna with A. Widemann, although there are no documents to support the assertion. Giovanni executed a series of struck medals of the earlier Medici. His cast medals indicate the end of the tradition begun by Soldani.

See Forrer 6, pp. 403–04; Thieme-Becker 35, p. 219; Lankheit, pp. 195, 219 (n. 159).

161 MARIA MADDALENA MORELLI FERNANDEZ ("Corilla Olimpica") (1728–1800), poet, on her coronation 1776

Obv. Bust to right, laureate. Around, M · MAGD · MORELLI · FERNANDEZ · PISTOR · IN · ARCAD · CORILLA · OLYMP · ; below, IN · CAPITOLIO · CORONATA · | PRID · KAL · SEPT · MDCCL-XXVI ·

Rev. Indians attempting to shoot arrows at the sun. Around, QVI MALEDICVNT DIEI; in exergue, I · V ·

Bronze, 82 mm. Piece missing from rim

1966.125.4

Maria Maddalena Morelli was born in Pistoia in 1728. In 1776 she received a crown of laurel at the capitol. The reverse alludes to a poem in honor of the poet on the occasion of her being crowned. A variant of the medal dated 1779 is noted by Forrer (6, p. 404) and Brescia (1, p. 193, no. 1244).

Bibl.: C. Johnson, "Tre medaglie e tre donne 'colte' nell'Italia settecentesca," in *Medaglia,* anno 3, no. 6 (1973), pp. 29–39 (at pp. 35–37), fig. 20.

162 GIOVANNI BOTTARI (1689–1775)

Obv. Bust to right, in cap and robes. Around, IOHAN-NES BOTTARIVS; under truncation, G · Z · VE

Rev. Above, a radiating triangle. At right a woman leans against a column which is being broken by a lightning bolt. Three putto heads blow rays toward top of column. At lower left a wolf attacks a dragon. Below, an anchor. In background, a ship with a broken mast on a stormy sea. Around, IN · HOC · EGO

Bronze, 91 mm.

1966.125.6

In Rome Bottari was the historian to the Sapienza and custodian of the Biblioteca Vaticana. He annotated old Italian texts, including the *Decameron,* and was the major compiler for the *Accademia della Crusca vocabolario* of 1729–37. An archaeologist and art lover, he annotated Vasari in 1757 and with Giacomo Carrara wrote seven volumes of *Lettere sulla sculture, pittura e architettura scritte dai più celebri professori dal sec. XV al XVIII* (1754–73).

163 THE FIRST MEDICI—1201   1785

Obv. Bust to right, in hat. Around, CLARISS · MEDIC · FAMIL · AVCTOR · 1201 ·

Rev. Inscription, MEDICE AE · GENTIS | NVMIS-MATA · | A · CLARISS · AD · M · ALOYSIAM | ELECT · PALAT · CONIVGEM | ELEGANTIORI-BVS · FORMIS | IAMDIV · EXPETITA · | IO · VEBER · EXCVDEBAT | FLORENTIAE | A · D · MDCCLXXXV

Bronze, struck, 49 mm.

1966.130.20

Restitution. This and the following four medals are part of Giovanni's series of medals of the earlier Medici. They are attributed by Forrer (6, pp. 404–06) to Lorenzo Maria Weber.

164 ELEANORA OF TOLEDO (d. 1562), wife of Cosimo I de' Medici, 1539

Obv. Bust to right. Around, ELEONORA · TOLE-TANA · COS · M · I · M · D · ETR · VXOR; below to left of bust, I . V .

Rev. Table with medals on it. Around, SPLENDET · VSV · TEMPERATO · ; in exergue, I · VEBER ·

Bronze, struck, 48 mm.

1966.130.21

Restitution. See no. 163.

165 BIANCA CAPPELLO (1543–87), second wife of Francesco I de' Medici, 1579

Obv. Bust to right. Around, BLANCA · CAPPELLI · FRANCISCI · I · M · D · VXOR; below, I · V ·

Rev. Stork standing among flora. Around, CANDORE · ET · VATICINIO · ; in exergue, I · VEBER ·

Bronze, struck, 48 mm.

1966.130.29

Restitution. See no. 163.

166 CHRISTINA OF LORRAINE (1565–1636), wife of Ferdinand I de' Medici, 1589

Obv. Bust to right. Around, CHRISTINA · PR · LOTHARINGIÆ · MAG · DVC · ETR · ; below, I · V ·

Rev. Single column with Corinthian capital. Around, NE · PRORVAT · ; in exergue, I · VEBER ·

Bronze, struck, 47 mm.

1966.130.28

Restitution. See no. 163.

167 MARIA MAGDALENA, Grand Duchess of Tuscany (d. 1631), wife of Cosimo II, 1608

Obv. Bust to right, in high ruffed collar. Around, M ·

MAGDALENA · AVSTRIACA · M · D · ETR · ; below, I · V ·

Rev. Bush growing from rocks in a stream. Around, ACQVIRIT · ET · SERVAT; in exergue, I · VEBER

Bronze, struck, 48 mm.

1966.130.22

Restitution. See no. 163.

Seventeenth-Eighteenth Century, Bologna

FELICE ANTONIO CASONI
(1559–1634)

Architect, sculptor, wax modeler, medalist, born at Ancona, trained in Bologna and working there by 1592. By 1624 he is noted as an architect in Rome where he died.

See D. Pollak in Thieme-Becker 6, pp. 118–19; Forrer 1, p. 358; Arm. 1, pp. 303–04; 3, p. 147; *Kress,* p. 91.

168 PIETRO ALDOBRANDINI (1572–1621), Cardinal 1593 1598

Obv. Bust to left. In border at left, female figure; at right, old man. Above, PET : S . R . E . CAR : ALDOB : ECCLE . | EXERC : SVPREM : MODERAT . | CLEM : VIII : NEPOS; below, FERRÆR : ET IN VNIVERSA | ITAL : DE LAT : LEGATVS

Rev. A large procession moving toward a town (Ferrara ?) in the background. Around, HOC VIRTVTIS OPVS; below, [AN] TONIV [S · CASONIVS · F] 1598

Bronze, late cast, 88 mm.

1966.106.20

In 1598, Cardinal Aldobrandini, nephew of Clement VIII, brought the town of Ferrara directly under papal rule.

Bibl.: Arm. 1, p. 303,1; Forrer 1, p. 358; Brescia 1, p. 62, no. 407; *MM.* 1, p. 451, pl. 100,3.

169 ALFONSO PALEOTTI, Archbishop of Bologna (d. 1619) 1605

Obv. Bust to left. Around, ALFONSVS · PALÆOIVS · ARCHIEP(?)BON·SAC·ROM·IMP·PRINCEPS·

Rev. Stemma surmounted by cross. Around, · ANNO · GRATIÆ · M · D · C · V ·

Bronze, 64 mm.

1966.119.1

One of four medals made for foundation of Church of S. Pietro Bologna, dedicated in 1605.

Bibl.: Brescia 1, p. 114, no. 801; *MM.* 1, p. 444, pl. 99,4.

ANTONIO LAZARI
(active 1709–34)

From 1709–13 and 1728–34 Lazari was mint master at Bologna.

See Forrer 3, pp. 350–51; Thieme-Becker 22, p. 489.

170 LAURA MARIA CATERINA BASSI, professor of philosophy at the University of Bologna 1732

Obv. Bust to left, laureate. Around, LAVRA MAR · CATH · BASSI BON · PHIL · DOCT · COLLEG · LECT · PVB · | INST · SCIEN · SOC · AN · XX · MDCCXXXII

Rev. Minerva with lamp and shield facing female figure with open book and laurel wreath; between them an owl on a globe. Around, * SOLI CUI FAS VIDISSE MINERVAM * ; on listel, · ANT · LAZARI · FEC ·

Gilt bronze, struck, 70 mm. Ring attached at top

1966.107.8

Brescia calls the woman on the reverse Laura Bassi; Houston calls her Philosophy. The medal commemorates Bassi's completion of her laureate, appointment to the faculty of the University of Bologna and acceptance into the Society of Science and Letters, all at the age of twenty.

Bibl.: Houston, no. 306; Forrer 3, p. 350; Brescia 1, p. 165, no. 1103; *MM.* 2, p. 413, pl. 202,2; Michelangelo Gualandi, "Medaglia e ricordi dell' antico reggimento in Lode di Laura Bassi," *Almanacco Bolognese,* num. 13 (1842); C. Johnson, "Tre medaglie e tre donne 'colte' nell'Italia settecentesca," in *Medaglia,* anno. 3, no. 6 (1973), pp. 29–39 (at pp. 29–34), fig. 19.

FILIPPO BALUGANI
(1734–80)

Bolognese sculptor, medalist and coin engraver, trained

by Vittorio Bigari. He held the office of coin engraver for the city of Bologna.

See Forrer 1, pp. 119–20; Thieme-Becker 2, p. 427.

171 VICENZO RICCATI (1707–75), physician and mathematician 1776

Obv. Bust three-quarters to left. Around, VINCEN-TIVS RICCATVS * ; on truncation, F . BALV [G] AN [I]

Rev. Two standing, draped women (Religion and Mathematics?); at left, podium with book and at right, globe; Holy Spirit above. Around, MAGNVS VTRA-QVE; in exergue, MDCCLXXVI

Bronze, struck, 53 mm.

1966.131.66

Bibl.: Forrer 1, p. 120.

172 FRANCESCO MARCHI (1504–77), military engineer and architect

Obv. Bust to left, bearded, in cuirass. Around, FRAN-CISCVS MARCHI BONONIEN · ARCHITECTVS BELLICVS; on truncation, F · B · F

Rev. Athena (?) seated on spears, drum, shield, cannon, holding spear in right hand and parchment in left. Around, EXEMPLA OMNIA PINXIT

Bronze, struck, 67 mm. Reverse slightly smaller than obverse

1966.131.68

Restitution.

BOLOGNESE SCHOOL— UNATTRIBUTED

173 GUIDO ZANETTI (1741–91), Italian numismatist

Obv. Bust three-quarters to left. Around, EQ · GVIDO ZANETTVS ITALICÆ MONETÆ SCRIPTOR

Rev. A scale. Around, IN HAC HISTORIAM CAS-TIGES

Bronze, black patina, 59 mm.

1966.131.65

Zanetti was conservator of the museum of antiquities at Ferrara and a writer on coins. His major work was *Nuova raccolta delle monete e zecche d' Italia,* Bologna 1775–89, five volumes. This and the following two medals are quite similarly treated and must be from the

same series. All three are described in Giovanni Fantuzzi, *Notizie degli scrittori bolognesi,* Bologna 1790; however, the medalist remains unknown. For Zanetti, see Fantuzzi 9, 1794, p. 197ff.

Bibl.: Durand, pp. 221–22, pl. 16, no. 9.

174 GIACOMO BIANCANI TAZZI (1729–89), classicist, scientist, numismatist 1789

Obv. Bust to right. Around, IAC · TATIVS BLAN-CANVS BON · Æ · A · LX · O · 1789 ·

Rev. Inscription, EX ACAD · | BENEDICTINA | ATQ · ETRVSC · | ANTIQVIT · | IN INSTIT · SCIENTIAR · | PRIMVS DOCVIT | AGRIC · ET HIST · NAT · | PERITISSIMVS

White metal (pewter?), 60 mm.

1966.131.79

Giancarlo Susini in his article on Biancani in *Dizionario Biografico degli Italiani* (10, pp. 35–36) notes that Biancani's appearance was recorded in a medal engraved by his son-in-law Guido Zanetti (see no. 173). However, Fantuzzi (see no. 173; Vol. 8, 1790, p. 104) says the medal was merely commissioned by Zanetti: "...havvi pure di esso una medaglia di metallo fatto fondere dal suo genero, Guido Zanetti."

Bibl.: Zanetti 5, p. 11; Durand, p. 229, pl. 17,7.

175 GIOVANNI CRISOSTOMO TROMBELLI (1697–1784), Jesuit, classicist 1784

Obv. Bust to left, wearing cap and mozzetta. Around, D · IO · CHRYS · TROMBELLI BON · AB · EXG · CAN · R · OB · A · 1784 ÆT · 87

Rev. Inscription, POETICA | THEOLOGICA | HIS-TORICA · ASCETICA | SCRIPTA · EDIDIT | MV-SEVM · CONDIDIT | BIBLIOTHECAM | CODICI-BVS | AVXIT

Bronze, 62 mm.

1966.114.67

As in nos. 173 and 174, Fantuzzi here (Vol. 8, 1790, p. 125) says this medal was commissioned by Zanetti, and not made by him: "il padre abate Luigi Mingarelli e il Sig. Giulio Zanetti...gli fecero fondere una medaglia ...e nel rovescio si legge questo verso: 'FERTILIS ET VARIUS, NAM BENE CULTUS AGER.'" This latter inscription refers to another medal of the sitter. This reference was discovered by Dr. Ulrich Middeldorf.

Bibl.: Zanetti 4, p. 3; Durand, p. 204, pl. 15,1.

176 PIETRO PAOLO MOLINELLI (1702–64), Bolognese doctor and surgeon   1768

Obv. Bust to right. Around, PETRVS PAVLVS MO-LINELLI MED . ET CHIRVR . DOCTOR

Rev. Inscription on shield, CIVI | OPTIMO . CLINI-CO | INCOMPARABILI | AMICI | MDCC | LXVIII

Bronze, 74 mm.

1966.131.97

Bibl.: Brettauer, no. 774 (as by Francesco Bruttini?).

177 SAINT CATHERINE OF BOLOGNA (1413–63)

Obv. Saint Catherine seated to right, painting a putto on canvas supported by a putto on clouds. Around, SANC-TA CATHARINA [V]IGRI DE BONONIA

Rev. Stemma. Around, MARCVS ANTONIVS A FLORE DONO DEDIT

Silver, struck, 45 mm. Hole at top

1966.131.76

Caterina Vigri of Bologna was canonized by Pope Clement XI in 1712. The medal probably celebrates this event.

Seventeenth-Eighteenth Century, Venice

JOHANN FRANZ NEIDINGER

Medalist active in Venice from 1678–92.

See Forrer 4, p. 238; Thieme-Becker 25, p. 383.

178 FRANCISCO MOROSINI (1616–94), Doge of Venice 1688–94   1687

Obv. Bust to right. Around, FRAN : MAVROCENO . EQ · D · M · S · N · PROC · CONT · T · IMP III; on truncation, NEIDINGER

Rev. Winged victory blowing horn, globe at lower left. Inscribed on globe, MOREA | [capta]; around, SPAR-GET ET VLTRA

Bronze, 41 mm.

1966.114.71

Morosini led the conquest of the Morea from the Turks in 1687. Venice held all of the area from 1687 to 1715.

Bibl.: Forrer 4, p. 238; Brescia 1, p. 122, no. 862; Cicogna, vol. 2, pt. 2.

AGOSTINO FRANCHI

Venetian medalist of the first half of the eighteenth century, best known for his medals of Flaminio Cornaro and Cardinal Angelo Quirini.

See Forrer 2, pp. 136–39; Thieme-Becker 12, p. 312.

179 FLAMINIO CORNARO (1693–1778), Venetian senator and author   1750

Obv. Bust to right, in peruke. Around, FLAMINIVS CORNELIVS SENAT · VENET · ; on truncation, A · FRANCHI F ·

Rev. Facade of church of S. Nicolo Tolentino. On scroll around, OB · ECCLESIAS · INLVSTRATAS · OR-DO · ANTISTITVM · VENET · ; on ends of scroll, A F; in exergue, MDCCL

Bronze, struck, 44 mm. Left and right edges scraped away; medal nearly oval

1966.131.70

Cornaro was a Venetian senator who wrote a history in Latin of the churches of Venice and Torcello. The eighteen volumes were published in 1749.

Bibl.: Forrer 2, p. 137; Brescia 1, p. 180, no. 1178; *MM.* 2, pp. 391–92, pl. 198,5.

VENETIAN SCHOOL—UNATTRIBUTED

180 FRANCESCO MOROSINI (1616–94)

Obv. Bust three-quarters to left. Around, FR · MAV · EQ · D · M · PR · ✕E · III · IM · C · T; on truncation, G M [F]

Without reverse

Gilt bronze, 53 mm.

1966.119.4

For a note on Morosini see no. 178.

181 RELIGION   1721

Obv. Standing figure of religion, veiled, holding book and censer. In field, CŒLO SOLI | SOLA SUM . ; around, : NON E'MAMURIO ANCILE SUM EGO : Æ ANCILLA DEI ÆB ÆRCANIS : | QVEM EX THURE COLO : PRO UNDIQ · RÆTIS DOGMA-TA : INQ · | CÆTEROS MECUM FERO SEMPER FERRUM; below, VEN · 1721 ·

Without reverse

Bronze, 65 mm.

1966.116.2

182 JACOPO NANI (1725–97) & MOCENIGA VEND-
RAMIN, married, 1772   1772

Obv. Man on a chariot drawn by eagles to left over a
cloud holds a putto out in his hands. Two stemmae flank
putto. In field, LVXEIT COLLECTA | MAIOR and
SIT TIBI CVRÆIVNO; around, VIRTVTVM EX-
EMPLAR AD PARVOS VSQVE PENATES VTER-
QVE PARENS VTRVMQVE NATVS ·

Rev. Inscription, VIRI OPTIMI | PHILOSOPHI
HVMANISSIMI | PROCONSVLIS MAXIMI | MA-
TRONÆQVE EIVS SPONSÆ | NEONATVS IN-
CLYITVS | POSCENTIBVS POPVLIS | CVM
PERENNI OBSEQVIO VNIVERSIT | HEBRÆ-
ORVM CORCYRENSIVM | PATRIAS VIRTVTES-
PANDAT | IN ÆVVM, | HVMANA REPLEN-
SVOTA | 1772 (1778?); around, PROCONSVL
IACOB NANI ÆQVES ET MOCENIGA VENDRA-
MINA SVAVIVM MORVM PRÆSTANTIÆ THA-
LAMIQVE CONSORTES ·

Bronze, 82 mm.

1966.131.96

183 PORTRAIT OF A DOGE

Obv. Bust three-quarters to right, wearing the ducal cap

Without reverse

Bronze, 42 mm.

1966.132.1

Seventeenth-Eighteenth Century, Naples

GIOVANNI COSTANZI
(1664–1754)

Neapolitan gem engraver, known as one of the first engravers on diamond.

See Thieme-Becker 7, p. 537; Forrer 1, p. 461; 7, p. 193.

184 SAINT JANUARIUS   1707

Obv. Bust to left, wearing cope and mitre. Around, D ·
IANV · M · PATR · NEAPO · VERO · PATRI ·
PATRIÆ · ; below, COSTANZI

Rev. Inscription, IN · CAPITE · EST · | ANIMA ·
EST · NOBIS · | IN · SANGVINE · VITA · | PAT ·
B · M · D · G · A · M · | F · M · D · S · VI · ID · DEC · |
A · MDCCVII | G · C ·

Bronze, struck, 37 mm.

1966.114.56

After the change in government and the eruption of
Vesuvius, the citizens of Naples struck medals in grati-
tude to their patron, San Gennaro. Several other examples of this type of medal exist. See Siciliano, nos. 73–
80.

MARIA ANTONIO DI GENNARO (Januario)
(1679–1744)

Son of a die engraver at the mint of Naples where he engraved the medal for Philip V's visit in 1702 (see below).
He went to Vienna via Mantua in 1713 and worked for
the imperial mint as well as in Salzburg (1722–25),
Saxony and Poland. In 1731 he was named director of
the *Graveur-Akademie* of the Vienna mint.

See Forrer 2, pp. 240–41; Thieme-Becker 13, p. 394.

185 PHILIP V (1683–1746), King of Spain, 1700   1702

Obv. Philip on horseback to left. Around, PHILIPPVS ·
V · HISPANIARVM · ET · VTRIVSQ : SICIL : REX;
on listel, ANT : DE · IANVARIO · F :

Rev. Minerva seated with shield and cornucopia. Vesu-
vius in background. Around, ADVENTVI · PRINCI-
PIS · FŒLICISSIMO . ; on listel, ANT · DE · IANV-
ARIO · NEAPOLITANVS · F · ; in exergue, NEA-
POLIS | 1702

Gilt bronze, struck, 59 mm.

1966.107.16

This seems to be one of the artist's earliest medals. It is
one of 462 medals (390 bronze, 70 silver, 2 gold) struck
for the visit of Philip to Naples in 1702. For the occasion,
an equestrian statue, depicted on the obverse, was commissioned for the Largo del Gesù Nuovo. The master-
piece of the sculptor Lorenzo Vaccaro, it was begun in
1702, completed in 1705, and destroyed by a mob when
the Austrians occupied Naples in 1707.

Bibl.: Siciliano, no. 69.

186 ANTONIO MAGLIABECCHI (1633–1714), librarian
at Florence   1710

Obv. Bust to right. Around, ANTONIVS MAGLIA-

BECHIVS FLORENTINVS; on truncation, ANT ·
.... (illegible)

Rev. Magliabecchi seated to right in garden, reading.
Books on the ground. In right background a philoso-
pher (?) stands facing left. Around, SCIRE NOS-
TRVM REMINISCI; in exergue, A · D · IANVARIO
F ·

Bronzed lead, struck, 43 mm.

1966.124.4

Bibl.: Forrer 2, p. 240 (ill.); Brescia 1, p. 163, no. 1095;
MM. 2, pp. 233–34, pl. 157,5; Thieme-Becker 13, p. 394.

ARTIST UNKNOWN

187 ELIZABETH DE MONTAPERTO 1616

Obv. Bust to left, in ruff. Around, D ELISAB DE
MŌTE APTO MARCHESA DE M APER ··

Rev. Knight mounted on Pegasus over two mountains,
with flames between them. Above, AD - ASTRA; below, 1616

Bronze, 47 mm.

1966.108.17

The reverse shows the crest and motto of the Montaperto
family.

Seventeenth-Eighteenth Century, Various Locations

LORENZO LAVY
(1720–89)

Member of a Torinese family of sculptors and medalists.
He studied first in Turin with André Boucheron, then
from 1740–45 in Paris under Thomas Germain. From
1745–49 he worked in Rome for both the church and
the House of Savoy. Back in Turin, he was employed at
the mint, where he became engraver in 1763. From
1757 to 1772 Lorenzo engraved seventy-seven medals for
a medallic series of the House of Savoy.

See Forrer 3, p. 350; Thieme-Becker 22, p. 480; Assandria, pp. 212–25.

188 POLISSENA CRISTINA of Rheinsfeld-Rottenburg
(1701–73), second wife of Carlo Emmanuel, 1724

Obv. Bust to left. Around, POLIXENA · CHRIS-
TINA · E · RHEINSF · CAR · EM · VXOR · II · ;
below, LAVY

Rev. Draped female figure hands palm branch to small
boy. Tree behind. Around, CERTVM · SALVTIS ·
PVBLICAE · PIGNVS

Bronze, struck, 52 mm.

1966.137.283

The medal celebrates the fact that Polissena Cristina
gave Carlo Emmanuele an heir.

Bibl.: Gianfrancesco Galeani Napione, *Storia Metallica
della Real Casa di Savoia,* Turin 1828, pl. 25,3.

ANTON GUILLEMARD
(doc. 1765–1812)

Medalist and coin engraver, trained in Günzburg and
active there until 1777. From 1777–92 he worked at the
Milan mint. With Napoleon's arrival he fled to Vienna
and Prague, where he was first engraver at the mint
from 1796. Often worked with F. Stuckhardt.

See Forrer 2, pp. 342–43; 7, p. 405; Thieme-Becker 15,
pp. 309–10.

189 MARIO LUPO (1720–89), historian 1785

Obv. Bust to right. Around, MARIO LVPO PRIMI-
CERIO BERGOMATI HISTOR · ET ANTIQVAR · ;
below, A · GUILLEMARD · F ·

Rev. Lupo standing in landscape holding map in right
hand. At right a plaque inscribed, DE VOTA | VENE-
TIA | CONLOCA | VIT. Around, BERGOMEI AS-
SERTIS ANTIQVI FINIBVS AGRI; in exergue,
CVRATORVM D · S · | MDCCLXXXV

Bronze, struck, 42 mm.

1966.114.68

In 1784 Lupo published the first volume of his much
praised *Codex diplomaticus civitatis et ecclesiae ber-
gomatis.*

Bibl.: Forrer 7, p. 405; Brescia 1, p. 200, no. 1282; Durand, p. 119, pl. 9,1.

190 NICCOLÒ VENIER and ELEANORA BENTIVO-
GLIO 1786

Obv. Bust of Niccolò to right. Around, NICOLAO
VENERIO PRAEF · BERGOMI; below, CIVES ·
BERG · MDCCLXXXVI; on truncation, A · G · F ·

Rev. Bust of Eleanora to right. Around, ELEONORAE BENTIVOLAE CONIVGI

Bronze, struck, 42 mm.

1966.131.73

Bibl.: Brescia 1, p. 200, no. 1283.

191 ERMOLAO PISANI, Prefect of Verona 1791

Obv. Bust to right. Around, HERMOLAVS · III · PISANVS · PRAET · PROPRAEF · ; below, A · GUILLEMARD · F ·

Rev. Meat market at Verona. On wall of market, MA-CELLVM · MCCCLXVIII; around, ANNONA · RESTITVTA · ; in exergue, ORDO · VERONEN-SIS | EX · DECR · | MDCCXCI

Bronze, struck, 54 mm.

1966.131.80

Bibl.: Forrer 2, p. 343; Brescia 1, p. 200, no. 1284.

B. CIANTOGNI

Italian medalist of the first half of the eighteenth century.

See Forrer 1, p. 430.

192 GIAN PAOLO SIMONE BIANCHI (1693–1775), naturalist

Obv. Head to left, horned. Around, IANVS * PLAN-CVS * ARIMINENSIS; below truncation, B · CIAN-TOGNI

Rev. Lynx standing to left. Around, LYNCEIS * RE-STITVTIS

Bronze, dark patina, 82 mm.

1966.137.107

Bianchi was widely known under his Latin name of Janus Plancus. He was born in Rimini. His first names are recorded as Gian Paolo Simone in *MM,* and as simply Giovanni by A. Fabi in *DBdI* 10, pp. 110–12. The horn of Ammon on the obverse refers to Bianchi's publications on shells, and appears on his tomb in Saint Agostino at Rimini. The reverse refers to his revival in Rimini of the Academy of the Lincei. He was secretary to the Academy, and wrote a history of it.

Bibl.: Forrer 1, p. 430; Brescia 1, p. 181, no. 1184; *MM.* 2, pp. 399–401, pl. 199,2.

S. A. B. A.
(late seventeenth or early eighteenth century)

193 GIOVANNI BATTISTA AND CATERINA F . . .

Obv. Jugate busts to right. Around, IOANNES BAPT · F · CAT · AMAT · CONG; on truncation, · S · A · B · A

Rev. Triangle surrounded by clouds, with sun rays above. Inscription in triangle, IN | TE | SPES · MEA

Bronze, 38 mm.

1966.130.16

See Brescia 1, p. 168, no. 1117 for a medal of Giovanni Battista Franceschi.

ITALIAN—UNATTRIBUTED
(Seventeenth–Eighteenth Century)

194 OTTAVIO TASSONE ESTENSE 1606

Obv. Bust to left, with double cross and eagle on chest. Around, + COMES · OCT · TASSONVS ESTEN COM · S · SP .ˢ ; below, 1606

Rev. Castle, with tower topped by a cross at each end. Around, + ARCE ANTIQVA LABENTE NOVAM EXTRVXIT

Bronze, 52 mm.

1966.106.14

Bibl.: Brescia, no. 788 (as medalist of the sign of the heart); Supino, no. 629.

195 ENEA MONTECUCCOLI (d. 1614), Governor of Carpi, distinguished captain and general of the Este cavalry

Obv. Bust to left, wearing medal. Around, ÆNEAS · MONTECVC · CAPRARA · AVSTRIAC · AGMI-NIB · PRÆFECT · PONTIFICII · EXERCITVS · DVX *

Rev. Pallas Athena seated to left on shields, holding double cross in left hand, two helmets below. Around, VIRES RESTITVIT; in exergue, ROMAE

Bronze, struck, 68 mm.

1966.131.67

Bibl.: Brescia 1, p. 159, no. 1072.

196 AMICO SINIBALDO (b. 1619) 1674

Obv. Bust to left. Around, AMICVS SINIBALDVS AN ÆTAT · SVÆ · LV; below, 1674

Rev. Oval shield with inscription on banderole, VERVS PRÆSTAT AMICVS

Bronze, 54 mm.

1966.130.14
Bibl.: Brescia 1, p. 157, no. 1059.

197 JACOPO OTTAVIO NICOLO DE BECCADELLI & ANTONIO BARTOLOMMEO DE BONFILIOLI 1685

Obv. Three stemmae surmounted by cardinal's hat. Around, IACOB : OCTAV : NICOL : DE : BECCADELLIS * ANTON : BARTHOL : DE BONFILIOLIS * | PALVT : S · R · E · CARD : DE ALTERIIS PRAESIDIO * ECCL : PAROCH · MARIMORTÆ FVNDATORES : *

Rev. In border of thorns with four crosses, inscription, ECCLESIAM | DIŒCES : RAVEN : S . CRVCI DICAT | PATRONI | AGRO DOTARVNT | SACR : SVPELLEC : INSTRVXERVNT | A FVNDAMENTIS EXCITARV̄T | ANNO SALVTIS | MDCLXXXV

Bronze, struck, 42 mm.

1966.130.31

The cardinal referred to is Paluzzo Paluzzi degli Albertoni Altieri (1613–98), politician, Bishop of Ravezza, 1670–74.

198 CARLO LABIA (d. 1701) 1696

Obv. Inscription, CARŌLI | ARCHIEP . LABIA | EPISC : ADRIEN : | PIE LARGITATI | CANONICI RHO | DIGINI

Rev. Facade of church. Around, TEMPLVM · S · STEPHANI P · M · RHODIGII RENOVATVR AN 1696 *

Bronze, 45 mm.

1966.130.15

Foundation medal for renovation of the church of S. Stefano at Rovigo.

Bibl.: Brescia 1, p. 158, no. 1067; *MM.* 2, pp. 183–84, pl. 145,2.

199 ORATORY OF S. FILIPPO NERI 1697

Obv. Facade of Oratory. In field, D · PHILIP · NERIO; around, HIERVSALEM NOVAM DESCENDENDE COELO; below, LV · GREGORINI ARCHI

Rev. Inscription, ECCLESIAM | CONG . ORAT .

MACER | ATÆ PRIMAM INTOTO | ORB . D . PHILIP . NER . DI : | CAT . IN AMPLIOR . HVI : | VS TEMPL . FORMAMPP . | EIVSD . CONG . FVNDA | RVNT ÆRE IOSEPHI | MARCONI DIE 17 | AMBRIS | 1697

Bronze, 58 mm.

1966.130.1

200 LUCREZIA CAPRANICA

Obv. Bust to right. Around, LVCRETIA · CAPRANICA · COM · ANTELMINELLA ·

Rev. Prudence, holding a mirror, leans on an altar; to the right, below, a snake. Around, RERVM . FATO . PRVDENTIA . MAIOR ·

Bronze, 42 mm.

1966.130.13

For a medal of her by Selvi, see Brescia 1, p. 180, no. 1176 (Lucrezia Capranica Antelminelli Castracani).

201 NICCOLÒ MACHIAVELLI (1469–1527), author and statesman

Obv. Bust to right, in cap and doublet. Around, NICOLAVS MACCHIAVELLIVS

Rev. A serpent leaving a bush

Bronze, 72 mm.

1966.130.27

One of a group, with nos. 202 and 203, of later restitutions which have in common the unusual technique of engraved legends and which in several instances even share portrait types for different sitters. The fabric suggests a date in the nineteenth century for the production of the medals, although a medal of Torquato Tasso which belongs to the group is in the collection of Goethe at Weimar, and is published in an exhibition catalog by G. Femmel (*"Merkwürdige Frauen" und "bedeutende Männer ihrer Zeit kunstreich abgebildet." Porträtmedaillen der Renaissance und der Klassik aus Goethes Besitz,* Weimar and Leipzig 1971, no. 49). A medal of Fra Domenico da Pescia (*Corpus,* no. 1300, illustrated in B. Morsolin, "Medaglia in onore di Fra Domenico da Pescia," *Rivista Italiana di Numismatica* 5 [1892], pp. 494–500) is related to these restitutions, as is also a portrait plaque of Casimir Poniatowski illustrated in A. Busiri Vici, *I Poniatowski e Roma,* Florence 1971, fig. 47.

Bibl.: Corpus, no. 1284 (not ill.).

202 GIROLAMO DA CARPI (1501–1556/69)

Obv. Bust to left. Around, HYERONIMVS · A · CAR-PI · PICTOR · FERRARIENSIS · OB · 1556 · ÆT · 55 ·

Without reverse

Bronze, greyish patina, 68 mm.

1966.106.17

See no. 201.

203 ALEXANDER MALEGONNELLE

Obv. Bust to right, in cap and ruff collar. Around, ALEXANDER MALEGONNELLE

Without reverse

Bronze, leaded or silvered, 59 mm.

1966.130.26

See no. 201.

204 GIUSEPPE COMPAGNIUCCI 1773

Obv. Bust to right. Around, IOSEPH COMPAGNIVC-CIVS; below CIɔIɔCCLXXIII

Rev. Two river gods and an eagle. Around, MVLCEN-DAS · NATVS AD · AVRES; on rock, 1773; below, PERVSIÆ

Gilt bronze, 78 mm. Hole at top

1966.131.100

Perugian artist, probably a musician.

Bibl.: Mario Bellucci, *Medaglie Perugine dal XV al XX Secolo. Fonti per la Storia dell' Umbria,* no. 9, Perugia 1971, pp. 38–39.

205 FRANCESCO I FARNESE (1678–1727), Duke of Parma and Piacenza, 1694

Obv. Bust to right, in peruke and armor with battle scene on cuirass. Around, FRANC · I · PAR · ET · PLAC · DVX; below, GL · F

Rev. Zodiac band, above Phaeton and Zeus; below, River God and town. Around, MEDIO TVTI […] MVS IBIS

Bronze, 53 mm. Hole at top

1966.130.18

For an earlier medal of Francesco by Giovanni Hamerani, see no. 112.

206 VINCENZO BELLINI (1708–83), Ferrarese antiquarian and numismatist

Obv. Bust to left. Around, in border, VINCENTIVS * BELLINI · ANTIQVARIS * FERRARIENSIS ·

Rev. Two palm trees, flowers, bees and a beehive. Above, in scroll, EGO · PLANTAVI · ·

Bronze, 79 mm.

1966.130.35

One of three medals of this sitter, all of which have the same subject on the reverse. The reverse compares Bellini's advances in the study of numismatics to the bees taking pollen from palms and flowers and producing honey. For Bellini see N. Parise in *DBdI* 7, pp. 716–18.

Bibl.: Brescia 1, p. 218, no. 1377 (dated 1756); Zanetti 3, p. 10; Durand, p. 228,1.

207 FRANCIS HYACINTH OF SAVOY (d. 1638), son of Victor Amadeus I

Obv. Bust to right. Around, FRANCISCVS · HYA-CIN · VIC · AM · FIL · SAB · DVX · XIII · CYP · REX

Rev. Boy in cloak protected by Minerva holding shield. Around, OPPORTVNA · MATRIS · TVTELA

Bronze, struck, silvered, 53 mm.

1966.130.2

Restitution.

One of the series of medals of the House of Savoy begun by Lorenzo Lavy in 1757.

Bibl.: Brescia 2, p. 56, no. 70.

Nineteenth-Twentieth Century, Rome

TOMMASO MERCANDETTI (1758–1821)

The son of Pietro Mercandetti, engraver at the papal mint, Tommaso was apprenticed at age nine to Girolamo Rossi, a gem engraver. By 1773 he was employed at the papal mint, and beginning in 1780 he worked on a number of commissions transferred to him by the silver smith and brass founder Luigi Valadier. In 1796 Mercandetti was appointed chief engraver at the papal mint, sharing the post with Gioacchino Hamerani. After

Hamerani's death ca. 1807, he retired to Umbria, but in 1810 returned to Rome where he made medals of Napoleon and of the popes.

See Forrer 4, pp. 28–32; 8, p. 54; Thieme-Becker 24, p. 407; Bulgari 2, pp. 139–40; F. Bartolotti, "Le medaglie di Tommaso Mercandetti," in *Medaglia,* anno. 1, no. 2 (1971), pp. 18–37; 2, no. 3 (1972), pp. 25–41 (a full and illustrated catalogue of the medals).

208 PIUS VII Chiaramonti, Pope 1800–23   1818

Obv. Bust to left, wearing tiara and cope. Around, PIO VII · PONT · MAX · ANN · XVIII · ; below, monogram · ᵀM ·

Rev. The Laocoon. Around, MONVMENTORVM VETERVM RESTITVTORI

Bronze, struck, 42 mm.

1966.114.34

Celebrates the return to Rome in 1818 of the objects of art which had been taken by Napoleon's armies and placed in the Louvre.

Bibl.: Patrignani, *Pio VII,* no. 85; Forrer 4, p. 32; Mazio, no. 559; *Trésor Papes,* pl. 46,7; Martinori, fasc. xxiii–xxiv, p. 33, no. 23; Rinaldi, no. 12 (silver); Bartolotti, no. E. 817; Bartolotti, *Mercandetti,* no. 98, fig. 45.

209 PIUS VII Chiaramonti   1820

Obv. Bust to left, wearing skullcap, mozzetta and stole. Around, PIVS VII PONT · MAX · ANN · XXI; in exergue, T . MERCANDETTI | F . ROMAE MDCCCXX

Rev. Christ washing the feet of Saint Peter. Around, TV DOMINVS ET MAGISTER; on listel, · T · M · I · ; in exergue, EXEMP . DEDI | VOBIS

Bronze, struck, 33 mm.

1966.114.35

Bibl.: Patrignani, *Pio VII,* no. 100; Mazio, no. 549; Martinori, fasc. xxiii–xxiv, p. 33, no. 30; Bartolotti, *Mercandetti,* no. 109, fig. 53.

GIUSEPPE GIROMETTI
(1780–1851)

Gem engraver, medalist, and sculptor, student of the sculptor Pacetti at the *Accademia di San Luca.* After winning prizes for four statues for the Duomo of Foligno, he turned to die engraving and from 1822 was engraver at the papal mint under Popes Pius VII, Leo

XIII, Pius VIII and Gregory XVI. Girometti also worked for the Grand Duke of Tuscany and the Kings of Sardinia and England.

See Thieme-Becker 14, pp. 189–90; Forrer 2, pp. 273–74; 7, pp. 367–68; Bulgari 1, p. 552.

210 LEO XII della Genga, Pope 1823–29   1827

Obv. Bust to left, wearing skullcap, mozzetta and stole. Around, LEO · XII · PONT · MAX · ANNO · IV · ; below, G · GIROMETTI · F ·

Rev. The baptistry and font at Santa Maria Maggiore. In exergue, BAPTISTERIO LIBERIANO | ERECTO DEDICATO; below, GIROMETTI · F ·

Bronze, struck, 43 mm.

1966.114.19

Leo XII restored the baptistry in Santa Maria Maggiore. The font, erected according to a project of Giuseppe Valadier, was made from a large antique porphyry basin moved from the Appartamenti Borgia in the Vatican.

Bibl.: A. Patrignani, *Le medaglie di Leone XII (1823–29),* Catania 1933, no. 60; *Trésor Papes,* pl. 48,1; Martinori, fasc. xxiii–xxiv, p. 50; Bartolotti, no. E. 827.

211 PIUS IX Mastai Ferretti, Pope 1846–78

Obv. Bust to right, wearing skullcap, mozzetta and stole. Around, PIVS · IX · PONTIFEX · MAXIMVS ·

Rev. Ruins of Saint Paul's. In exergue, BASILIC · S · PAVLI EX INCENDIO | XV · IVL · MDCCCXXIII | GIROMETTI FEC ·

Bronze, struck, black patina, 51 mm.

1966.114.23

Ruins of Saint Paul's Outside the Walls, which burned in 1823. For restored church, see no. 216.

Bibl.: Brescia 2, p. 43, no. 537.

212 PIUS IX Mastai Ferretti   1850

Obv. Bust to left, wearing skullcap, mozzetta and stole. Around, PIVS IX · PONTIFEX MAXIMVS ANNO V · ; below, G . GIROMETTI F .

Rev. Daniel standing with slain dragon at his feet; broken column at right. Around, DIRVPTVS EST DRACO ET DIXIT DANIEL ECCE QVEM COLEBATIS; in exergue, G . GIROMETTI F .

Bronze, struck, 44 mm.

1966.114.21

The biblical source for the reverse is Daniel 7:11. The allusion is to Pius' return to Rome in 1850 and the Fall of the Roman Republic.

Bibl.: Rinaldi, no. 44 (silver); Mazio (1885), no. 681; Martinori, fasc. xxiii–xxiv, p. 137; Bartolotti, no. E. 850.

PIETRO GIROMETTI
(1811–59)

Medalist and gem engraver, the son of Giuseppe, he worked with Niccolò Cerbara on his series of medals of famous Italians. Member of the Florentine Academy in 1835, and director general of the mint at Rome from 1849.

See Forrer 2, p. 274; 7, p. 368; Thieme-Becker 14, p. 190; Bulgari 1, p. 552.

213 GREGORY XVI Capellari, Pope 1831–46   1837

Obv. Bust to left, wearing skullcap, mozzetta and stole. Around, GREGORIVS · XVI · PONT · MAX · A · VII · ; below, PETRVS · GIROMETTI · FECIT ·

Rev. In entrance to Pauline Chapel, pope kneels before a vision of the Madonna flanked by angels carrying a tablet and the Host. On tablet above, inscription, GREGORIVS · XVI | RESTITVIT | A · VII S · PRINCIP; in exergue, SACRARIVM · PAVLINVM · PAVLVS · III · COND · | GREGORIVS · XVI · REST · | MDCCCXXXVII

Bronze, struck, 60 mm.

1966.114.12

Commemorates restoration of the Pauline Chapel in Santa Maria Maggiore.

Bibl.: A. Patrignani, *Le medaglie di Gregorio XVI,* Rome 1929, p. 88, no. 49; Mazio (1885), no. 629.

NICCOLÒ CERBARA
(1793–1869)

Medalist and gem engraver, brother of Guiseppe, and active 1829–58 as engraver of gems and dies at the Rome mint. He is known for his *Serie iconografica numismatica dei piu famosi Italiani,* begun in 1843, and engraved in collaboration with Pietro Girometti. Cerbara is said to have been influenced by the Bavarian Karl Friedrich Voigt.

See Forrer 1, pp. 386–88; 7, p. 172; Thieme-Becker 6, p. 291; Bulgari 1, p. 275.

214 MICHELANGELO (1475–1564)   1828

Obv. Intaglio bust to left. Around, reversed, MICHAEL· ANGELVS · BONARROTIVS; below, NIC · CER-BARA F · ROM · AN · 1828 ·

Without reverse

Trial piece, 61 mm.

1966.137.287

Bibl.: Forrer 7, p. 172.

215 ANGELO POLIZIANO (1454–94), poet and humanist

Obv. Bust to left. Around, ANGELVS POLITIANVS; below, NIC . CERBARA F .

Rev. In laurel wreath, inscription, POETAE | ET VETERVM | VTRIVSQ · LINGVAE | SCRIPTO-RVM | RESTITVTORI | SAGACISS; stamped on rim, head of Minerva to left

Bronze, struck, black patina, 42 mm.

1966.137.286

This is one of Cerbara's series of famous Italians.

IGNAZIO BIANCHI

A coin engraver and medalist active at the papal mint at Rome from 1848–69.

See H. V. in Thieme-Becker 3, p. 584; Forrer 1, p. 185; 7, p. 81.

216 PIUS IX Mastai-Ferretti, Pope 1846–78   1854

Obv. Bust to left, wearing skullcap, mozzetta and stole. Around, PIVS IX · PONT · MAX · ; below, I · BIAN-CHI F ·

Rev. Interior of Basilica of Saint Paul. Around, PIVS · IX · P · M · BASILICAM · PAVLI · APOST · AB · IN-CENDIO · REFECTAM · SOLEMNI · RITV · CON-SECRAVIT · IV · ID · DEC · MDCCCLIV * ; below, I · BIANCHI · F · ; in exergue, AL · POLETTI · ARCH · INV ·

Bronze, struck, 82 mm.

1966.114.2

The Basilica of Saint Paul, which had burned in 1823, was rebuilt under Pius and his predecessors. Although a team of architects was employed, most of the work was done by Luigi Poletti (1793–1869), beginning in 1833. This medal commemorates the reconsecration of the church in 1854.

Bibl.: Mazio (1885), no. 730; Martinori, fasc. xxiii–xxiv, p. 138.

217 PIUS IX Mastai-Ferretti 1876

Obv. Bust to left, wearing skullcap, mozzetta and stole. Around, PIVS · IX · PONT · MAX · AN · XXX · ; below, BIANCHI

Rev. View of piazza with fountain in lower foreground. In exergue, PAVPERVM · COMMODITATI | AEDES · A · SOLO | EXSTRVCTAE; below, I · BIANCHI · S ·

Bronze, struck, 44 mm.

1966.114.25

Refers to the construction of a new hospital for the poor.

Bibl.: Rinaldi, no. 69 (silver); Bartolotti, no. E. 875.

Nineteenth-Twentieth Century, Milan

LUIGI MANFREDINI
(1771–1840)

Sculptor, engraver, medalist, born at Bologna. Manfredini was active at the Milan mint from 1798–1830 and became chief engraver in 1808. He was professor of medallic art at the Academy of Arts in Milan. Manfredini designed the coins and medals for Napoleon I, Francis I, the Empress Maria Luisa and Francis IV d'Este, often using designs of the painter Andrea Appiani.

See Forrer 3, pp. 552–55; Thieme-Becker 24, pp. 10–11.

218 FRANCIS IV, Duke of Modena (1814–46) 1814

Obv. Head to left. Around, FRANCISCO . IIII . A . A . PR . H . ET . B . DVCI . MVT . REG . MIR . ; below, MDCCCXIIII; on truncation, L . M .

Rev. Female (Peace) leads nude winged male figure carrying shield toward left. City of Modena in left background under rainbow. Around, ADVENTV OPTIMI PRINCIPIS; on listel, L · M · F · ; in exergue, MVTINA | RESTITVTA

Bronze, struck, black patina, 42 mm.

1966.137.184

Commemorates the return of the rule of the House of Austria—Este after the defeat of Napoleon.

Bibl.: Forrer 3, p. 554; Brescia 2, p. 157, no. 144; Bianchi, p. 207; Crespellani, p. 55.

219 FERDINAND I (1793–1875), Emperor of Austria (1835–48) 1838

Obv. Head to right, laureate. Around, FERDINANDVS · I · D · G · AVSTRIAE · IMPERATOR · LONGOB · ET · VENET · REX; below, · RECTA TVERI · ; on truncation, L · MANFREDINI F ·

Rev. Ferdinand kneeling on a dais before a bishop who crowns him; around them, two noblemen and two priests. Around, CORONA · FERREA · FAVSTE · FELICITER · INAVGVRATO | AVITA · ET · AVCTA · ; below, L · MANFREDINI F · ; in exergue, LONGOBARDI · VENETIQVE | MENS · SEPT · A · MDCCCXXXVIII ·

Bronze, struck, black patina, 52 mm.

1966.137.276

Bibl.: Forrer 3, p. 554 (dated 1831).

LUIGI COSSA
(1789–1867)

Coin engraver and medalist from Cernusio near Como. A student of Albertolli and Manfredini, he was mint engraver at Milan from 1820–41.

See Forrer 1, p. 459; 7, p. 192; Thieme-Becker 7, p. 510.

220 GIUSEPPE UGOLINI (1783–1863), Cardinal, 1838, Apostolic Legate to Ferrara 1839

Obv. Bust to left. Around, G · CARDINAL LEGATO UGOLINI PROVEDENTE ANNO MDCCCXXX-IX · ; below, L . COSSA F .

Rev. Two female figures, left one (Fama?) kneeling and Victory standing, holding fasces in left hand and placing laurel wreaths on altar. Behind, city of Ferrara (?) at left and reclining male river god at right. Inscribed on altar, NATALI | RAVALLI | SCUTELLARI | MAGNONI | COPPI | BERTONI | COSTANTINI | PASSEGA | ZANARDI | MAZZARINI; in exergue, PROVINCIA DI FERRARA | L . COSSA F .

Gilt bronze, struck, 52 mm.

1966.137.281

FRANCESCO PUTINATI
(1775–1848)

Medalist, sculptor, steel engraver; second engraver at the mint of Milan for many years.

See Forrer 4, pp. 711–12; 8, p. 147; Thieme-Becker 27, p. 472.

221 ANTONIO CANOVA, sculptor (1757–1822)

Obv. Head to right. Around, ANTONIO CANOVA; on truncation, PUTINATI F ·

Rev. Snake biting its tail around inscription, AL SECOLO DECIMO NONO; above inscription a winged hat; below, a head of Minerva to right

Bronze, struck, 34 mm.

1966.137.210

Bibl.: Houston, no. 319; Forrer 4, p. 711; Brescia 2, p. 162, nos. 213–16; Bianchi, p. 152.

222 LUIGI MALASPINA, Marquis of Sannazaro (1754–1834), writer and political economist 1835

Obv. Head to left. Around, ALOISIVS · MALASPINA · A · S · NAZAR · MARCH · ; below truncation, F · PUTINATI

Rev. Palace facade. Above, BONIS · ARTIB · ; below, CONDITORI · AC · CIVI | B · M · TICINENSES | A · MDCCCXXXV

Bronze, struck, black patina, 43 mm.

1966.137.181

Malaspina founded a school of fine arts in Pavia and ran charitable institutions there.

Bibl.: Forrer 4, p. 712.

DEMETRIO CANZANI
(b. 1813)

Born in Milan, Canzani was engraver at the mint there from 1841–57, then worked for the Italian government. He executed a number of medals of the Emperor Francis Joseph.

See Forrer 1, p. 339; 7, p. 150; Thieme-Becker 5, p. 532.

223 COUNTESS GIULIA SAMOYLOFF 1845

Obv. Head to right. Around, CONTESSA GIULIA

SAMOYLOFF NATA PAHLEN; below, D. CANZANI F .

Rev. Inscription, ALLA | PROTETTRICE | DELLE ARTI BELLE | MILANO | MDCCCXLV

Bronze, struck, 60 mm.

1966.137.1

Bibl.: Brescia 2, p. 148, no. 14.

FRANCESCO BROGGI
(1811–57)

Born in Milan, assistant engraver at the mint there in 1831, second engraver in 1841, active there until his death.

See Forrer 1, p. 296; 7, p. 124; Thieme-Becker 5, p. 50.

224 CESARE CANTÙ (1804–95), Italian historian 1883

Obv. Bust to right. Around, CÆSARI CANTÙ; below truncation, P . FUMEO MODELLO; below, FRAN . BROGGI INCISE

Rev. Inscription, HISTORICORUM | ITALORUM | SUI TEMPORIS | CLARISSIMO | AN . MDCCCLXXXIII

Bronze, struck, 53 mm.

1966.137.26

Bibl.: Brescia 2, p. 148, no. 12 ("In omaggio a Cesare Cantù").

STEFANO JOHNSON

A firm of medalists founded in Milan in 1868.

See Forrer 3, pp. 79–81.

225 REBUILDING OF CAMPANILE, VENICE, 1912

Obv. Campanile seen over domes of Saint Mark's. Center below, lion of Saint Mark. Around, in border, XXV APRILE MCMXII IL VOTO E COMPIVTO; in field, COME ERA DOVE ERA

Rev. Loggetta of Campanile; in front, two virtues flank tablet inscribed, NEL GIORNO DELLA ROVINA | IL COMVNE | VOTA | LA RIEDIFICAZIONE | XIV LVGLIO MCMII | ; below, G . MORETTI DIS . S . JOHNSON

Bronze, struck, 43 mm.

1966.138.1

Nineteenth-Twentieth Century, Turin

AMADEO LAVY
(1777–1864)

Sculptor, painter, medalist, son of Lorenzo Lavy. A student at the Academy of Art at Turin in 1792–93, he worked at the Turin mint from 1794–1826, becoming sole engraver there at the death of his brother Carlo in 1813. In Rome in 1805–06, he met Canova and made copies after him and the antique. Lavy became a professor at the Turin academy in 1822 and a member of the *Accademia di San Luca* in Rome in 1823.

See Forrer 3, pp. 349–50; 7, pp. 538–39; Thieme-Becker 22, p. 480; Assandria, pp. 245–64.

226 VICTOR EMMANUEL I (1759–1824), King of Sardinia, 1802–21 1814

Obv. Bust to right. Around, VICTORIVS EMMAN-VEL; below, A · LAVY F ·

Rev. City tyche of Turin, holding a shield with a bull on it, kneels before Victor Emmanuel. Around, AD-VENTVS REGIS; on listel, A · LAVY F · ; in exergue, AVG · TAVRINORVM | AN · MDCCCXIV

Bronze, struck, 52 mm.

1966.137.27

Commemorates the return of King Victor Emmanuel I to Turin in 1814, following the fall of Napoleon.

Bibl.: Forrer 3, pp. 348–49.

GASPARE GALEAZZI

Medalist and coin engraver from Turin, active in the middle of the nineteenth century.

See Forrer 2, p. 189; 7, p. 336 (as Giuseppe); Thieme-Becker 13, p. 90 (as Gaspare).

227 VITTORIO ALFIERI (1749–1803), dramatist and poet

Obv. Head to left. Around, VICTORIVS ALFIERI; on truncation, G. GALEAZZI . F

Rev. In laurel wreath, inscription, ITALICAE | MEL-POMENIS | VINDEX

Copper, struck, 46 mm. In frame with ring at top

1966.137.272

228 LORENZO CIGNA

Obv. Head to left. Around, LAVRENTIVS CIGNA; on truncation, G · GALEAZZI · F

Rev. In laurel wreath, inscription, SIMPLICITATE | ANTIQVIS PAR | DOCTRINA | AEQVALIBVS

Copper, struck, 46 mm. In frame with loop at top

1966.137.273

Bibl.: Forrer 7, p. 336.

229 GIOVANNI BATTISTA BECCARIA (1716–81), experimental physicist

Obv. Head to left. Around, JOANNES B · BECCARIA; on truncation, G · GALEAZZI · F

Rev. In laurel wreath, inscription, ASTRA | SERVA-VIT | FVLMEN COELO | DEDVXIT

Copper, struck, 44 mm.

1966.137.277

Bibl.: Forrer 7, p. 336.

230 GEORGE, LORD BYRON (1788–1824), English poet

Obv. Head to right. Around, GEORGIVS BYRON; below, G · GALEAZZI F ·

Rev. Winged young man playing lyre. Around, AGI-TANTE CALESCIMVS ILLO

Bronze, struck, 57 mm. In frame with ring at top

1966.137.106

Bibl.: Forrer 7, p. 336.

Nineteenth-Twentieth Century, Florence

GIOVANNI ANTONIO SANTARELLI
(1758–1826)

Gem engraver, wax sculptor and medalist, born in the Abruzzi. He was a student of Niccolò Ranieri and was first active in Chieti (1780) and Rome (1785), where he was a friend of Antonio Canova. After 1797 he worked in Florence where he became a teacher of cameo and gem engraving at the academy in 1808.

See Forrer 5, pp. 334–35; 8, pp. 187–88; Thieme-Becker 29, p. 428; Pyke, pp. 127–28; C. Johnson, "'La storia metallica' di Maria Luigia Duchessa di Parma," in *Medaglia,* anno. 2, no. 3 (1972), pp. 42–82.

231 MARIE LOUISE (1791–1847), sister of Ferdinand, Emperor of Austria; Empress of France (1810–15); Duchess of Parma, Piacenza and Guastalla, 1816   1816

Obv. Head to right, wearing diadem and necklace. Around, M · LVDOV · ARCH · AVSTR · D · G · PARM · PLAC · ET · VAST · DVX; below, SANTA-RELLI · F ·

Rev. In a wreath of oak leaves, inscription, ADVENTV | PRINCIPIS · SVAE | PARMA | VOTI · COMPOS | XX · APR · | M · DCCC · XVI ·

Bronze, struck, 41 mm.

1966.137.285

The obverse is after a scudo by Manfredini. Marie-Louise was married to Napoleon I in 1810 and was the mother of Napoleon II. In 1814 she fled to Venice where her duchies were awarded to her in 1816.

Bibl.: Jean-Paul Divo, "Les médailles historiques frappées sous le règne de Marie-Louise d'Autriche à Parma," *Revue Suisse de Numismatique* 46 (1967), p. 70, no. 2; Forrer 5, p. 335; Bramsen, no. 1780; Brescia 2, p. 164, no. 250; Bianchi, pp. 207–08; Johnson, p. 78, no. 3, fig. 63.

232 MARIE LOUISE

Obv. Same as no. 231

Rev. Inscription, TREBIA | HANNIBALIS | A . DXXXV . V . C . | LICHTENSTEINII | A . MDCC-XXXXVI . | SOVWAROFII . ET . MELAS | A . MDCCLXXXXVIIII . | VICTORIIS . MAGNA | EX DECRETO . AVGVSTAE | A . MDCCCXXI . | PONTE . IMPOSITO | VTILITATE . POPVLOR . | FELIX

Bronze, struck, 41 mm.

1966.137.275

Medal for the bridge over the Trebbia.

Bibl.: Forrer 5, 335; Brescia 2, p. 164, nos. 248–49; Johnson at pp. 56–58, p. 79, no. 9, fig. 72.

DOMENICO TRENTACOSTE
(1859–1933)

A sculptor, medalist, coin engraver and painter, born in Palermo. Trentacoste studied first in Palermo with Delisi and Domenico Costantino. From 1880 he worked in Paris with A. G. Lanzirotti, C. Ceribelli and Arthur de Gravillon. He was in London in 1891 and finally settled in Florence in 1895. In that year he won the Grand Prize at the Venice Biennale. A teacher and director of the academy in Florence, he became a member of the Italian Academy in 1932.

See Forrer 6, p. 132; Thieme-Becker 33, pp. 377–78; Pyke, p. 150.

233 DANTE

Obv. Bust to left, laureate. Around, MOSTRO · CIO · CHE POTEA LA LINGUA NOSTRA; on truncation, D . TRENTACOSTE

Rev. Draped female figure standing on scroll, holds open book above her head. Rays of light flow from book. Around, SOCIETÁ NAZIONALE DANTE ALIGHIERI; below, a crown over Z; in left field, AI BE-NEME | RITI DELLA | ITALIANI | TÁ; in right field, PREMIO | PASQUALE | VILLARI

Bronze, struck, 43 mm.

1966.138.3

Pasquale Villari (1826–1917) was president of the *Societá Nazionale Dante Alighieri* from 1896 to 1903.

Nineteenth-Twentieth Century, Various Locations

PICCIOLI

Bolognese sculptor of the first half of the nineteenth century. Modeled medals of the composer G. A. Rossini and of Cardinal Ugo Spinola in 1842.

See Forrer 4, pp. 506–07.

234 PIUS IX Mastai Ferretti, Pope 1846–78   1846

Obv. Bust to left, wearing skullcap, mozzetta and stole. Around, PIO · IX · PON · MAS · ; on truncation, PICIOLI [F (?)]

Rev. In wreath, inscription, ALL'ELETTO DA DIO | SPERANZA DÈ POPOLI | 1846

Bronze, 80 mm.

1966.114.30

Coronation medal.

DONNINO BENTELLI
(1807–85)

Born at Piacenza and trained at the *Istituto Gazzola,* Bentelli was a die engraver, medalist, mechanical engineer and designer. In Parma by 1844, he was master and engraver at the mint until it closed in 1869, and professor at the Academy of Fine Arts. He engraved coins for Parma, Turin and Bologna.

See St. Lottici in Thieme-Becker 3, p. 353; Forrer 1, p. 164; 7, pp. 67–70.

235 GIAN DOMENICO ROMAGNOSI (1761–1835), Italian jurist and philosopher

Obv. Head to right. Around, GIAN DOMENICO ROMAGNOSI PIACENTINO NATO IL 1761 · ; below truncation, D · BENTELLI · F

Rev. In laurel wreath, inscription, INSEGNÒ | NUOVA E NECESSARIA | SAVIEZZA | ALLE LEGGI · ; below, U⚓F

Bronze, struck, 46 mm. Traces of black patina

1966.137.280

Romagnosi lectured on law in Milan. In 1806 he participated in the formation of a new Italian criminal code at Milan.

Bibl.: Forrer 7, p. 68.

LUIGI DE FEO
(active late nineteenth-early twentieth century)

From Apulia, de Feo was a painter, sculptor, and medalist active in Paris and Venice. He exhibited in Paris in 1907, Venice in 1909, and New York in 1910. Inspired by French relief sculpture, he is particularly noted for plaquette portraits of aristocratic women and children.

See Forrer 7, p. 296; Thieme-Becker 11, p. 393.

236 MARIE LOUISE BOURBON DEL MONTE S. MARIA 1908

Obv. Bust of child to left, with long hair. Below, – L . de FEO – 1908 – ; down left side, MARIE LOUISE; in band at bottom, BOURBON DEL MONTE S . MARIA

Without reverse

Bronze, rectangular, 139 x 106 mm. Ring at top

1966.137.46

PIVETTI
(unknown medalist)

237 LUDOVICO PAVONI (1784–1849), founder of the Congregation of the Sons of the Immaculate Virgin

Obv. Bust to right. Around, LUDOVICUS PAVONI CAN . EQUES ORD . III; below, Pivetti . F . dis .

Rev. Inscription, CONDITOR | SODAL . FILIOR . | A MARIA | SINE LABE | CONCEPTA .

Bronze, struck, 43 mm.

1966.114.69

Bibl.: Brescia 2, p. 161, no. 199 (attr. to Adolfo Pieroni).

Nineteenth-Twentieth Century, Artist Unknown

———

238 LUDOVICO ANTONIO MURATORI (1672–1750), Modenese historian and archeologist 1853

Obv. Bust to right. Around, Λ . LODOVICO . ΛNTONIO MURΛTORI . LΛ . PΛTRIΛ

Rev. Statue on a pedestal. Around, ΛDEODΛTO . MΛLΛTESTΛ . FECE; in exergue, MDCCCLIII

Silver, gilt, 80 mm. Loop attached at top

1966.137.108

The medal depicts the statue of Muratori which was commissioned in 1847 and erected in the Piazzale Muratori by the Modenese artist Adeodato Malatesta (1805–91[?]).

The medal is not recorded in Forrer, who gives only three other medals of Muratori by N. Cerbara (1, p. 388), by T. Mercandetti, 1806 (4, p. 31) and by F. Speranza (1848–1903) (5, p. 599).

FRANCE
Sixteenth Century

———

MARC BECHOT
(1520–57)

Medalist under Henry II, probably trained by Matteo dal Nassaro of Verona. Henry II appointed Bechot the first engraver general of the mints in 1547. Mazerolle says that in Bechot's medals the fine style of the French Renaissance begins to be combined with the broader Italian manner.

See Forrer 1, p. 141; Hill, *Med. Ren.* p. 143; Alvin in Thieme-Becker 3, p. 135.

239 HENRY II (1519–59), King of France 1547   1552

Obv. Bust to right, in cuirass. Around, HENRICVS · II · REX · CHRISTIANISSIMVS

Rev. Fame, Abundance and a third female figure on Quadriga to left. Around, OB · RES · IN · ITAL · GERM · ET · GAL · FORTITER · GESTAS; in exergue, EX · VOTO · PVB | 1552

Bronze, struck, 60 mm.

1966.117.3

Commemorates Henry's victory over the emperor Charles V.

Bibl.: Mazerolle 2, no. 90; *Trésor France* 1, pl. 13,2; De Haye, no. 17 (obv.), no. 20 (rev.); Robert, p. 58, no. 2 (rev.); Van Mieris, vol. 3, p. 314 (rev.).

ÉTIENNE DELAUNE
(1518/19–83)

Primarily known as a copperplate engraver, Delaune was originally an engraver of medals and seems to have worked with Benvenuto Cellini during his sojourn in Paris. In 1552 Delaune was briefly engraver to the newly mechanized Paris mint. Some of his drawings for medals and coins are at the Bibliothèque Nationale.

See H. Stöcklein in Thieme-Becker 9, pp. 2–3; Forrer 3, pp. 335–39; *Kress*, p. 103; H. Stöcklein, "Die Medaillen von E. Delaune in der Staatlichen Münzsammlung München," in *Georg Habich zum 60. Geburtstag*, Munich 1928, pp. 53–62; B. Thomas, "Die münchner Harnischvorzeichnungen des Etienne Delaune für die Emblem und die Schlangen-Garniture Heinrichs II von Frankreich," *Jahrbuch der Kunsthistorischen Sammlungen in Wien* 56 (1960), pp. 7–62 (at pp. 24–25, figs. 19–27, drawings for medals); C. Eisler, "Étienne Delaune et les graveurs de son entourage," *L'Oeil*, no. 132 (1965), pp. 10–19, 78; Y. Hackenbroch, "New knowledge on jewels and designs after Etienne Delaune," *Connoisseur* (June 1966), pp. 83–89.

240 HENRY II   1552

Obv. Bust to right, laureate, in cuirass. Around, HENRICVS · II · GALLIARVM REX INVICTISS · P P ·

Rev. Fame, Abundance and Victory on Quadriga to right. Around, OB RES IN ITAL · GERM · ET GAL · FORTITER AC FOELIC · GESTAS; in exergue, EX VOTO PVB | 1552

Gilt bronze, 55 mm.

1966.117.37

Commemorates victory over Emperor Charles V. (See note to no. 241.)

Bibl.: Arm. 3, p. 285B; Naples, p. 198; Supino, no. 818; Mazerolle 2, no. 99; *Trésor France* 1, pl. 12,1; De Haye, no. 27; Robert, p. 59, no. 3; Van Mieris 3, p. 314,2; W. McA. Johnson, "Numismatic Propaganda in Renaissance France," *Art Quarterly* 31 (1968), pp. 123–53 (p. 124 on the obverse legend, 139; figs. 26a,b; 30 for related drawing).

241 HENRY II   1552

Obv. Bust to right, in armor. Around, HENRICVS · II · GALLIARVM REX INVICTISS · PP ·

Rev. In laurel wreath, inscription, RESTITVTA | REP · SENENSI · | LIBERATIS OBSID · | MEDIOMAT · PARMA | MIRAND · SANDAMI · | · ET RECEPTO | HEDINIO · | ORBIS CONSENSV | 1552

Bronze, 55 mm.

1966.117.4

Commemorates the liberation of Siena and victory over the forces of Emperor Charles V and the pope.

Bibl.: Arm. 3, p. 285C; Houston, no. 152; Naples, p. 198; Supino, no. 819; Mazerolle 2, no. 101; *Trésor France* 1, pl. 12,2; Robert, pl. 8; Van Mieris 3, p. 313.

242 HENRY II

Obv. Bust to right, laureate, in cuirass. Around, HENRICVS · II · FRANCOR$_x$ · REX · INVICTISS° · P · P ·

Rev. Fame, Abundance and Victory on Quadriga to right. Around, TE · COPIA LAVRO · ET · FAMA · BEARVNT; in exergue, N$\widehat{V}$IA

Bronze, traces of gilt, 53 mm. Hole at top

1966.117.2

Dated 1551 to early 1553. Robert (p. 60) calls N$\widehat{V}$IA an abbreviation for NV [M] I [N] A, as the symbol over the V usually refers to an omitted N or M.

Bibl.: Arm. 3, p. 285D; Houston, no. 151; *Salton*, no. 79; *Kress*, no. 542; Naples, p. 199; Mazerolle 2, no. 103

(bronze gilt recorded); *Trésor France* 1, pl. 11,5 (proposes NŪĪA as abbreviation for N [O] V [AR] IA); Johnson (cited at no. 240), p. 124 (on the obverse legend), p. 139, fig. 27.

UNATTRIBUTED

243   HENRI D'ORLEANS (1519–59), Dauphin of France, later Henry II, King of France, 1547   1535

Obv. Bust to left, in plumed hat. **Around**, HEИR : AVREL · DVX : 1535 | AИИORVM 17

Rev. In a landscape, Saint Michael killing a monster

Bronze, 69 mm.

1966.117.40

This medal is similar in style and organization to medals of Charles of Angoulême illustrated in Rondot, *Les Médailleurs et les Graveurs de Monnaies, Jetons et Médailles en France,* Paris 1904, pl. 13,5 and to a medal of François de Tournon of 1535 in G. Combrouse, *Monuments de la Maison de France,* Paris 1856, pl. 21. The portrait type is also similar to that of a medal of Henry's brother Francis, first son of Francis I (*Trésor France* 1, pl. 6,3). The medals are so clumsy that they may well be restitutions. This specimen in Hotel Drouet sale catalog, 15 June 1923, lot 3.

Bibl.: Madrid, p. 134, no. 176 (as by François Thevenot); *Trésor France* 1, pl. 9,4.

244   HENRY OF LORRAINE, Duke of Guise (1550–88)

Obv. Bust to right, laureate, in cuirass. Around, + HENRY + DE + LOR + DVC + DE + GVISE +

Rev. In a landscape, a man plowing; above, sun dispelling clouds. Around, DISCVTIT · VT · COELO · PHOEBVS · PAX · NVBILA · TERRIS

Bronze, struck, 48 mm. Obverse struck from cracked die

1966.117.30

Except for the identification of the subject, this medal is identical to *Kress,* no. 550, of Charles III de Lorraine. Both appear to be modern restitutions.

Bibl.: Mazerolle 2, no. 409; *Trésor France* 1, pl. 27,1,2.

245   ANTOINE DE BOURBON (1518–62), King of Navarre and JEANNE D' ALBRET (1528–72)

Obv. Bust to left, in armor. Around, ANTONIVS · DEI · G · REX · NAVARRAE

Rev. Bust of Jeanne, consort of Antoine, to right.

Around, IOANNA · REGINA · NAVARRIE; below, 1572

Bronze, 54 mm.

1966.117.27

Parents of Henri de Navarre. (Henri IV, King of France, 1589–1610.)

Bibl.: Mazerolle 2, no. 387.

Seventeenth Century

GUILLAUME DUPRÉ
(ca. 1576–1643)

Dupré is considered the outstanding French medalist of the High Renaissance. His medallic activity dates from 1597. From 1604–39 he was *contrôleur général* of the French mint. He seems to have been in Italy from ca. 1611 to 1613 and from this date his medals lose some of their French delicacy in exchange for an Italianate vigor. Dupré's medals are extremely finely cast.

See Alvin in Thieme-Becker 10, pp. 173–74; Forrer 1, pp. 654–60; 7, p. 239; *Kress,* pp. 105–06.

246   FRANCESCO DE' MEDICI (1594–1614), brother of Cosimo II   1613

Obv. Bust to right, in armor. Around, D · PRINCEPS FRANCISCVS MEDICES; on truncation, GDP 1613

Without reverse

Bronze, 93 mm. Hollow cast

1966.117.15

Mazerolle reports a version of this medal with Dupré's Maria Magdalena of Austria, no. 247 as a reverse.

Bibl.: Supino, no. 849; Brescia 1, p. 112, no. 790; Migeon, no. 595; Mazerolle 2, no. 673; *Trésor France* 2, pl. 11,1; *MM.* 1, pp. 394–97, pl. 89,4.

247   MARIA MAGDALENA OF AUSTRIA, Grand Duchess of Tuscany (1591–1631), wife of Cosimo II, 1608   1613

Obv. Bust to left, in court costume. Around, MAR · MAGDALENÆ · ARCH · AVSTR · MAG · D · ETR; below, GDP 1613

Without reverse

Bronze, 93 mm. Hollow cast

1966.117.36

See no. 246. A duplicate of this medal is also in the Molinari Collection (1966.117.14; bronze, dark brown patina, 94 mm.).

Bibl.: Kress, no. 562; Supino, no. 848; Brescia 1, p. 112, no. 792; Migeon, no. 594; Mazerolle 2, no. 671 (as the reverse of a medal of Cosimo II); *Trésor France* 2, pl. 10,3; Heraeus, pl. 63,2 (as reverse of medal of Cosimo II, unsigned); Fabriczy, p. 183, pl. 36,5 (as Mola); Habich, p. 119 (as signed by Mola and Dupré).

248 ARMAND-JEAN DUPLESSIS (1585–1642), Cardinal of Richelieu, 1622   1627

Obv. Bust to left. Around, ARMAND · SANCT · ROM · ECCL · CARD · DE RICHELIEV NVNCV-PATVS; below, 1627

Rev. Hands binding laurel wreath. In scroll, EX O [T] ERE GLORIAM

Bronze, 51 mm. Old aftercast

1966.117.23

Bibl.: Mazerolle 2, no. 701; *Trésor France* 1, pl. 63,4.

249 MARSHAL D'ARGENCOURT   1630

Obv. Bust to right. Around, P . D . C . Sᴿ DARGEN-COVR . MARECH . D . BATAILLE . ; below, G . DVPRE . F . 1630

Rev. Sword, shield and ribbon, crossed. Around, IN-FERT . ET . SVSTINET; in exergue, 1630

Bronze, 65 mm. Good later cast

1966.130.46

Bibl.: Forrer 1, p. 657; Mazerolle 2, no. 704; *Trésor France* 2, pl. 16,1.

JEAN VARIN
(ca. 1604–72)

Born at Liège, Varin worked at Rochefort in 1615 and at Liège and Sedan ca. 1623. He arrived in Paris in 1625 and succeeded René Olivier at the mint in 1629 (marrying his widow in 1630). By 1646 he was engraver general of the mint of France and in 1647 he became *Contrôleur Général des Poinçons et Effigies.* Varin established the style of the seventeenth-century French medal and reorganized the French mint. He was also a noted portrait sculptor and was received into the Academy of Painting and Sculpture in 1665.

See Forrer 6, pp. 361–72; Jean de Foville in Michel 5, pp. 769–72; Thieme-Becker 35, p. 161; Jacquiot, pp. 79–

93; Mazerolle, *Varin*; V. Tourneur, "Les origines de Jean Varin," *Revue belge de Numismatique* 84 (1932), pp. 65–76.

250 ARMAND-JEAN DUPLESSIS (1585–1642), Cardinal of Richelieu, 1622   1630

Obv. Bust to right, wearing the Order of Saint Esprit. Around, · ARMANDVS IOANNES CARDINALIS DE RICHELIEV

Rev. France seated with Fortune and Fame in chariot drawn by horses; flying Victory crowns France with laurel wreath. Around, TANDEM VICTA SEQVOR; below, WARIN | · 1630 ·

Bronze, 77 mm. Later cast

1966.117.20

Bibl.: (All of the following are variations on this medal.) Houston, nos. 165, 166; *Salton,* no. 84; *Kress,* no. 575a; Mazerolle-*Varin* 1, p. 86, no. 5; Brescia 2, p. 97, no. 8; *Trésor France* 2, pl. 21,3; *MM.* 2, pl. 108,1.

251 ARMAND-JEAN DUPLESSIS, Cardinal of Richelieu 1631

Obv. Bust to right. Around, ARMANVS · IOAN · CARD · DE RICHELIEV · ; below, I · WARIN ·

Rev. Globe within circle of planets guided by winged genius. Around, · MENS SIDERA VOLVIT · ; in exergue, * 1631 *

Bronze, 50 mm.

1966.117.22

This medal with a device of the Cardinal de Richelieu was probably struck after the famous *journée des Dupes,* in which the cardinal, having thought himself lost, overcame the intrigues of the queen mother. (*Trésor*)

Bibl.: Kress, no. 576; *Médailles Françaises,* no. 83; *Trésor France* 2, pl. 28,1; Mazerolle-*Varin* 1, p. 87, no. 13.

252 LOUIS XIV (1638–1715) and ANNE OF AUSTRIA (1601–66)   1643

Obv. Bust of Louis to right, laureate. Around, · LV-DOVICVS · XIIII · D · G · FR · ET · NAV · REX · ; below, · WARIN · 1643 ·

Rev. Bust of Anne to right in mourning. Around, ANNA · D · G · FR · ET · NAV · REG; below, WARIN

Bronze, struck, 54 mm. Hole at top

1966.117.25

Married to Louis XIII in 1615, Anne became Regent of France at his death in 1643.

Bibl.: De Haye, no. 50; Jacquiot, no. 118; no. 532 (die for reverse); Menestrier, p. 14,G; Mazerolle-*Varin,* cat. pl. 3, no. 14; *Trésor France* 2, pl. 22,4.

PIERRE AURY
(b. 1622)

A French medalist, son of Augustin Aury, who was probably briefly in Holland in 1672. He later executed in France a number of medals of Louis XIV, one of which he signed with Bertinet in 1673.

See Alvin in Thieme-Becker 2, p. 258; Forrer 1, p. 91; 7, p. 34; Babelon in Michel 7, p. 410.

253 JOHANN (1625–72) and CORNELIUS (1623–72) DE WITT

Obv. Two busts confronted. Around, CORNELIVS · DE · WITT · NAT · A · 1623 * IOHANNES DE WITT · NAT · A 1625 | SCELERIS = QVE PVRVS INTEGER VITÆ; below bust of Cornelius, AVRY, below Johann, FEC; on scroll below busts, HIC ARMIS ILLE TOGA | MAXIMVS

Rev. Brothers consumed by many-headed allegorical beast, framed in a wreath of thorns entwined with ribbon inscribed, MENS | AGITAT | MOLEM | ET MAGNO · | SE COR | PORE | MISCET. At left, AVRY · F · ; around, * NUNC REDEUNT · ANIMIS INGENTIA CONSULIS · ACTA * ET FORMIDATI · SCEPTRIS ORACLA MINISTRI; in exergue, NOBILE PAR FRATRVM SÆVO | FVROR ORE TRVCIDAT · | XXAVGVSTI ·

Silver, struck, 67 mm.

1966.142

As leader of the Republican party, Johann de Witt was in effect the leader of the union of the Netherlands from 1653–72, a period of great prosperity. However, when Louis XIV invaded Holland in 1672, Johann and his brother Cornelius were hacked to pieces in a riot at the Hague provoked by the supporters of William of Orange (later William III of England). The medal has also been attributed to Reinier Arondeaux (W. Meijer, "G. H. Schuller, het Swart Toneel-Gordijn en de penning met het veelhoofdig monster," *De Navorscher* [1900], pp. 57–69). Gay van der Meer (private communication) has suggested that on stylistic grounds the medal could be

by Christoffel Adolphi, but that neither attribution has any proof.

Bibl.: Houston, no. 349; Forrer 1, p. 94 (as F. Avry); 7, p. 34 (as P. Aury); Hill-*Historical,* no. 54; Van Loon 3, p. 81 (ill.), p. 82, no. 1; *MM.* 2, pp. 87–88, pl. 120,3 (unsigned).

CHARLES JEAN FRANÇOIS CHÉRON
(1635–98)

Born at Lunéville, trained by his father, Jean-Charles Chéron, engraver to Charles IV, Duke of Lorraine, Chéron went to Rome and became engraver of medals for Clement IX and Innocent X. He returned to France in 1675 to contribute to the medallic series of Louis XIV, and was received into the academy in 1676. Chéron's style in his Roman medals is of remarkable boldness, and his medals of Pope Clement IX and of Bernini are grandiloquent and among the finest Italian medals of the period. On his return to France he was employed on the *Histoire Métallique* for the king, and his medals are consequently in an international baroque style.

See H. V. in Thieme-Becker 6, p. 466; Forrer 1, p. 420; 7, p. 179; Jacquiot, pp. 119–35.

254 PIETRO DA CORTONA (1596–1669), painter

Obv. Bust to right, in cape. Around, . PETRVS . BERETINVS . E . CORTONNA . ; on truncation, F . CHERON . F . R .

Rev. Fame recumbent, pointing with a scepter to a wreath above. Around, BENE . SVPER . VIRTVS . TE . CORONAT . ANAGR . ; below, F . CHERON . F . R .

Bronze, 72 mm.

1966.118.2

The reverse legend is an anagram of the obverse titles. This medal may have been commissioned from France. An oval ivory relief after this medal was lot 119, Sotheby sale, London, 17 November 1970.

Bibl.: Jacquiot, no. 183 (silver); Forrer 7, p. 179; Brescia 1, p. 126, no. 885; *MM.* 2, p. 86, pl. 120,2; G. Pollard, "Some Roman Seventeenth-Century Portrait Medals," *Studi Secenteschi* 7 (1966), p. 99, pl. 6b.

255 GIOVANNI PAOLO OLIVA (1600–81), eleventh Preceptor-General of the Jesuits, 1664

Obv. Bust to right, in cape. Around, I · P · OLIVA · SOC · IESV · PR · GEN · XI · PP · M · IV · A · SAC · CONC; on truncation, F . CHERON

Rev. Saint being borne to heaven by angels. Around, PROC . HONORIB . SS . DECESS . SVO . F . BORGIÆ . ; below, F . CHERON

Bronze, 68 mm.

1966.118.1

Saint Francis Borgia was canonized by Pope Clement X (1670–76) on 12 April 1671.

Bibl.: Forrer 1, p. 420; Brescia 1, p. 126, no. 887; *MM.* 2, p. 131, pl. 130,1.

256 COSIMO III DE' MEDICI (1642–1723), Grand Duke of Tuscany, 1670 and MARGARET D'ORLEANS (1645–1721)

Obv. Bust to right. Around, COSMVS . III . D . G . MAGN . DVX . ETRVRIÆ .

Rev. Bust of Margaret to right. Around, MARG^TA . ALOYS . AVRELIANENSIS . D . G . M . D . ETRVRIÆ

Bronze, 58 mm. Hole at top

1966.118.3

Cosimo married Margaret of Orleans, the daughter of Louis XIV, in 1661. She returned to France in 1675.

Bibl.: Heraeus, pl. 63,9 (rev. insc. MARG . ALOYS . . . . ETRVRIÆ; below, F . CHERON .).

257 LOUIS XIV (1638–1715), King of France, 1643

Obv. Bust to right, in peruke. Around, LVD · MAG · FRA · ET · NAV · REX · P · P · ; on truncation, CHERON

Rev. Helios riding across heavens in quadriga. Around, SOLIS QVE LABORES. Encircling scene are twelve representations of fortress plans. Around, · ARNHEM · DOESBOVPG · ZUTPHEN · DEVENTER · NIMEGVE · GRAVE · BOMEL · ORSOY · RHINBERG · VESEL · EMERICK · SCHINCK · ; stamped on rim, BRONZE

Silvered bronze, struck, 65 mm. Modern restrike

1966.118.4

The Dutch war, begun 1672; for the taking of twelve cities in Holland. From the Royal Series of the *Histoire Métallique du roi Louis XIV*.

Bibl.: Jacquiot, no. 188 (reverse undescribed); Forrer 1, p. 420; Brescia 2, p. 97, no. 12; *Trésor France* 3, pl. 14,1

(rev. 70 mm., cut down to fit smaller obverse); *Choix de Médailles en vente a la Monnaie,* Paris 1926, p. 7.

NICOLAS DELAHAYE
(1645/54–ca. 1695)

Perhaps from Lyons, Delahaye was a goldsmith and medalist in Paris, noted in the king's payment books from 1684. He worked on the medallic history of Louis XIV.

See Thieme-Becker 22, p. 225; Forrer 1, p. 548.

258 MARIE DESCORAILLE, Duchess of Fontagnes   1684

Obv. Bust to left. Around, · MARIE · DESCORAILLE · DVCHESSE · DE · FONTANGE · ; below, · DELAHAYE · F ·

Without reverse

Bronze, 59 mm.

1966.131.85

Bibl.: Forrer 1, p. 548.

ANTOINE BENOIST
(1632–1717)

Known primarily as a sculptor in wax, Benoist was also a painter and a sculptor in metal and stone. Beginning in 1657 he was one of the twenty *Peintres Ordinaires du Roi* and he was elected to the academy in 1691. Benoist executed a few medals and painted in grisaille the portraits of Louis XIV used as obverses for the *Histoire Métallique*.

See S. Lami in Thieme-Becker 3, pp. 336–37; Babelon in Michel 7, p. 408; Jacquiot, pp. 345–47; Pyke, p. 13.

259 LOUIS XIV, Portrait Bust at Age Sixty-Eight   1706

Obv. Bust to right. Around, LUDOVICUS MAGNUS REX CHRISTIANISSIMUS · ; below, incised, Ænoist. Eques ad Vivum F.

Rev. Inscription, VOTUM GALLIÆ | SIT MIHI REX TALIS SEMPER | ET ISTE DIU · | ANN · DOM · M · DCC · VI · ÆT · LXVIII · | REG · LXIIII ·

Bronze, 88 mm.

1966.131.2

Bibl.: Houston, no. 186 (with different rev.).

THOMAS BERNARD
(1650–1713)

Medalist for Louis XIV, first mentioned in his service in 1679. After 1685 Bernard worked almost exclusively for the Paris mint on the *Histoire Métallique* of the king. In 1690 he was received into the academy for a medallic portrait of the painter Mignard. He executed also a medallic series of the kings of France and made medals for the courts of England and Bavaria.

See Thieme-Becker 3, p. 433; Forrer 1, pp. 172–73; 7, p. 74; Jacquiot, pp. 95–117.

260 THE VOW OF LOUIS XIII (1601–43), King of France, 1610

Without obverse

Rev. Louis XIII kneels before the Pietà on the altar of Notre Dame and offers up his crown. Around, in border, SE ET REGNUM DEO SUB B . MARIÆ TUTELA CONSECRAVIT; at base of altar steps, T · BERNARD · F · ; in exergue, ARAM VOVIT | M . DC . XXXVIII .

Pewter, 69 mm.

1966.131.86

From the first Royal Series of the *Histoire Métallique du roi Louis XIV*. On 15 August 1638, Louis put himself, his crown, and France under the special protection of the Virgin.

Bibl.: Jacquiot, no. 132; Forrer 1, p. 173; *Médailles Françaises,* no. 85, p. 24; *Trésor France* 1, pl. 40,4.

261 HENRI DE LA TOUR OF AUVERGNE, Prince Viscount of Turenne (1611–75), Marshal of France, one of the greatest of French commanders 1683

Obv. Bust to right, in cuirass and lace scarf. Around, · HENR · DE · LA · TOVR · DAVVERGNE · PRINC · VICEC · DE · TVRENNE · ; on truncation, BERNARD

Rev. A tree, with wreaths hanging from its branches, being struck by lightning. Around, * NON * LAVRI * MILLE * TVENTVR * ; in exergue, M · DCL · XXXIII

Bronze, struck, 54 mm.

1966.131.87

The reverse refers to a legend that laurel is never struck by lightning.

Bibl.: Jacquiot, no. 173; Forrer 1, p. 173; *Médailles Françaises,* no. 506, p. 207.

262 LOUIS XIV (1638–1715), Embellishment of Paris (1670)

Obv. Head to right. Around, LUDOVICUS XIIII · REX CHRISTIANISSIMUS *

Rev. Tyche of Paris, seated turned to left, holding cornucopia and ship; at her feet, river god representing the Seine; behind, portals of Saint Denis and Saint Martin. Around, ORNATA ET AMPLIATA URBE · ; below, left, B̄ (artist's monogram); in exergue, M · DC · LXX ·

Bronze, struck, 41 mm.

1966.131.7

From the Uniform Series of the *Histoire Métallique du roi Louis XIV*.

Bibl.: Jacquiot, no. 150 (notes a payment of 1702 for this medal); Forrer 1, p. 173; *Louis XIV,* p. 115.

JEAN DOLLIN
(d. 1725)

Medalist, active from 1680 in Paris. He is documented at the French medal mint from 1714–25, but must have worked there earlier, since he assisted Jean Mauger with the Uniform Series of the *Histoire Métallique du roi Louis XIV*.

See Forrer 1, pp. 598–99; 7, p. 228; Thieme-Becker 4, p. 394; Jacquiot, pp. 137–49.

JEAN MAUGER
(1648–1722)

Born at Dieppe, Mauger may have been a student of Jean Varin. Having settled at Paris ca. 1677, he was primarily engaged on the medallic series of Louis XIV, first engraving large medals for the Royal Series, then engraving the entire first Uniform Series of Louis XIV between 1695 and 1703. Mauger executed the obverse portraits for the Uniform Series after designs by Antoine Coypel and was assisted on the series by Jean Dollin, Thomas Bernard, Hercule Breton, Joseph Roettiers and Jerome Roussel. After 1702 he worked, assisted by Dollin, Roeg, Le Blanc, Benjamin Duvivier, and Roettiers, on the reformed Uniform Series, which remained unfinished at the death of Louis XIV.

See Forrer 3, pp. 616–24 (extensive list of Mauger's medals); 8, p. 34; Thieme-Becker 24, p. 274; Jacquiot, pp. 175–201.

Jean Mauger/Jean Duvivier (See biog. after no. 282)

263 LOUIS XIV, Raising of the Siege of Guise (1650)

Obv. Head to right. Around, LUDOVICUS XIIII · REX CHRISTIANISS · ; below, I · MAVGER · F ·

Rev. Male figure (War), standing over weapons and armor, hands laurel wreath to female figure (France). Around, HISPANORUM COMMEATU INTERCEPTO · ; lower right, D . V . ; in exergue, GUSIA LIBERATA | I · JULII M · DC · L ·

Bronze, 41 mm.

1966.131.5

From the first Uniform Series of the *Histoire Métallique* of Louis XIV.

Bibl.: Forrer 1, p. 684 (rev.); Jacquiot, no. 257 (obverse is similar); *Louis XIV*, p. 31.

Jean Mauger/Jean Dollin

264 LOUIS XIV, Reception of the Queen of Sweden (1656)

Obv. Head to right. Around, LUDOVICUS XIIII · REX CHRISTIANISSIMUS · ; below, J · MAVGER · F ·

Rev. Louis receiving the queen. Around, HOSPITALITAS AUGUSTA . ; lower right, D; in exergue, CHRISTINA SUECORUM REGINA | IN GALLIA EXCEPTA | M . DC . LVI

Bronze, 41 mm.

1966.131.8

From the reformed Uniform Series.

Bibl.: Jacquiot, no. 257 (obverse similar); no. 211 (reverse); Jacquiot, *Médailles*, p. 108, pl. 20,5; Forrer 1, p. 598; *Louis XIV*, p. 44.

Jean Mauger/Jean Dollin

265 LOUIS XIV, Audience Granted to the Pontifical Legate (1664)

Obv. Head to right. Around, LUDOVICUS XIIII · REX CHRISTIANISSIMUS · ; below, I · MAVGER · F ·

Rev. Louis XIV seated in court dress at left, listens to Cardinal Chigi, seated at right. Around, CORSICVM FACINVS EXCVSATVM; in exergue, LEGATO A LATERE MISSO | M . DC . LXIV . ; on rim, BRONZE

Bronze, struck, 41 mm. (Restrike)

1966.131.9

From the first Uniform Series.

Bibl.: Jacquiot, no. 214 (reverse); Jacquiot, *Médailles*, p. 170, pl. 32,5; Forrer 3, p. 618; cp *Louis XIV*, p. 79 (insc. in exergue adds XXVIII JULII to MDCLXIV).

Jean Mauger

266 LOUIS XIV, Institution of the Military Order of Saint Louis (1693)

Obv. Head to right. Around, LUDOVICUS MAGNUS REX CHRISTIANISSIMUS · ; below, J · MAVGER · F ·

Rev. Cross of the Order of Saint Louis, with inscription, BELLICAE VIRTVTIS PRAEMIUM · ; around, ORDOMILITARIS · S · LVDOVICI ALVDOVICO MAGNO INSTITVTVS · M · DC · XCIII ·

Bronze, struck, 41 mm.

1966.131.15

From the reformed Uniform Series.

Reverse designed by Jean Racine.

Bibl.: Jacquiot, no. 59 (larger version, rev.); Jacquiot, *Médailles*, p. 568, pl. 113,2; Forrer 3, p. 622; *Médailles Françaises*, no. 312B, p. 147.

Jean Mauger

267 LOUIS XIV

Obv. Head to right. Around, LUDOVICUS MAGNUS REX CHRISTIANISSIMUS · ; below, J · MAVGER · F ·

Without reverse

Bronze, struck, 41 mm.

1966.131.10

Jean Mauger

268 LOUIS XIV, Chamber of Commerce (1700)

Obv. Head to right. Around, LUDOVICUS MAGNUS REX CHRISTIANISSIMUS · ; below, I · MAVGER · F ·

Rev. Justice and Mercury. Around, SEXVIRI COMMERCIIS REGUNDIS · ; in exergue, M · DCC ·

Bronze, partly gilt and silvered, struck, 41 mm.

1966.131.1

From the first Uniform Series.

Bibl.: *Médailles Françaises*, no. 350, p. 158; *Louis XIV*, p. 283.

Jean Dollin/Jean Mauger

269 LOUIS XIV, The Palace of Versailles (1680)

Obv. Head to right. Around, LUDOVICUS MAGNUS REX CHRISTIANISSIMUS · ; below, I · D . . . LI

Rev. View of the palace and gardens of Versailles from above. Around, REGIA VERSALIARUM; in exergue, M · DC · LXXX ·

Bronze, struck, 41 mm.

1966.131.14

From the first Uniform Series.

Bibl.: Jacquiot, no. 461; Forrer 3, p. 621; *Médailles Françaises*, no. 243, p. 116; *Louis XIV*, p. 184.

Jean Dollin/Jean Mauger

270 LOUIS XIV, The Citadel of Casale Surrenders to Louis XIV (1681)

Obv. Head to right. Around, LUDOVICUS MAGNUS REX CHRISTIANISSIMUS; below, I D . . . LI . . . · F ·

Rev. Louis, enthroned on dais at left, receives shield with the plan of Casale on it from kneeling female personification of Casale; behind her the Duke of Mantua hands his standard to Louis. Around, TUTELA ITA-LIAE · ; in exergue, CASALIS ARCE IN FIDEM | RECEPTA · | M · DC · LXXXI ·

Bronze, struck, 41 mm.

1966.131.11

From the first Uniform Series.

A larger version of this reverse by Hercule le Breton exists (Jacquiot, no. 252).

Bibl.: Forrer 3, 621; Menestrier, no. 70; *Louis XIV*, p. 187 (adds XXX SEPTEMB · to reverse insc.).

Jean Dollin/Jean Mauger

271 LOUIS XIV, Institution of Cadet Corps (1683)

Obv. Same as no. 269.

Rev. Officer in center, flanked by two cadets; in background, ship. Around, LECTI JUVENES INNAVAL-EM MILITIAM CONSCRIPTI· DCCC; in exergue, M · DC · LXXXIII ·

Bronze, struck, 41 mm.

1966.131.13

From the first Uniform Series.

Bibl.: Forrer 3, p. 621; *Médailles Françaises*, no. 258; p. 123 (by Mauger, *Gardes de la marine et de l'étendard*); *Louis XIV*, p. 199.

Jean Dollin/Jean Mauger

272 LOUIS XIV, Institution of the Military Order of Saint Louis (1693)

Obv. Same as no. 270

Rev. At left, king, armor behind him, awarding order to kneeling officer while two others stand at right; in background, military camp and two ships. Around, in scroll, VIRTUTIS BELLICAE PRAEMIUM; in exergue, ORDO MILIT · S · LUDOVICI | INSTITUTUS · | M · DC · XCIII ·

Bronze, struck, 41 mm.

1966.131.12

From the first Uniform Series.

Bibl.: Forrer 3, p. 622; Jacquiot, no. 288 (large version with different inscription); Jacquiot, *Médailles*, p. 574, pl. 114,11; *Médailles Françaises*, no. 311c, p. 146; *Louis XIV*, p. 246.

UNATTRIBUTED

273 LOUIS XIV (?)

Obv. Bust to right, laureate

Without reverse

Copper, gilt, 85 mm.

1966.131.4

274 NICOLAS DE BAILLEUL (d. 1662), member of Parliament, Provost of the Paris Guilds (1622–28)   1623

Obv. Bust to right, in magistrate's gown. Around, NICO · DE · BAILLEVL · PROPRÆT · VRB · ET · PRÆF · ÆDIL · CVRANTE; below, · 1623

Rev. Nymph of the Seine reclining in a landscape. Around, ÆTERNOS · PRÆBET · LVTETIA · FONTES ·

Bronze, 53 mm.

1966.117.28

Bibl.: Mazerolle 2, no. 842; *Trésor France* 2, pl. 18,4; *Kress*, no. 577.

275 ALLEGORY OF PRUDENCE

Obv. Woman seated among masks. Around, STVLTI-TIAM SIMVLARE LOCO SVMMA PRVDENTIA EST

Rev. Prudence, Bellona and Bona Fortuna. Around, PROVIDENTIA DVCIS FORTISS · AC FOELI-CISS · ; incised in exergue, 1626

Gilt bronze, 56 mm. Reverse is smaller than obverse (52 mm.)

1966.119.8

The reverse of this medal is published as the reverse of a medal of Anne de Montmorency.

Bibl.: Arm. 2, p. 191,20; Mazerolle 2, no. 461; *Trésor France* 1, pl. 46,3.

276 ANNE OF AUSTRIA (1602–66), married Louis XIII, 1615   1645

Without obverse

Rev. Facade of Church of Val de Grâce. Around, · OB · GRATIAM · DIV · DESIDERATI · REGII · ET · SECVNDI · PARTVS · ; below, · QVINTO · CAL · SEPT · | · 1638 ·

Bronze, 94 mm. Hole at top

1966.130.44

Foundation medal of Val de Grâce.

Queen Anne of Austria made a vow during her twenty-two childless years that if she became a mother she would build a church. Louis XIV was born on 8 September 1638, but the church was not begun until after the death of Louis XIII. On 1 April 1645 Anne placed the first stone of the Val de Grâce. The convent was completed in 1662, the church in 1665. The first architect was François Mansart, and his design is probably represented on the medal. He was dismissed after one year and the design was altered by Lemercier. The medal was issued on 1 April 1645.

Bibl.: *Trésor France* 2, pl. 22,2; Anthony Blunt, *Art and Architecture in France, 1500–1700*, Pelican History of Art, 1954, pp. 149–50 (for Val de Grâce); A. Braham, "Mansart Studies I: The Val-de-Grâce," *Burlington Magazine* 105 (1963), pp. 351–63, fig. 15 (medal by Jean Varin); P. Smith, "Mansart Studies II: The Val-de-Grâce," *Burlington Magazine* 106 (1964), p. 115 (for date of medal); Anthony Blunt, *François Mansart*, London 1941, pp. 14–16 (medal as image of Mansart's design compared to later changes).

277 LOUIS XIII (1601–43), King of France, 1610; medal for the foundation of the Church of Saint Louis   1627

Obv. Bust to right of Saint Louis. Around, PRO · SCEP-TRIS · ARAS · DAT · TELLVS · ET · DEVS · ASTRA

Rev. Facade of Church of Saint Louis. Around, LV-DOVICVS XIII . D . G . FRANCOR . ET . NAV . REX . FVNDAVIT AN . MDCXXVII

Bronze, 58 mm. Hole at top

1966.131.88

This medal was one of those placed in the foundation of the Church of Saint Louis, built by Louis XIII from 1627 to 1641 for the Jesuits of Rue Saint-Antoine, called "les Grands Jesuites." The design of the church was changed during construction.

Bibl.: Mazerolle 2, no. 819; *Trésor France* 1, pl. 36,3.

278 LOUIS XIV (1643–1715), The New Ordinances (1667)

Obv. Head to right. Around, LUDOVICUS XIIII · REX CHRISTIANISSIMUS *

Rev. At right, king enthroned holding scales. Justice before him at left. Around, LITIUM SERIES RESCIS-SAE; in exergue, NOVO CODICE LATO · | M · DC · LXVII ·

Bronze, struck, 41 mm.

1966.131.6

Bibl.: *Louis XIV*, p. 95 (with different inscription on reverse).

Eighteenth Century

SIMONE CURÉ
(ca. 1681–1734)

Curé executed a series of medals of famous Frenchmen and engraved the medals for E. Titon du Tillet's *Parnasse Français,* after models by the sculptor Louis Garnier.

See Forrer 1, pp. 483–84; 7, p. 198; Michel 7, pp. 413–14; Fréd. Alvin in Thieme-Becker 8, pp. 203–04.

279 VINCENT VOITURE (1598–1648), writer and diplomat   1718

Obv. Bust to left, laureate. Around, VINCENT VOI-TURE

Rev. The Three Graces. Around, IE LES FAIS A MON BADINAGE · ; lower right, CURÉ; in exergue, M DCC XVIII

Bronze, 53 mm.

1966.130.36

This is one of thirty-four medals executed for the *Parnasse Français,* conceived by Evrard Titon du Tillet and designed by Louis Garnier. The sculptured group represented the summit of Parnassus, on which Louis XIV as Apollo presided over images and medallions of leading artistic figures. The bronze model was finished in 1718, but the full-scale sculpture was never made.

Bibl.: Houston, no. 189; Forrer 1, p. 483; Brescia 2, p. 103, no. 6; *MM.* 2, p. 38, pl. 109,2.

280 RENÉ RAPIN (1621–87), Jesuit poet 1718

Obv. Bust to left, wearing cap. Around, RENATUS RAPINUS · ; below, S · CURÉ · F

Rev. Fountain with a high jet of water in a garden. Around, FŒCUNDAT ET ORNAT; in exergue, M DCC XVIII

Bronze, 51 mm.

1966.130.43

For the *Parnasse Français.* See no. 279.

Bibl.: Forrer 1, p. 483; Brescia 2, p. 103, no. 8; *MM.* 2, p. 150, pl. 137,3.

NORBERT ROETTIERS
(ca. 1666–1727)

The son of Jean Roettiers, Norbert was apprenticed to his father and worked at the London mint from 1684–95, becoming assistant engraver in 1690. He later went to France where he was given a position at the mint through his uncle Joseph Roettiers, whom he succeeded as engraver general in 1703.

See Forrer 5, pp. 183–87; 8, p. 358; Thieme-Becker 28, p. 508.

JOSEPH CHARLES ROETTIERS
(1692–1779)

Son of Joseph Roettiers, he became *Graveur des Médailles du Roi* in 1715 and was admitted to the Paris Academy in 1717. He succeeded his cousin Norbert as first engraver at the Paris mint and held the post from 1727–53 and 1772–74.

See Forrer 5, pp. 178–82; Thieme-Becker 28, p. 508.

Norbert Roettiers/Joseph Charles Roettiers

281 ELIZABETH, Duchess of Orleans, Princess Palatine (d. 1722) 1717

Obv. Bust to left. Around, ELIZ · CAR · PALATINA RHENI DVCISSA AVRELIAN · ; below, N · R ·

Rev. Tyche of Orleans seated, flanked by two lions. Around, DIS GENITA ET GENITRIX DEVM; on listel, I : C : ROETTIERS . F : ; in exergue, M . D . CC . XVII .

Bronze, struck, 72 mm.

1966.130.45

Bibl.: Forrer 5, p. 186.

JEAN LE BLANC
(ca. 1676–1749)

A goldsmith, medalist and coin engraver, Le Blanc won the Rome Prize in 1704 and studied in Italy for several years. From 1715 to his death he worked in Paris at the *Monnaie des Médailles du Roi.* He became a member of the Paris Academy in 1718.

See Forrer 1, pp. 194–96; 3, p. 355; 7, p. 84; Thieme-Becker 8, p. 90.

282 LOUIS XV (1710–74), King of France, 1715, Audience of the Turkish Ambassador (1721)

Obv. Bust to right. Around, LUDOVICUS XV · REX CHRISTIANISS · ; on truncation, LE BLANC . F .

Rev. Turkish ambassador bowing before the king on dais. Around, SPLENDOR NOMINIS GALLICI · ; lower left, I · B · ; in exergue, ORATOR IMP · TURCARUM | M · DCC · XXI ·

Bronze, struck, 41 mm.

1966.131.17

Bibl.: Forrer 1, p. 195; *Louis XV,* no. 20; *Médailles Françaises,* no. 26 (rev.), p. 215.

JEAN DUVIVIER
(1687–1761)

Born at Liège, Duvivier was a student of his father Gandolphe. In 1710/11 he went to Paris, where he was active as a copperplate engraver until 1714, when, under the influence of his patron, Jean-Baptiste de Valdor, he turned to medals. He succeeded Mauger at the medal mint in 1719, remaining there until 1729. A dispute with Bouchardon caused him to lose the king's patronage in 1738, but he returned to court in 1748. A prolific medalist,

Duvivier designed over 400 medals and engraved portraits of Louis XV at seventeen different ages.

See Forrer 1, pp. 683–85; 6, pp. 293–96; Thieme-Becker 10, pp. 252–53; H. Nocq, *Les Duvivier,* Paris 1911.

MICHAEL ROEG
(ca. 1679–1736/7)

Norwegian medalist who was trained in Copenhagen and worked there until 1715 when he went to France. From 1720 to his death he was engraver of medals to Louis XV.

See Forrer 5, pp. 147–48; Arist Pander in Thieme-Becker 28, pp. 483–84.

Jean Duvivier

283 LOUIS XV, The Congress of Cambrai (1721)

Obv. Bust to right, laureate. Around, LUDOVICUS XV . D . G . FRAN . ET NAV . REX . ; on truncation, DU VIVIER F ·

Rev. Female figures representing Victory and Peace touching hands. Around, FELIX CONGRESSUS . ; at lower right, D . V . ; in exergue, M · DCC · XXI

Bronze, struck, 41 mm.

1966.131.16

The Congress of Cambrai was convened to attempt to solve the problems of the Spanish Succession. It ended unsuccessfully in 1725.

Bibl.: Forrer 1, p. 684; Nocq, no. 54, p. 150; *Louis XV,* no. 17; *Médailles Françaises,* no. 32, p. 216.

Jean Duvivier/Michael Roeg

284 LOUIS XV, Conquest of the Milanese Provinces (1733)

Obv. Bust to right, laureate. Around, LUDOVICUS XV . REX CHRISTIANISSIMUS; on truncation, DUVIVIER

Rev. Figure of Mars holding shield with French coat of arms, receiving supplicant tyche of city of Milan. Around, MARS ULTOR; lower right, RÖG; in exergue, INSUBRIA | AUSTRIACIS EREPTA | M D CCXXXIII .

Bronze, struck, 41 mm.

1966.131.18

Bibl.: Forrer 5, p. 148; *Louis XV,* no. 49; *Médailles Françaises,* no. 75, p. 228.

FRANÇOIS JOSEPH MARTEAU
(ca. 1720–57)

Goldsmith and medalist in Paris, living in the Louvre as goldsmith to the king from 1741. Marteau engraved medals of Louis XIV and Louis XV.

See Forrer 3, pp. 587–88; Thieme-Becker 24, p. 145.

François Marteau

285 PHILIP STOSCH (1691–1757), German archaeologist who lived in Italy   1727

Obv. Head to right. Around, PHILIPP · L · BARO · DE · STOSCH · GERMANVS; below, F · MARTEAU · F · | 1727

Rev. In front of a wall Diogenes, seated in his barrel at left, converses with Alexander, who stands at right. On barrel, a dog. From openings in wall emerge an owl and a tree branch. On wall at right, a bird. In background, a temple. In exergue, ΑΡΙΣΤΟΝ · ΜΕΤΡΟΝ

Gilt bronze, struck, 41 mm. Reverse struck from cracked die

1966.130.38

Bibl.: Forrer 3, p. 587; Brescia 2, p. 101, no. 35; *MM.* 2, pp. 379–80, pl. 193,4.

François Marteau/Joseph Charles Roettiers (See biog. before no. 281)

286 LOUIS XV, Pacification of Corsica (1740)

Obv. Head to right. Around, LUD · XV · REX · CHRISTIANISS · ; below, F . M .

Rev. Corsica, a woman kneeling before Mars, who carries a drape covered with *fleurs de lis,* is directed to submit to the republic of Genoa, represented by the woman at the left. Around, REBELLES CORSICÆ MOTUS COMPRESSI; lower right, J · C · R · ; in exergue, M . DCC . XL

Bronze, struck, 42 mm.

1966.131.19

Bibl.: Forrer 5, p. 180; 3, p. 587 (obv. ill.); *Médailles Françaises,* no. 90, p. 232.

François Marteau

287 LOUIS XV, Departure for the Campaign in Flanders (1744)

Obv. Head to right. Around, LUD · XV · REX CHRISTIANISS · ; below, F . M .

Rev. King on horseback, to right, crowned by flying Victory and led by a soldier carrying the *fleur de lis* standard. Around, SPES EXERCITUUM; lower right, M; in exergue, PROFECTIO AUGUSTI | IN BELGIUM | M·DCC·XLIV·

Bronze, struck, 42 mm.

1966.131.20

Bibl.: Médailles Françaises, no. 94, p. 233.

JAMES OR JACQUES ROETTIERS DE LA TOUR
(1707–84)

Known primarily as a goldsmith, Jacques Roettiers, the son of Norbert, was trained under Thomas Germain. He went to London in 1732 and was appointed engraver at the English mint. Returning to Paris in 1733, he was engraver general from 1733–72 and he succeeded Nicholas Besnier as court goldsmith to Louis XV in 1737. Roettiers was ennobled when he retired in 1772 and in 1773 he was admitted into the Académie des Beaux Arts as a medalist.

See Thieme-Becker 28, p. 508; Forrer 5, pp. 159–61; 8, p. 358; J. Bingen, *Les Roettiers, graveurs en Médaille des Pays-Bas Meridionaux,* Bruxelles 1952, pp. 37–46, 109–46; H. Honour, *Goldsmiths and Silversmiths,* London 1971, pp. 192–97, 315.

288 ISAAC NEWTON (1642–1727), English mathematician, physicist and natural philosopher 1739

Obv. Bust to right. Around, ISAACVS NEWTONVS; below, Jac · Roettiers ·

Rev. Figure of woman in classical robes holding shield with solar system drawn upon it. At her feet, a globe. Around, ERIT QUI DEMONSTRET IN QUIBUS COELI PARTIBUS ERRENT, SEN COM : ; below right, R; in exergue, 1739

Lead, struck, 53 mm.

1966.131.53

The rev. insc. (a quotation from Seneca, *de cometis*) was reused in the 1735 medal for the Antwerp Academy.

Bibl.: Forrer 5, pp. 160 (illustrates reversed copy by Croker), 161; Bingen (cited above), pp. 38, 110, no. 2; *Med. Ill.* 2, p. 471,86; pl. 147, no. 7.

BENJAMIN DUVIVIER
(1730–1819)

The son of Jean Duvivier. Trained as a medalist at the academy (1756–58), he took over his deceased father's studio at the Louvre in 1761. In 1764 he became *Graveur des Médailles du Roi,* in 1774 *Graveur général des Monnaies de France,* and in 1776 a member of the Royal Academy. During the Revolution, in 1791, he was replaced by Augustin Dupré, but continued to be active as a medalist.

See Forrer 1, pp. 685–89; 6, pp. 296–301; Fréd. Alvin in Thieme-Becker 10, pp. 249–50; H. Nocq, *Les Duvivier,* Paris 1911; "Les dessins des Duvivier au Cabinet des Médailles," *Aréthuse,* fasc. 28 (1930), pp. 73–77.

LAURENT LÉONARD
(1709–88)

Medalist and engraver, active at the Paris medal mint on the medallic series of Louis XV. Léonard temporarily succeeded Charles Norbert Roettiers as mint engraver between 1772 and 1774.

See Forrer 3, pp. 395–96; Thieme-Becker 23, p. 72.

AUGUSTIN DUPRÉ
(1748–1833)

Dupré learned engraving and sculpture at the school of Jacques Olanier in Saint Étienne (Loire). He went to Paris in 1768, working first for an armorer and then independently through the aid of the Spanish ambassador. His first medals date from 1776, and in the 1780s he did a number of medals for American independence. A supporter of the Revolution, he succeeded Benjamin Duvivier as *Graveur général des monnaies françaises* and held the office from 1791 to 1803.

See Forrer 1, pp. 647–52; 7, p. 239; F. Alvin in Thieme-Becker 10, pp. 169–70; C. Saunier, *Augustin Dupré, orfèvre, médailleur et graveur Général des monnaies,* Paris 1894; C. Zigrosser, "Medallic Sketches of Augustin Dupré," *Proceedings of the American Philosophical Society* 101 (1957), pp. 535–50; J. Mazard, "Un Directeur ignoré de la monnaie de Paris: Le citoyen Anfrye," *Revue Numismatique* (1964), pp. 141–48 (including two unpublished drawings for medals by Dupré).

Benjamin Duvivier/Laurent Léonard

289 LOUIS XV, Construction of the Pont de Neuilly   1772

Obv. Head to right, laureate. Around, LUD . XV . REX CHRISTIANISS . ; below, B . DUVIVIER F .

Rev. View of the Pont de Neuilly and the Seine with environs. Around, NOVAM ARTIS AUDACIAM MIRANTE SEQUANA; in exergue, PONS | AD LUGNIACUM | EXTRUCTUS | M · DCC · LXXII | L · LEON · F ·

Bronze, struck, 42 mm.

1966.131.21

Bibl.: Médailles Françaises, no. 153B, p. 251.

Benjamin Duvivier

290 MARIE ANTOINETTE (1755–93), Birth of Marie Thérèse Charlotte   1778

Obv. Bust to left. Around, MARIA ANT . AUSTR . FR . ET NAV . REGINA; below, B . DUVIVIER

Rev. Figure representing France holding infant. Around, FŒCUNDITATIS AUGUSTÆ PIGNUS ET OMEN; on listel, B . DU VIV . ; in exergue, · NATAL · MARIÆ THER · CAR · | REGIS PRIMOG · | XIX · DEC · | MDCCLXXVIII .

Bronze, struck, 42 mm.

1966.131.22

Bibl.: Forrer 1, p. 686; Nocq, no. 196 (rev.); *Médailles Françaises,* no. 16 (rev.), p. 277; no. 13 (this rev. is our obv.), p. 276.

Benjamin Duvivier

291 LOUIS XVI (1754–93), King of France, 1774, and MARIE ANTOINETTE, Birth of the Dauphin   1781

Obv. Busts to left, jugate. Around, LUD · XVI · REX CHRISTIANISS : MAR · ANT · AUSTR · REGINA; below, DUVIVIER

Rev. Enthroned figure of France holding up infant. Around, FELICITAS PUBLICA; lower left, D . V . ; in exergue, NATALES DELPHINI | DIE XXII OCTOBRIS | MDCCLXXXI

Bronze, struck, 42 mm.

1966.131.23

Bibl.: Forrer 1, p. 686; Nocq, no. 207; *Médailles Françaises,* no. 22, p. 278 (variant in obv. insc.).

Benjamin Duvivier/Augustin Dupré

292 LOUIS XVI, Establishment of the Paris Mayorality   1789

Obv. Bust to right. Around, LOUIS XVI ROI DES FRANÇOIS; on truncation, B . DUVIVIER F . ; in exergue, VILLE DE PARIS

Rev. Paris leaning on pedestal holding staff with Phrygian cap. Around, ÉTABLISSEMENT DE LA MAIRIE DE PARIS * ; left center, DUPRÉ F . ; in exergue, J. SILVAIN BAILLY PREMIER MAIRE | ÉLULE 15 JUILLET | 1789 ·

Bronze, struck, 53 mm.

1966.131.25

Dupré had also engraved a head of the king to serve as the obverse of this medal, but the die was not used and the medal was struck with an obverse by Duvivier.

Bibl.: Forrer 1, p. 648; Nocq, no. 239; *Médailles Françaises,* no. 4, p. 297; *Trésor Revolution,* pl. 9,5.

Benjamin Duvivier

293 LOUIS XVI, The Assembly of Nobles at Paris   1789

Obv. Bust to left. Around, LUDOV · XVI · FRANC · ET NAVARRÆ REX; below, DU VIVIER . F .

Rev. In laurel wreath, inscription, CONVENTUS | NOBILIUM | PARISIEN- | SIUM; around, LEGI REGIQUE FIDELES; below, LUTETIÆ MAIO | MDCCLXXXIX

Bronze, struck, 42 mm.

1966.131.27

Assembly of nobility held at the Church of the Oratory, beginning 26 April 1789 and lasting through part of May.

Bibl.: Forrer 1, p. 687; Nocq, no. 234; *Médailles Françaises,* no. 2, p. 297; *Trésor Revolution,* pl. 2,3.

Benjamin Duvivier

294 LOUIS XVI, Entry of Louis XVI into Paris   1789

Obv. Same as no. 292

Rev. King, queen and dauphin being led by city tyche of Paris, to the Tuileries palace, where a large crowd waits. Around, J'Y FERAI DESORMAIS MA DEMEURE HABITUELLE; lower right, DUVIV; in exergue, ARRIVEE DU ROI A PARIS | LE 6 . OCT . 1789

Bronze, struck, 53 mm.

1966.131.26

A drawing for this medal is published in *Aréthuse,* fasc. 28 (1930), pl. 14.

Bibl.: Forrer 1, p. 686; Nocq, no. 242; *Médailles Françaises,* no. 10, p. 299; *Trésor Revolution,* pl. 12,4; Roger Marx, *Les Médailleurs Français depuis 1789,* Paris 1897, p. 4.

Benjamin Duvivier

295 CHARLES-MICHEL, Abbé de l'Épée (1712–89)   1801

Obv. Bust to left. Around, CH · MICHEL DE L'ÉPÉE NÉ A VERSAILLES 1712, MORT A PARIS 1789 · ; on truncation, B DUVIVIER F .

Rev. Inscription, AU GÉNIE | INVENTEUR | DE L'ART D'INSTRUIRE | LES SOURDS - ET - MUETS | DANS LES SCIENCES | ET LES ARTS | B . DUVIVIER | 1801

Bronze, struck, 42 mm.

1966.131.38

The Abbé de l'Épée interested himself in the education of poor deaf and dumb children, and founded in 1755 a school for such pupils, which he supported until his death. The medal was used as a prize awarded by the government in the institutions for the deaf and dumb.

Bibl.: Forrer 1, p. 688; Nocq, p. 109; *Médailles Françaises,* no. 111, p. 335; *Trésor Révolution,* pl. 88, no. 9; Bramsen 1, no. 185; Brettauer, no. 1648; Freeman, no. 312.

NICOLAS MARIE GATTEAUX
(1751–1832)

A student of Delorme and Gros, Gatteaux was at the Paris medal mint from 1773, and was named *Graveur des Médailles du Roi* in 1781. He was a prolific medalist.

See Forrer 2, pp. 209–13; 7, p. 342; Thieme-Becker 13, p. 248; Pyke, p. 52.

296 LOUIS XVI (1754–93), Aerostatic Experiments of the Montgolfier Brothers   1783

Obv. Bust to right. Around, LUD XVI · REX CHRISTIANISS · ; below, GATTEAUX

Rev. Cybele, seated on a lion, raises arms toward one Montgolfier brother seated on a cloud, holding fire under balloon. Around, ATTONITUS ORBIS TERRARUM; lower right, GATTEAUX; in exergue, ITINERE PER AERA FELICITER | TENTATO ANNO | MDCCLXXXIII

Bronze, struck, 42 mm.

1966.131.24

Bibl.: Forrer 2, p. 210; *Médailles Françaises,* no. 37, p. 283.

297 JOSEPH JEROME LEFRANÇOIS DE LALANDE (1732–1807), French astronomer   1787

Obv. Bust to left. Around, JOS . HIER . LE FRANÇOIS DE LA LANDE , N . BURGI 1732 . ; below, GATTEAUX . F .

Rev. Inscription, ACADEMIÆ | REG . SCIENT . PARIS . | ASTRONOMUS . | ACAD . LONDIN . BEROLIN . | PETROP . HOLMI . HAFNIENS . | ROTER . BRUXEL . GOTTING . | DUBLIN . EDIMB . BONON . | FLORENT . ROM . PATAV . MANT . | TAURIN . BOSTONIENSIS | MONSPEL . TOLOS . & . . | SOCIUS | 1787

Bronze, struck, 42 mm.

1966.130.41

Bibl.: Forrer 2, p. 210; *Médailles Françaises,* no. 64, p. 290.

NICHOLAS PIERRE TIOLIER
(1784–1853)

Sculptor and medalist, trained by his father Pierre Joseph Tiolier, Jeuffroy and Dejoux. Tiolier won the Rome Prize in 1805 and, succeeding his father, was engraver general at the French mint from 1816–43. He exhibited at the Salons from 1812–31 and designed many coins as well as medals of Louis XVIII and Charles X.

See Forrer 6, pp. 99–102; Thieme-Becker 33, p. 200.

298 LOUIS XVII, Death of the King   1795

Obv. Bust to left. Around, LUDOV · XVII D · G · FRANC · ET NAV · REX; on truncation, N · TIOLIER F ·

Rev. Lily with broken stem. Around, CECIDIT UT FLOS; in exergue, VIII JUNII | MDCCLXXXXV

Bronze, struck, 41 mm.

1966.131.30

Nineteenth-Twentieth Century

JEAN PIERRE DROZ
(1746–1823)

Swiss medalist and coin engraver, who went to Paris in 1764. His medals and technical innovations of the 1780s brought him attention and he was called to England by Matthew Boulton where he was employed at the Soho mint, Birmingham, between 1788–91, when he returned to Paris. Droz was made administrator of coins and medals of France in 1802 and from 1803–14 was keeper of the mint museum. Droz executed coins for England, for Louis XVI and for Napoleon, as well as a great variety of medals.

See Forrer 1, pp. 618–28; 7, pp. 234–35; Thieme-Becker 9, pp. 585–86; J. G. Pollard, "Matthew Boulton and J.-P. Droz," *Numismatic Chronicle* (1968), pp. 241–65.

LOUIS JALEY
(1763–1838)

A medalist, student of Moitte and Dupré, active for the court from 1799. He did many medals of the Napoleonic series.

See Forrer 3, p. 54; Thieme-Becker 18, p. 356.

Jean-Pierre Droz/Louis Jaley

299 PIUS VII Chiaramonti, Pope 1800–23   1804

Obv. Bust to right, wearing tiara and cope. Around, PIVS VII P . M . HOSPES NEAPOLIONIS IMP . ; in exergue, DROZ F . | AN XIII .

Rev. Church of Notre Dame, Paris. Monogram of initials M A for Virgin Mary at upper left. Around, IMPERATOR SACRATVS; in exergue, PARISIIS · II · DEC · M · DCCCIV · | XI · FRIM · AN · XIII · ; below, DEN · DIR · JALEY · FEC ·

Bronze, struck, 41 mm.

1966.114.33

Coronation of Napoleon.

Bibl.: Houston, no. 217; Patrignani, *Pius VII,* no. 22; Forrer 1, p. 624 (Droz obv.); 3, p. 54 (Jaley rev.); E. Edwards, *The Napoleon Medals,* London 1837, pl. 3, 14.

BERTRAND ANDRIEU
(1761–1822)

Andrieu was born in Bordeaux, where he studied at the academy and under André Lavau. In 1786 he went to Paris where he made such progress in the shop of Gatteaux that in 1789 he engraved the medal of the Storming of the Bastille. He executed many medals during the Revolution, Empire, and Restoration, engraving the portraits used for the obverse of medals of Napoleon and Louis XVIII.

See A. Évrard de Fayolle, *Recherches sur Bertrand Andrieu,* Chalon-sur Saone/Paris 1902; Forrer 1, pp. 51–56; 7, p. 19; Fréd. Alvin in Thieme-Becker 1, pp. 285–86.

JEAN JACQUES BARRE
(1793–1855)

A student of Tiolier Barre exhibited first at the Salon of 1819 with considerable success. He worked at the mint under Puymaurin and was *Graveur général des monnaies* from 1843 to his death. Barre engraved both coins and copper plates for paper money.

See Forrer 1, pp. 127–31; 7, p. 51; Fréd. Alvin in Thieme-Becker 2, pp. 528–29.

Bertrand Andrieu

300 ALEXANDER I (1777–1825), Emperor of Russia, 1801   1814

Obv. Head to right, laureate. Around, ALEXANDRE I . EMPEREUR DE TOUTES LES RUSSIES . ; below, DENON . D . ; on truncation, ANDRIEU F .

Rev. A winged, draped female (History) sits in profile to left before a tree and writes on plaque, Sejour | d'Alex · 1 · | à Paris. Around, ANDRIEU . F . DENON . D . ; in exergue, MDCCCXIV .

Bronze, struck, 40 mm.

1966.137.48

Commemorates Alexander's visit to Paris in 1814.

Dominique Vivant Denon was director of the Paris mint from 1804 to 1815.

Bibl.: Forrer 1, p. 54; Évrard de Fayolle, p. 199, no. 140; *Médailles Françaises,* p. 423, no. 17.

Bertrand Andrieu/Jean Jacques Barre

301 LOUIS XVIII (1755–1824), Rededication of the Church of Saint Geneviève 1822

Obv. Bust to right. Around, LVDOVICVS · XVIII FRANC · ET · NAV · REX; below, DE PUYMAU-RIN DIREXIT; on truncation, ANDRIEU F .

Rev. Facade of Saint Geneviève with figures representing the saint (on a cloud, gesturing to the church), the city of Paris and Religion, holding the cross. Around, PROPRIAS · IN · AEDES · REDVX SVORVM · VOTIS · EXCIPITVR; in exergue, ALMAE · GE-NOVEFAE · PARISINORVM · PATRONAE | BASILICA · RELIGIONI · VINDICATA | REGIS · EX · EDICTO · MDCCCXXII | BARRE FT .

Bronze, struck, 51 mm.

1966.131.35

Bibl.: Médailles Françaises, p. 439, no. 66.

JACQUES ÉDOUARD GATTEAUX
(1788–1881)

A student of his father, Nicolas Marie, and of the sculptor Moitte, Gatteaux won the Rome Prize in 1809. On his return to Paris in 1814 he was named medalist to King Louis XVIII, a post which he held until 1855. In 1845 he became a member of the Institute of France, where he lived and worked until his death. Gatteaux was a close friend of the painter Ingres. He had a large art collection, much of which was destroyed during the Paris Commune of 1871.

See Forrer 2, pp. 206–09; 7, p. 342; Thieme-Becker 13, pp. 247–48; Pyke, p. 52.

Jacques Édouard Gatteaux/Jean Jacques Barre (See biog. before no. 300)

302 CHARLES X (1757–1836), King of France, 1824–30 1825

Obv. Bust to right, crowned. Around, CAROLUS · X · REX · CHRISTIANISSIMUS; on truncation, E. GAT-TEAUX

Rev. Bishop anoints kneeling king while seven men observe. Around, REX · CAROLUS · COELESTI · OLEO UNCTUS; in exergue, ADSTANTIBUS · FRANCIAE · PARIBUS | REGIONUMQUE · DE-LECTIS · SUMMIS · LEGUM | ADMINISTRIS ·

EXERCIT · PROCERIBUS | GENTIUM · EXTER-AR · LEGATIS | REMIS XXIX MAI | MDCCCXXV; below, BARRE FT. DE PUYMAURIN N . P .

Bronze, struck, 68 mm. Dies cracked, on obv. at truncation line, on rev. diagonally through center

1966.137.152

Coronation medal. Charles was the brother of Louis XVI and Louis XVIII. He abdicated during the July Revolution of 1830. Jean Casimir de Mercassus, Baron de Puymaurin, was master of the Paris mint from 1816–30.

Bibl.: Forrer 2, p. 207; 4, p. 714 (for de Puymaurin).

JOSEPH EUGÈNE DUBOIS
(1795–1863)

Born in Paris, Dubois was a student of Droz and Bridan at the École des Beaux-Arts from 1810. He exhibited frequently at the Salon from 1827 to 1848.

See Forrer 1, p. 638; 7, pp. 236–37; Thieme-Becker 9, p. 604.

Joseph Eugène Dubois

303 MARIE CAROLINE DE BOURBON-SICILES (1798–1870), Duchess of Berry, 1816 1824

Obv. Head to right, wearing tiara. Around, ME CAROLNE FERDE LSE DUCHESSE DE BERRI . ; below, E . DUBOIS F . DE PUYMAURIN D ·

Rev. Inscription, JE ME SUIS BIEN | APPERÇUE HIER QU'HENRI IV | AVAIT RAISON LORS-QU'IL | APPELAIT LES DIEPPOIS | SES BONS AMIS, J'IMITERAI | MON AYEUL DANS MON | AMOUR POUR EUX | PAROLES DE S · A · R · | 30 JUILLET 1824 . ; around, SEJOUR DE S · A · R · MADAME DUCHESSE DE BERRI A DIEPPE .

Bronze, struck, traces of gilding, 42 mm.

1966.131.90

Commemorates a visit to Dieppe in 1824.

Bibl.: Houston, no. 222; Forrer 1, p. 638; H. Bauquier, *Album Numismatique et Souvenirs Iconographiques de S. A. R. Marie Caroline de Sicile, Duchesse de Berry,* Paris 1951, no. 90.

Joseph Eugène Dubois

304 MARIA CHRISTINA (1806–78), Princess of Naples 1829

Obv. Head to left. Around, MARIE · CHRISTINE PRINCESSE · DE · NAPLES; below, DE PUY-MAURIN D . E · DUBOIS F ·

Rev. Inscription, NÉE | LE XXVII AVRIL | MD-CCCVI | MARIÉE | A FERDINAND VII | ROI D'ESPAGNE | ET | DES INDES | LE XI DÉCEM-BRE | MDCCCXXIX

Copper, struck, 51 mm.

1966.137.182

Commemorates Maria Christina's marriage to Ferdinand VII of Spain.

Bibl.: Forrer 8, p. 237.

Joseph Eugène Dubois/Jean Jacques Barre (See biog. before no. 300)

305 HYACINTH LOUIS DE QUELEN (1778–1839), Archbishop of Paris 1840

Obv. Bust three-quarters to right. Around, HYA-CINTHVS · LVD · DE · QVELEN · ARCHIEPIS-COPVS · PARISIENSIS; in field, NATVS · PARISIIS | AN · MDCCLXXVIII and DEFVNCTVS | AN · MDCCCXXXIX; on truncation, BARRE

Rev. Church of Notre Dame in Paris. Around, · · · ET · DE · FORTI · EGRESSA · EST · DVLCEDO; in field, JVD . CAP . XIV and VERS . XIV; below, E · DUBOIS · 1840

Bronze, struck, 57 mm.

1966.114.70

Bibl.: Forrer 1, p. 131.

PIERRE JEAN DAVID D'ANGERS (1788–1856)

Born in Angers, the son of a wood sculptor, David went to Paris and learned drawing from Delusse and sculpture from Roland. In 1811 he won the *Prix de Rome;* he lived in Rome from 1811 to 1816 studying the work of Canova, Thorwaldsen, and the antique. During his career in Paris he received many private and state sculptural commissions and executed more than 500 portrait medallions. David achieved great fame as a sculptor and was considered a chief exponent of romanticism in sculpture and in the medal.

See Forrer 1, pp. 522–35; 7, pp. 210–11; H. Vollmer in Thieme-Becker 8, pp. 464–67; *Les Médaillons de David d'Angers réunis et publiés par son fils,* Paris 1867; G.

Chesneau & C. Metzger, *Les oeuvres de David d'Angers,* Angers (Musée des Beaux-Arts), 1934; Pyke, p. 37.

306 DIEUDONNÉ, COMTE DE LAS-CASES (1766–1842), historian 1830

Obv. Bust to right. At left, M . J . E . A . D . | LAS-CASES; below, DAVID | 1830 .

Without reverse

Bronze, 127 mm.

1966.135.6

Las-Cases was a companion of Napoleon during his exile on Saint Helena.

Bibl.: Forrer 1, p. 529; *David d'Angers,* pl. 33 (unsigned); Chesneau, no. 651 (signed, not dated).

307 JEAN PAUL MARAT (1743–93), French revolutionary pamphleteer 1830

Obv. Bust to left. At right, a dagger piercing a letter inscribed C . CORDAY; at left, MARAT; below, DAVID | 1830

Without reverse

Bronze, 123 mm.

1966.135.5

Bibl.: Forrer 1, p. 526; *David d'Angers,* pl. 34; Chesneau, no. 686.

308 ABBÉ DE LA MENNAIS (1782–1854), religious and political writer

Obv. Bust to right. At left, ABBE | DE LA MENNAIS; below, DAVID

Without reverse

Bronze, 70 mm. Ring at top

1966.135.2

Bibl.: Forrer 1, p. 526; *David d'Angers,* pl. 32; Chesneau, no. 643 (dated 1831).

ÉMILE ROGAT (d. 1852)

Sculptor, medalist, and coin engraver, Rogat lived and worked all his life in Paris, exhibiting often at the Salon after 1815. He made patterns for several coins for France and Monaco, and also worked on the Napoleonic and Durand medallic series.

See Forrer 5, pp. 191–93; Thieme-Becker 28, p. 510.

309 CLAUDE JOSEPH ROUGET DE LISLE (1760–1836), author of the *Marseillaise* 1833

Obv. Head to right. Around, À ROUGET DE LISLE AUTEUR DE LA MARSEILLAISE . ; below truncation, E . ROGAT DIRIGÉ PAR | P . J . DAVID 1833 .

Rev. All six verses of the *Marseillaise,* the first set to music. Fasces in center

Bronze, struck, 51 mm.

1966.137.28

While an officer at Strasbourg in 1792 Rouget de Lisle wrote the words and music of the *Marseillaise* for the soldiers of the Army of the Rhine. Although the song later became inseparably associated with the Revolution, he himself was a royalist and barely escaped the guillotine. The medal was executed after a portrait medallion by David d'Angers, done in 1827 (Forrer 1, p. 524).

Bibl.: Forrer 5, pp. 191–92.

JEAN FRANÇOIS ANTOINE BOVY (1795–1877)

Member of a celebrated Geneva family of medalists, Bovy studied in Geneva and in Paris under Pradier. In order to compete for the French coinage, Bovy became a French citizen in 1835. He worked in both France and Switzerland, engraving the Swiss coinage in 1850 and 1873.

See Forrer 1, pp. 243–47; 7, p. 106.

310 LOUIS PHILIPPE I (1773–1850), King of France (1830–48) 1842

Obv. Head to left, laureate. Around, LOUIS PHILIPPE I ROI DES FRANÇAIS · ; below, A . BOVY .

Rev. Flying Mercury and Mars flank a female figure, nude to the waist and seated on a throne, who holds tablets inscribed CHEMINS | DE | FER in her left hand and points to Mercury with her right; in distance, four trains. Inscribed on throne, LOI DU XI JUIN | M . D . CCC . XLII . | · LOUIS PHILIPPE · | REGNANT; around, DANT IGNOTAS MARTI NOVASQUE MERCURIO ALAS · ; in exergue, Mᴿ TESTE MINISTRE DES TRAVAUX PUBLICS . | Mᴿ LEGRAND SOUS-SECRÉTAIRE D'ÉTAT . | A . BOVY FECIT · ; stamped on rim, CUIVRE

Copper, struck, 113 mm.

1966.137.173

Commemorates promulgation of railway laws in France. This is one of the largest medals ever struck, and won for its engraver, in 1843, the Legion of Honor.

Bibl.: Forrer 1, p. 246; Jean Babelon, "Les Médailles à L'Exposition Romantique de la Bibliothèque Nationale," *Aréthuse,* fasc. 27 (1930), p. 68, pl. 11, no. 4; Auguste Moyaux, *Les Chemins de Fer Autrefois et Aujourd'hui et Leurs Médailles Commemoratives,* Brussels 1905, no. 121.

VALENTIN MAURICE BORREL (1804–82)

A student of J. J. Barre, Borrel began engraving medals in 1828. In 1831 he was appointed to the Monaco mint under Honoré V and he soon began engraving official medals of Louis Philippe and the House of Orleans. He won numerous prizes at the Salons from 1832 to 1878.

See Forrer 1, pp. 222–25; 7, p. 100; Geffroy in Thieme-Becker 4, p. 374.

311 N. TH. OLIVIER, Bishop of Évreux (1798–1854) 1860

Obv. Bust to left. Around, N . TH . OLIVIER EPISC . EBROÏC . NAT . MDCCXCVIII . CONSECR . MDCCCXLI . OB . MDCCCLIV; below, BORREL 1860.

Rev. Cardinal's coat of arms, inscribed, FERO PACEM; around, FUIT POTENS IN OPERE ET SERMONE | LUC . XXIV . XIX . and, IN SÆCULUM MEMORIA EJUS IN BENEDICTIONE | I . MACCH . III . VII · ; stamped on rim, CUIVRE

Copper, struck, 51 mm.

1966.137.279

Bibl.: Forrer 1, p. 224.

FRANÇOIS JOSEPH HUBERT PONSCARME (1827–1903)

A sculptor, medalist, coin and gem engraver, Ponscarme was a student of Oudiné, Vauthié and Dumont. He was highly praised as a teacher of medal engraving at the *École des Beaux-Arts* from 1871. Most of Ponscarme's medals are cast.

See Forrer 4, pp. 654–64; Thieme-Becker 27, p. 244; Chevreux (cited below).

312 JULES BRAME, Deputy de Nord   1870

Obv. Head to left. Around, IVLES BRAME; below, PONSCARME

Without reverse

Bronze, struck, 68 mm. On reverse, V 8

1966.138.37

Bibl.: Forrer 4, p. 656; P. Chevreux, "Le Sculpteur Medailleur Hubert Ponscarme, Biographie et Catalogue de Son Oeuvre," *Gazette numismatique française* 2 (1907), pp. 209–65, at p. 245, no. 47 (with reverse insc. A | JULES BRAME | DÉPUTÉ | PROTECT · DE · L'AGRICVLTVRE | ET · DE · L'INDVSTRIE | DÉFENSEVR · DE · LA · LIBERTÉ | LA VILLE · DE · ROVBAIX | RECONNAISSANTE | MDCCCLXX ·).

LOUIS OSCAR ROTY
(1846–1911)

The most important French medalist of the second half of the nineteenth century, Roty studied at the *École des Beaux-Arts* with Lecoq de Boisbaudran, Augustin Dumont and Hubert Ponscarme. He won the *Prix de Rome* in 1875, became a professor at the *Académie des Beaux-Arts* in 1888, and its president in 1897.

See Forrer 5, pp. 228–49; Thieme-Becker 29, p. 106.

313 PRIZE MEDAL OF THE MINISTRY OF THE INTERIOR   1893

Obv. Bust to left, in elaborate Renaissance armor. Around, REPVBLIQVE FRANÇAISE; on truncation, O. Roty

Rev. In laurel and oak wreath, inscription, PRIX | OFFERT PAR | LE | MINISTRE; around, MINISTERE DE L'INTERIEVR; stamped on rim, BRONZE

Silvered bronze, struck, 36 mm.

1966.137.180

Bibl.: Forrer 5, p. 234 (notes two sizes, 36 and 50 mm.); Roger Marx, *Les Médailleurs français contemporains*, Paris, n.d., pl. 16.

JULES CLÉMENT CHAPLAIN
(1839–1909)

Born at Montagne, Chaplain entered the *École des Beaux-Arts* in 1857 and studied with the sculptor Fran-

cois Jouffroy and the medalist André Oudiné. He won the Rome Prize in 1863, and was in Italy from 1864–68. Returning to Paris, he exhibited extensively, and was a member of the *Académie des Beaux-Arts* from 1881. Chaplain worked as a sculptor, but he is best known for his medals. Inspired by the Italian Renaissance as well as contemporary sculptors, he made both cast and struck medals.

See Forrer 1, pp. 398–407; 7, p. 175; Thieme-Becker 6, pp. 372–73.

314 ALBERT DUMONT (1842–84), French historian of ancient Greece   1884

Obv. Bust to left. Around, ALBERT · DUMONT · M^{BRE} DE L'INSTITUT · DIRECTEUR DE L'ENSEIGNEMENT · SUPERIEUR; in field, J · C | CHAPLAIN and 1842 | 1884

Rev. Draped female figure raising her veil, standing amid classical ruins and artifacts. Around, AGREGATION D'HISTOIRE ·

Bronze, cast, 98 mm.

1966.137.174

Dumont and Chaplain were friends who fought together in the Franco-Prussian War. Chaplain did the drawings for Dumont's study, *Les ceramiques de la Grèce propre.*

Bibl.: Forrer 1, p. 403.

315 EMMANUEL BIBESCO   1891

Obv. Bust to left. Above, EMMANUEL · BIBESCO; on left side, MDCCCLXXXXI; on truncation, J · C · | CHAPLAIN

Without reverse

Bronze, cast, rectangular, 99 x 75 mm.

1966.137.47

Bibl.: Forrer 1, p. 403.

316 ÉMILE FRANÇOIS LOUBET (1838–1929), President of France (1899–1906)   1899

Obv. Bust to left. Around, EMILE · LOUBET · PRESIDENT · DE · LA REPUBLIQUE · FRANÇAISE · ; on truncation, J C | CHAPLAIN | 1899

Rev. Urn and spear with banner rest on altar decorated with fasces, crossed oak and laurel branches and inscribed [R] F. Around, ELU · PAR · L'ASSEMBLEE · NATIONALE · ; in field, LE · 18 | FEVRIER | 1899;

in exergue, J . C . CHAPLAIN; stamped on rim, BRONZE

Bronze, struck, 68 mm.

1966.138.32

Bibl.: Forrer 1, p. 403.

JEAN-BAPTISTE DANIEL DUPUIS
(1849–99)

The son of a painter, Daniel Dupuis studied painting at the *École des Beaux-Arts* under Cavelier and medal engraving with Farochon and Ponscarme. He won the Rome Prize for his medals and exhibited as a medalist first in the Salon of 1877 and continuing until 1896. In Italy Dupuis imitated the lost wax method of Renaissance medals. A major representative of the renewal of the French medal, Dupuis was a prolific artist.

See Forrer 1, pp. 660–67; 7, pp. 239–40; Bender in Thieme-Becker 10, pp. 181–82.

317 UNIVERSAL EXHIBITION OF 1900–HISTORY 1900

Obv. Seated on a bank of clouds, a woman writes 1900 on the front of a book held up by a small boy; below, DANIEL–DUPUIS

Rev. Putto, holding up torch in his right hand, leans on a die press. To right, a scales; to left an easel and artist's materials. Around, MONNAIE DE PARIS; in exergue, DANIEL-DUPUIS; stamped on rim, BRONZE

Bronze, struck, 51 mm.

1966.137.288

Bibl.: Forrer 1, p. 662; F. Mazerolle, "J.–B. Daniel–Dupuis, Catalogue de Son Oeuvre, Supplement," *Gazette Numismatique Française* 7 (1903), pp. 303–16, no. 350.

GEORGES DUPRÉ
(1869–1909)

Born at St. Étienne, Dupré studied first at the *École des Arts industriels* there, then went to Paris in 1883, where he became a student at the *École des Beaux-Arts* in 1892 under L. O. Roty and J. G. Thomas. He won the Rome Prize in 1896 and was in Rome for three years. During his short life Dupré executed a number of cast and struck medals.

See Forrer 1, pp. 652–53; 7, p. 239; Thieme-Becker 10, pp. 171–72.

318 REDEMPTION 1901

Obv. An old man in an animal skin kneels before a fully draped woman who holds up a baby, his arms outstretched. Rays of light around the child's head; to left altar with fire; to right, sheep in distance. Below, G . DUPRÉ .

Rev. Young man wearing animal skin holds crucifix over a book on altar inscribed, O CRVX AVE | SPES VNICA; classical ruins in left distance. In exergue, G . DUPRÉ . ; stamped on rim, BRONZE

Bronze, struck, 73 mm.

1966.137.289

Bibl.: Forrer 1, p. 653; F. Mazerolle, "Georges Dupré," *Gazette numismatique française* 6 (1902), pp. 225–33, no. 3.

OVIDE YENCESSE
(1867–1947)

Born in Dijon, Yencesse was a student of Ponscarme, F. Levillain and J. Thomas. He exhibited extensively and won gold medals at the Universal Exhibition of 1900 and the Salons of 1910 and 1920. He became director of the art school in Dijon.

See Forrer 6, pp. 692–701; 8, p. 304; Thieme-Becker 36, p. 353.

319 AMEDEO GODARD, publisher of medals, Paris 1912

Obv. Bust to right. Around, AMEDEE GODARD GRAVEVR EDITEVR; in field O . YENCESSE

Rev. Inscription, HOMMAGE | A | AMÉDÉE · GODARD | CINQVANTE · ANNÉES | · DE · LA-BEVR · ET · DE · | · DIRECTION · | · SES · AMIS · SES · ELÈVES | SES · COLLABORATEVRS | · M · CM · XII · ; stamped on rim, BRONZE

Bronze, 50 mm.

1966.138.2

Bibl.: Forrer 6, p. 695.

NETHERLANDS

JACOB JONGHELINCK
(1530–1606)

The most prolific Flemish medalist, also a sculptor and seal engraver, Jonghelinck was born in Antwerp. He visited Italy in 1552 and may have worked under Leone Leoni. He was seal engraver to the king in Brussels from 1556–72 and master of the mint after 1572. Jonghelinck's medals reflect the influence of Italian art.

See Thieme-Becker 19, pp. 135–37; Forrer 3, pp. 82–85; 7, pp. 487–89; *Kress,* p. 121.

ATTRIBUTED TO JONGHELINCK

320 ALESSANDRO FARNESE (1545–92), Governor of the Netherlands, third Duke of Parma, 1586 1585

Obv. Bust to right, wearing cuirass and ruff with Order of the Golden Fleece. Around, ALEXANDER FARNES : PAR : PLA · DVX · BELG : DVM : GVB · ; on truncation, ÆT · 40

Rev. Alexander the Great, seated in his tent, reaches out toward a satyr who gestures towards a river. In distance, the town of Antwerp. Around, CONCIPE CERTAS SPES 1585; below, [Σ] ATYRO [Σ]

Gilt bronze, 45 mm.

1966.106.9

A variant of this medal, with obverse inscribed PRIN instead of DVX (Houston, no. 337), is attributed to Jacob Jonghelinck. In 1585 the Duke of Parma confirmed Jonghelinck's appointment as mint warden at Antwerp (Forrer 3, p. 84).

The reverse compares the siege of Antwerp with the siege of Tyre by Alexander the Great (Houston).

Bibl.: Arm. 2, p. 265,14; Van Loon 1, p. 350; Hill-*Med. Ren.,* p. 131 (as not by Jonghelinck).

321 ANTON STRALE, Duke of Merxem and Dambrugge

Obv. Bust to right. Around, · ANTONII · A · STRALE · DVS : DE · MERXEM · ET · DAMBRVGGE ·

Rev. Nude female figure (Fortune or Venus) atop a globe in a conch shell on ocean, holding a sail. Around, · VIRTVTE · ET · CONSTANCIA

Bronze, 55 mm. Aftercast, heavily tooled

1966.131.64

Strale was governor of Antwerp, 1567, and was executed 1568. Armand reads on the obverse AET . XLIIII . 1565, after van Loon.

Bibl.: Arm. 2, p. 241,29; Van Loon 1, p. 95; Hill-*Med. Ren.,* p. 130, pl. 23,5; Forrer 3, p. 84.

SIXTEENTH CENTURY NETHERLANDS (?)

322 CHARLES V (1500–58), Holy Roman Emperor, 1519

Obv. Bust to right, laureate. Around, · IMP · CAES · CAROLVS · V · AVG ·

Rev. The Infante Philip in armor, on horseback, to right. Around, · PHILIPVS · AVSTR · CAROLI · V · CAES

Lead, 100 mm.

1966.111

A coarse variant of Leone Leoni's medal of the emperor. The medal is recorded by Bernhart and by Hill from an electrotype in the Victoria and Albert Museum, London.

Bibl.: Arm. 2, p. 182,13 (as Italian); Van Mieris 2, pp. 442–43 (without inscriptions); M. Bernhart, *Die Bildnismedaillen Karls des Fünften,* Munich 1919, no. 178 (as anonymous Italian); G. F. Hill in *Numismatic Chronicle* (1921), p. 159; *Catálogo de la Coleccion de Monedas y Medallas de Manuel Vidal Quadras y Ramón de Barcelona,* 4 vols., Barcelona 1892, 4, nos. 13529,13530. Auction catalog: Mezbacher, 1–2 May 1900, pl. 2, 508.

SEVENTEENTH CENTURY NETHERLANDS

323 JOHANN (1625–72) and CORNELIUS (1623–72) DE WITT 1672

Obv. Busts jugate to right. Around, ILLVSTRISSIMI . FRATRES . IOHAN : ET . CORNEL : DE . WIT .

Rev. Garlands above and below inscription, Twee Witten, eensgezint, | Gevloeckt, gehaet, gemint, | Ten fpiegel van de Grooten | Verheven en verftooten, | In alles Lotgemeen, | Staen naer hùn doot bijeen | Gelijck zij hier nae't leven | Zoo konftig zijn gedreven; on rim, * VIOLENTA MORTE DELETI · HAGÆ · COMITIS · 20 AVG : A'O · 1672 ·

Silver, struck, 48 mm.

1966.131.62

See no. 253 (Pierre Aury).

Bibl.: Van Loon 3, p. 81 (ill.); p. 83, no. 3.

324 JOHANN and CORNELIUS DE WITT

Obv. Same as no. 323

Rev. Two ships on heavy seas being driven against a cliff. Around, VNA MENTE ET SORTE · ; on rim,

* NAVEMQUE VIROSQUE SUB OEQUORE MER-
SIT * HAGÆ . 20 AVG . A'O . 1672 .

Silver, struck, 48 mm.

1966.131.63

See no. 253 (Pierre Aury).

Bibl.: Van Loon 3, p. 81 (ill.); p. 84, no. 4.

ENGLAND

JAN ROETTIERS
(1631–1703)

A member of a large family of Flemish medalists, Roettiers was trained by his father Philip Roettiers. He worked as an assistant at the Antwerp mint until 1661, when he moved to London. From 1670–98 he was chief engraver at the royal mint; from 1669 his family was given a monopoly of engraving and striking coins for Charles II.

See Thieme-Becker 28, p. 507; Forrer 5, pp. 161–73.

325 CHARLES I (1600–49), King of England 1629, Memorial Medal ca. 1670

Obv. Bust to right. Around, CAROL · D · G · M · B · F · ET · H · REX · & · GLOR · MEM · ; below, R

Rev. Arm from clouds, holding celestial crown; below, landscape with sheep. Around, VIRTVT EX · ME · FORTVNAM · EX · ALIJS ·

Copper, struck, 50 mm.

1966.131.54

Made by Roettiers after the Restoration, and highly praised by Evelyn as "incomparably the most resembling his serene countenance." The effigy is related to a similar medal signed by Norbert Roettiers (*Med. Ill.,* pl. 30, no. 10).

Bibl.: Forrer 5, p. 165 (dated 1649); *Med. Ill.,* pl. 30, no. 11; Houston, no. 83; J. Evelyn, *A Discourse of Medals,* London 1697, pp. 112–13, fig. 34 (medal signed by Norbert Roettiers).

WILLIAM WYON
(1795–1851)

The most important member of the family of English medalists, Wyon was trained by his father Peter, and strongly influenced by the art of Flaxman. He became second engraver at the royal mint in 1816 and, after a long dispute with Pistrucci, chief engraver in 1828. Wyon engraved many coins of the British Empire, as well as a large number of medals.

See Forrer 6, pp. 650–87; 8, pp. 300–03; Thieme-Becker 36, pp. 334–35; Pyke, pp. 161–62.

326 PRINCE ALBERT (1819–61), married Queen Victoria, 1840   1851

Obv. Head of Prince Albert to left. Around, H : R : H : PRINCE ALBERT PRESIDENT OF THE ROYAL COMMISSION · ; below truncation, W WYON . RA .

Rev. Globe with laurel wreath around and dove above. Continents inscribed, AMERICA, S AMERICA, EUROPE, AFRICA, ASIA. Scroll across globe inscribed, EXHIBITOR. Around, EXHIBITION OF THE WORKS OF INDUSTRY OF ALL NATIONS . ; below, MDCCCLI . ; on rim, FRANCE. Nọ 586.

Bronze, struck, 44 mm.

1966.137.183

Medal for the Crystal Palace Exhibition in London of 1851.

Bibl.: Forrer 6, p. 684.

SWITZERLAND

JEAN DASSIER
(1676–1763)

Swiss, son of the engraver Domaine Dassier of Geneva, Jean studied in Paris under Mauger and Roettiers from 1694–96. He returned to Geneva and in 1711 was made assistant engraver at the mint. In 1720 he succeeded his father as mint master, a post which he kept until he died. He visited England in 1728 and Turin in 1743. Dassier engraved several medallic series of which the first, of French celebrities of the time of Louis XIV, begun in 1720, established his reputation. Other series are of French rulers from Pharamund I to Louis XV, of religious reformers, Roman history (done with Jacques Antoine), Genevan theologians, and the sovereigns of England.

See Forrer 1, pp. 512–17; 7, pp. 206–08; Michel 7, pp. 412–13; Thieme-Becker 8, pp. 415–16.

327 VICTOR AMADEUS II (1666–1732), Duke of Savoy, King of Sicily and of Sardinia

Obv. Bust to right, laureate, in peruke and cuirass. Around, VICTOR AMED · D · G · REX SARD · CYP · ET IER ·

Rev. Justice, Fortitude and Prudence. Around, SCEPTRI COLUMEN ET DECUS; in exergue, · I · DASSIER · F ·

Copper, struck, 41 mm.

1966.131.71

A bronze version (no. 1966.131.72) also exists in the Molinari Collection. Victor Amadeus became King of Sicily, 1713–18, and King of Sardinia, 1720, until his abdication in 1730.

328 PHILIPPE, DUC D'ORLEANS (1674–1723), Regent of France, 1715   1723

Obv. Bust to right, in wig. Around, PHILIPPE DUC D'ORLEANS .

Rev. Inscription, LES HOMMES | ILLUSTRES | DU SIÉCLE DE LOUIS XIV | DEDIEZ | A S · A · Rᴸ . MONSEIGNEUR | DUC D'ORLEANS | PETIT FILS DE FRANCE . | PAR SON TRES HUMBLE ET TRES | OBEISSANT SERVITEUR | JEAN DASSIER | 1723 .

Bronze, struck, 28 mm.

1966.130.42

Dedication medal for Dassier's series of French celebrities, the *Gallerie métallique des grands hommes du siècle de Louis XIV*. The entire series contains seventy-two medals.

Bibl.: Forrer 1, p. 515.

329 LOUIS LEFORT (1668–1743), Chief Burgomaster of Geneva   1734

Obv. Bust three-quarters to left, in peruke. Around, LUD · LE FORT REIP · GENEV · CONSUL PRIMAR · ANN · J734 · ÆT · 66 · ; below, I · DASSIER · F ·

Rev. Seated female figure at left (Geneva), with cornucopia and holding book inscribed, BIBL . | SA = | CRA; four putti to right with symbols of commerce, the arts, government, and science. Around, DEI NUMINE · ; lower right, I · D · ; in exergue, JURA CIVIUM ASSERTA | ANNO 1734 ·

Bronze, struck, 55 mm.

1966.131.40

Bibl.: Houston, no. 395; Forrer 1, p. 516; 7, p. 206; Brescia 2, p. 91, nos. 95–96; *MM.* 2, p. 295, pl. 171,4.

330 D. F. COUNT OF LAUTREC, French Envoy to the Peace of Geneva   1738

Obv. Bust three-quarters to left, in peruke and cuirass. Around, D · F · COMES A LAUTREC LEGAT · REG · AD PAC · GENEV 1738; on truncation, I · DASSIER

Rev. Prudence in center, flanked by Fortitude (Mars) and Justice. Around, FORTITUDO PRUDENTIA AEQUITAS; in exergue, CONSPICUAE | IN VNO ·

Bronze, struck, 55 mm.

1966.131.39

From series, *Gallerie métallique des grands hommes du siècle de Louis XIV*.

Bibl.: Forrer 1, p. 515.

331 GEORGE II (1683–1760), King of England, 1727   1731

Obv. Bust to left, laureate, in peruke and armor. Around, GEORGIUS · II · D · G · MAG · BR · FR · ET · HIB · REX · ; below, J · DASSIER F ·

Rev. Inscription, NUMISMATA | REGUM ANGLIAE | A | GULIELMO PRIMO | AD HAEC USQUE TEMPORA | GEORGIO II . | MAGNAE BRITANNIAE | FRANCIAE ET HIBERNIAE | REGI SERENISSIMO ETC . | DICATA | A JOANNE DASSIER | GENEVENSIS REIPUB · | CÆLATORE MONETALI | ANNO M · DCC · XXXI ·

Copper, struck, 41 mm.

1966.131.57

Dedication medal of the series of medals of the kings and queens of England from William I to George II. The series was published by subscription at six guineas for all thirty-three in copper, fifteen guineas for silver.

Bibl.: Forrer 1, p. 515; *Med. Ill.*, pl. 151, no. 2.

JACQUES ANTOINE DASSIER (1715–59)

A son of Jean Dassier, born in Geneva, he studied in Paris with Thomas Germain and at the Academy of Design under Bernard and Roussel. He was in Italy in 1736 and 1737, worked with his father in Geneva, and in 1740 went to England where he became an assistant engraver at the mint in 1741. In 1756 he went to Saint

Petersburg where he was active at the Russian court for three years. He fell ill and on the return trip to Geneva died in Copenhagen. Jacques Antoine worked on several medals with his father, including the series of Roman history.

See Forrer 1, pp. 510–12; 7, p. 206; Thieme-Becker 8, pp. 414–15.

332 MARIA THERESA (1717–80), Queen of Hungary and Bohemia, 1740   1745

Obv. Bust to left. Around, MAR : THERESIA · D : G : REG : HUNG : BOH : ; below, I · D ·

Rev. Minerva seated on clouds over the earth, holding spear and Medusa-head shield; her right foot rests on portion of globe. Around, ET MENTE ET ARMIS · ; below, 1745 · I · D · F ·

Bronze, struck, traces of black patina, 55 mm.

1966.131.41

Bibl.: Forrer 1, p. 516 (as by Jean); Brescia 2, p. 92, no. 101.

333 CHARLES EMMANUEL III (1701–73) of Savoy, King of Sardinia, 1730   1739

Obv. Bust three-quarters to right, in cuirass. Around, CAR · EM · D · G · REX SAR · CYP · ET IER ·

Rev. The king with Minerva to right; winged Victory crowning him with laurel. Around, MINERVA DUX VICTORIA COMES . ; in exergue, JAC · ANT · DASSIER F · | 1739

Bronze, struck, 55 mm.

1966.131.78

Bibl.: Forrer 1, p. 511.

334 MARCHESE SCIPIONE MAFFEI (1675–1755), scholar and tragic poet   1755

Obv. Bust to right, in peruke. Around, SCIPIONI MAFFEIO MARCH · ; below, A · D · F ·

Rev. View of Museum of Verona. Around, MUSEI · VERONENSIS · CONDITORI · ; in exergue, ACADEMIA | PHILARMONICA · | AN · MDCCLV ·

Bronze, struck, 55 mm.

1966.131.74

The medal was commissioned by the Accademia Filarmonica to commemorate the founding by Maffei of the Verona Museum.

Bibl.: Forrer 1, p. 511; Brescia 2, p. 93, no. 119; *MM.* 2, pp. 371–72, pl. 190,5.

Jean Dassier (See biog. before no. 327) *and Jacques Antoine Dassier*

335 COUNT GIOVANNI MARIA MAZZUCCHELLI (1707–65), scholar and biographer   1752

Obv. Bust three-quarters to right. Around, COMES IO · MARIA MAZZUCHELLI ÆT · ANNO XLV · ; below, I · DAS · ET F ·

Rev. Lion of Saint Mark holding sword; view of Venice, the sea, a ship. Around, SENATUS CONSULTO · ; in exergue, M · DCCLII · | I · DASSIER ET FILS F ·

Bronze, struck, 55 mm.

1966.131.77

Mazzucchelli was a celebrated scholar whose home in Brescia was used as a private museum and academy, containing manuscripts, books, and collections, especially of portrait medals. The medals were published by P. A. Gaetani (see *MM.* in the bibliography), and are now in the Musei Civici, Brescia. For Mazzucchelli's career, publications, etc., see E. de Tipaldo, *Biografia degli Italiani Illustri,* vol. 9, Venice 1844, pp. 241–50.

Bibl.: Forrer 1, p. 516 (as Jean); Brescia 2, p. 92, nos. 106–08 (as Jean and Jacques-Antoine); Durand, pp. 124–25, no. 2.

Jacques Antoine Dassier and Jean Dassier (See biog. before no. 327)

336 MAURICE, COMTE DE SAXE (1696–1750), Marshal of France   1747

Obv. Bust to right, wearing cuirass and fur drape. Around, MAURITIUS SAXO GALL · MARESC · D · CURL · ET · SEM · ; below, I · D · ET FILS F ·

Rev. Victory seated on weapons, writing on oval plaque. Around, BELGI · GALL · PROPUG AUSTR · CAPT · FOED · VICT · ; in exergue, NUM · SIGN · A · MDCCXLVII | KAL · DECEM ·

Bronze, struck, 55 mm.

1966.130.37

Maurice of Saxony was one of the greatest military commanders of the eighteenth century. Louis XV gave him the title of marshal general in 1747. The rest of the obverse inscription refers to his title of duke of Courland, which he was unable to retain.

Bibl.: Houston, no. 199 (different obv.); Forrer 1, p. 511

(as Maurice, Duke of Saxony); 7, p. 206 (mentions that two versions exist); Brescia 2, p. 92, no. 105 (different obv.); *MM*. 2, p. 349, pl. 186,5 (different obv.).

JOHANN KARL HEDLINGER
(1691–1771)

Born in Switzerland, Hedlinger studied medal engraving with W. Krauer in Lucern where he became active at the mint in 1713. In 1717 he visited Saint-Urbain in Nancy and worked with de Launay and Coysevox in Paris. He became medalist at the royal mint in Stockholm in 1718 and remained there for twenty-seven years with the exception of trips to work in Italy in 1726, Copenhagen in 1732, Russia in 1735–37, and Switzerland in 1739. After 1745 he lived and worked in Switzerland. Hedlinger is one of the most important eighteenth-century medalists.

See Forrer 2, pp. 445–67; 7, p. 432; B. C. K. in Thieme-Becker 16, pp. 218–21; Pyke, p. 66.

337 NICOLAUS KEDER (1659–1735), Swedish antiquarian, numismatist ca. 1735

Obv. Bust to right. Around, NICOLAVS · KEDERVS · HOLMIENSIS · ; below, I · C · H · F ·

Rev. Phoenix rising from a fire. Around, VITAM · MIHI · MORS · RENOVABIT ·

Bronze, struck, 32 mm.

1966.131.58

Bibl.: Forrer 2, pp. 465–66; Durand, p. 94, no. 5; *MM*. 2, pp. 273–74, pl. 175,7.

338 ANNA IVANOWNA (1693–1740), Empress of Russia, 1730 1739

Obv. Bust to right. Around, АННА Б · М · ІМПЕ РАТРИЦАИСАМОΔЕР · ЖИЦА ВСЕРОСС (ANNA B · M · IMPERATRĪTSA Ī SAMODERCHĪTSA VSEROSS)

Rev. Eagle with laurel wreath in beak stands on trophies including Ottoman banners. Around, СΛАВА ІМПЕРІИ · (SLAVA · IMPERII); on listel, H; in exergue, МИР · СТУРК · ВОЗСТА · | 7 · СЕНТ · 1739 (MIR · STURK · VOZSTA · | 7 · SENT · 1739)

Bronze, struck, 60 mm.

1966.131.49

Commemorates peace after the second Crimean War.

Bibl.: Forrer 2, p. 462 (dated 1736–38).

GERMANY

JOHANN HÖHN
(active ca. 1637–93)

Medalist active from 1640 in Danzig for the mint and at the Court of Brandenburg from 1678. Höhn died near Danzig in 1693.

See Forrer 2, pp. 520–23; 7, p. 454; Thieme-Becker 17, p. 201.

339 IN MEMORY OF THE PEACE OF OLIVA 2/3 May 1660

Obv. Religion, holding chalice, kneels before a decorated column inscribed STA | TVA | PA | CIS mounted on a base inscribed in front · V · D · M · I · Æ · (*Verbum Dominae manet in aeternum*) and on right side IH. Atop the column the Eye of God, with inscription RE^(LI)GIO. Above, the divine eye surrounded by clouds and rays; above, PERVIGILI | UM DEI. In the background the city of Danzig. Around, IN VERA VITAM NOS RELLIGIONE PER OMNEM CEU PUPILLAM OCULI PROTEGE CHRISTE TUI | CUSTODI ME UT PUPILLAM OCULI . PS . 17

Rev. The triumphant Fortitude with column and palm seated in a chariot drawn to left by Faith with cross and Peace holding a dove. Above, an arm from clouds holds a crown. Around, FER PATIENTER ONUS CONSTANTI PECTORE SPERA IN COELO FIDEI CERTA CORONA DATUR . ; below, CONSTANTIA | TRIUMPHANS

Bronze, 70 mm. Hole at top

1966.131.48

Bibl.: Tentzel, *Saxonia Numismatica,* Linea Albertina, Dresden 1705, pl. 44,2; F. A. Vossberg, *Munzgeschichte der Stadt Danzig,* Berlin 1852, p. 945; Sale catalog, Coll. Le Maistre, J. Schulman, Amsterdam, 13–15 October 1913, no. 241.

JOHANN KITTEL
(1656–1740)

Member of a family of medalists, armorers and coin engravers in Breslau. Johann's first medals date from 1681.

See Forrer 3, pp. 168–69; 7, p. 507; Thieme-Becker 20, pp. 393–94.

340 ALLEGORY OF A VIRTUOUS WAY OF LIFE

Obv. Twisted column on base with grotesque masks divides field. At left, interior with cradle; above, a heart in the wall decoration; at right, grave with sunrise. Around, A TENERIS AD FATA SVPREMA; on column base, · I · K ·

Rev. Faith, Hope and Charity in a landscape. Above, a dove in rays of light. Around, . HÆ TIBI SINT CO-MITES . ; below, in waves, CW (?); on rim, WENN AUCH KEIN ANDER FREUND AUF ERDEN UBRIG BLIBE SO HALTE DU NUR FEST AN GLAUBE HOFFNUNG LIBE

Silver, struck, 78 mm.

1966.143.2

GEORG HAUTSCH
(active 1679–1712)

Medalist and coin engraver from Nürnberg, a student of J. J. Wolrab. Hautsch was active at the mint in Nürnberg from 1683–1712, replacing Hermann Haffner as assistant engraver in 1691. He moved to Vienna in 1712 and worked there until his death.

See Forrer 2, pp. 441–42; 7, p. 425; W. Fries in Thieme-Becker 16, p. 152.

341 MAXIMILIAN II EMMANUEL (1662–1726), Elector of Bavaria, 1679

Obv. Bust to right, in peruke and armor. Around, MAX · EMAN · D · G · V · BA & · P · S · D · C · P · R · S · R · I · AR & · E · L · L · ; below, GH ·

Rev. Map showing campaign against the Turks and the recapture of Belgrade. Around, QUOD PETIT | OB-TINET · IN VIA VIRTUTI NULLA EST VIA · · MONSTRAT ITER · ; below, PLUS ULTRA; in cartouche, ALBA GRÆCA | RECEPTA · | MDC-LXXXVIII | DIE 6 SEP ·

Bronze, struck, 43 mm. Hole at top

1966.131.43

Taking of Belgrade from the Turks.

The medal was issued as part of the large series commemorating contemporary history by Friedrich Kleinert and his associates L. G. and C. G. Lauffer in Nürnberg. Hautsch and several other medalists, including G. W. Vestner and Werner, contributed to the series, which was published in 1742 (C. G. Lauffer, *Das Laufferische Medaillen-Cabinet,* Nürnberg).

Bibl.: Houston, no. 71; Forrer 3, p. 326 (notes 4 varieties).

342 VENETIAN CONQUEST OF MOREA 1685

Obv. Lion of Saint Mark, in midst of five chained Turkish prisoners, being crowned from above with crown and palm. He holds a book inscribed, PAX TIBI | MARCE | EVANGE | LIS TA | MEVS · . Around, LEONI ULTORI · ; below, GH; in exergue, 1685

Rev. Map of the province of Morea

Gilt bronze, struck, 36 mm.

1966.130.19

See no. 341.

Bibl.: Brescia 1, p. 138, no. 954 (as FRANCESCO MOROSINI; with reverse inscribed VIRTVTE ET FORTVNA VENETORVM); Cicogna, vol. 2, pt. 2; Forrer 3, p. 326.

GERMAN–UNATTRIBUTED

343 JOHN GEORGE II, Elector of Saxony, Knight of the Garter, 1671 1678

Obv. Saint George and the Dragon. Around, EN HONNEUR DU SOUVERAIN DU TRÈS NOBLE ORDRE DE LA IARTIERE

Rev. In a wreath, inscription, DU TRÉ HAUT | TRÉ PUISSANT ET | TRES EXCELLENT PRIN | CE CHARLES II · PAR · LA | GRACE DE DIEU ROY DE | LA GRANDE BRETAG : | FRAN : ET IR-LANDE DE = | FENSEUR DE LA FOY · | MDC-LXXVIII ·

Silver, struck, 48 mm.

1966.131.56

Struck at Dresden, where a great festival in honor of the Order of the Garter was held on 23 April 1678.

Bibl.: Med. Ill., pl. 59, no. 3.

GEORG WILHELM VESTNER
(1677–1740)

Vestner learned die engraving from the medalist Suhl. He worked in Chur, Berlin, and Weimar before moving to Nürnberg in 1705. In 1720 he became engraver to the Episcopal See of Würzburg, in 1732 court medalist to the elector of Bavaria. He was assisted by his son from 1726.

See Forrer 6, pp. 252–57; Thieme-Becker 34, p. 313.

344 FABRIZIO PAOLUCCI (1650–1726), Cardinal, 1697 and GIULIO PIAZZA (1663–1726), Cardinal, 1712
1712

Obv. Busts, Paolucci facing right and Piazza left, wearing mozzettas. Around, FABRITI CARD · PAVLVTIVS SECRET · STATVS ET IVLIVS CARD · PIAZZA NVNTIVS AP · VIEN · FOROLIVIENSES · ; on truncation, G · W · V ·

Rev. City square of Forli. Atop a column is the Virgin, flanked by flying putti holding cardinal hats and haloes, one of lilies, the other of stars. Below, coats of arms of two cardinals. Around, CIRCVNDABANT EAM FLORES ROSARVM ET LILIA CONVALLIVM · & IN CAPITE EIVS CORONA STELLARVM · ; below, MDCCXII; in exergue, HÆC EST IMAGO B . MV . | AB IGNE PROTECTRIX | ET PATRONA | CIVITATIS | FORILIVII | G . W . V .

Lead, 54 mm.

1966.114.54

Bibl.: Forrer 6, pp. 254, 256 (ill.); *MM.* 2, pp. 265–66, pl. 163,6.

PETER PAUL WERNER
(1689–1771)

Born in Nürnberg, Werner's medallic activity dates from 1711. He replaced Philip Heinrich Müller as court medalist to Carl Albert of Bavaria in 1718, and later executed medals for German princes, cities and individuals.

See Forrer 6, pp. 453–55; M. B. in Thieme-Becker 35, pp. 417–18; Pyke, p. 156.

345 DEDICATION OF THE HEDWIGSKIRCHE, BERLIN

Obv. Facade of Church of Saint Hedwig. Around, ECCLES . CATHOLICOR . BEROLIN; below, P · P · WERNER · f ·

Rev. Rocaille decoration around inscription, FRIDERICI | REGIS | CLEMENTIÆ | MONVMENTVM | S · HEDVVIGI | SACRVM | ANG · MAR · QVIRINVS | S · R · E · CARDIN · | SVO AERE | PERFECIT

Gilt bronze, struck, 48 mm.

1966.131.46

The Church of Saint Hedwig in Berlin was built from 1747 to 1773 on ground donated by Frederick the Great,

to whom the church is dedicated. Cardinal Angelo Maria Quirini generously contributed to German missions, corresponded with Frederick, and in 1747 was elected to the Berlin Academy.

Bibl.: Brescia 1, p. 183, nos. 1189–90; *MM.* 2, pp. 375–76, pl. 191,9.

JOHANN PETER WERNER
(active ca. 1761–96)

Nürnberg medalist and gem engraver, probably the son of Peter Paul Werner.

See Forrer 6, pp. 452–53; M. B. in Thieme-Becker 35, p. 409; Pyke, p. 156.

346 PETER PAUL WERNER (1689–1771), medalist

Obv. Bust to right. Around, PETER PAUL WERNER . MEDAILLEUR . ; below, J . P . Werner . Fec .

Without reverse

Bronzed lead, 44 mm.

1966.131.47

Bibl.: Forrer 6, p. 453 (ill.).

GEORGE CHRISTIAN WAECHTER
(1729–ca. 1789)

Brother of Johann Georg. A student of Jean Dassier in Geneva, Waechter was active from 1770 as court medalist at Mannheim, and from 1771 in Saint Petersburg.

See Forrer 6, pp. 338–39; Thieme-Becker 35, p. 16.

347 VOLTAIRE (1694–1778) 1770

Obv. Bust to right. Around, VOLTAIRE NÉ LE XX · FEVRIER M · DC · XCIV · ; below, G . C . WAECHTER F . ; laurel border

Rev. On an altar surrounded by light rays, masks, a globe, a laurel wreath, flowers, musical instruments, books, one inscribed LA HENRIADE. On altar front, inscription, TIRÉ | D'APRÈS NATURE | AU CHÂTEAU | DE FERNEY . | G . C . WÆCHTER; below, GRAVÉ | M · DCC · LXX . ; floral border

Bronze, struck, 59 mm.

1966.130.40

The original medal of 1769 was inscribed "il ôte aux nations le bandeau de l'erreur," but this was objected to and the dies were destroyed and the new reverse cut.

Bibl.: Forrer 6, pp. 338–39; Brescia 2, p. 81, no. 159; E. Demole, "Voltaire, le Conseil de Genève et le graveur G.–C. Waechter en 1769 et 1770," *Revue belge de Numismatique* (1913), pp. 36–48. The medals of Voltaire are conveniently listed in J. Montagu, "Inventaire des tableaux, sculptures, estampes, etc. de l'Institut et musée Voltaire," *Studies on Voltaire and the Eighteenth Century* 20 (1962), pp. 223–47, at pp. 229–30.

LEONHARD POSCH
(1750–1831)

A wax sculptor, medalist and sculptor, Posch was born in the Tyrol and studied in Salzburg from 1766 with J. B. Hagenauer. In 1774 he went with Hagenauer to Vienna where he turned from monumental sculpture to wax portraits and medals. In Italy from 1793–95, he went to Berlin in 1804 and (except for a visit to Paris in 1810–14) remained active there as professor of modeling at the royal mint (1814) and a member of the Prussian Royal Academy (1816). Posch's medals, cast in iron, represent a monumental classicism which forms a bridge between the Austrian baroque style and the work of David d'Angers.

See Forrer 4, pp. 669–73; 8, p. 144; F. Dworschak in Thieme-Becker 27, p. 293; Pyke, p. 144 (useful bibliographical references).

348 UNKNOWN FEMALE SITTER

Obv. Bust to right

Without reverse

Iron, 80 mm.

1966.137.163

349 UNKNOWN MALE SITTER

Obv. Bust to left, wearing uniform

Without reverse

Iron, 81 mm.

1966.137.164

ABRAHAM ABRAMSON
(1754–1811)

Born in Potsdam, Abramson learned metal engraving from his father Jakob Abraham. His early work, much of it done in collaboration with his father, is dependent on the designs of others, but after a trip to Italy from 1788–92 he began to make his own designs. Besides medals of East European royalty, Abramson engraved a series of famous men of his time.

See Forrer 1, pp. 17–19; 7, p. 5; Thieme-Becker 1, pp. 30–31; Pyke, pp. 3–4.

350 FREDERICK WILHELM III (1770–1840), King of Prussia, 1797, Introduction of Vaccination ca. 1800

Obv. Bust to right. Around, FRID · WILHELMVS III BORVSS · REX PATER PATRIAE; below, ABRAMSON

Rev. Figure in classical robes (Hygeiea), holding bowl in left hand and left arm entwined by snake, seated upon cow rising from the sea onto a meadow. Around, IN TE SVPREMA SALVS; in exergue, VACCINATIONIS | PRAEMIVM

Silver, struck, 68 mm.

1966.131.42

Bibl.: T. Hoffmann, *Jacob Abraham und Abraham Abramson, 55 Jahre Berliner Medaillenkunst 1755–1810*, Frankfurt-am-Main 1927, no. 111, pl. 12; Brettauer, no. 1648.

KARL FRIEDRICH VOIGT
(1800–74)

Born in Berlin, Voigt studied first under the goldsmith Vollgold and the medalist Leonhard Posch. He worked in the medallic shop of Gottfried Loos from 1820 until he won an Academy Prize and went to London in 1825. In 1826 he went to Rome where he studied gem engraving with Girometti and came under the influence of Thorwaldsen. In 1829 he was called to be the chief engraver at the royal mint in Munich. He revisited Rome in 1836–37 and moved there permanently in 1857.

See Forrer 6, pp. 305–10; 8, p. 250; Thieme-Becker 34, pp. 508–09.

351 JOHN SCOTT (1751–1838), Earl of Eldon 1827

Obv. Bust to left, in a wig. Around, JOHN EARL OF ELDON LORD HIGH CHANCELLOR OF GREAT BRITAIN 1827; below, C . VOIGT F .

Rev. Inscription, BORN 4 . JUNE 1751 | CALLED TO THE BAR 1776 | SOL . GEN . 1788 . ATTORN . GEN . 1793 | BARON ELDON CH . JUST . COM . PL . 1799 | LORD CHANCELLOR 1801 | RESIG . THE SEALS 1806 . RECALLED 1807 | CONTINUED LORD CHANCELLOR UNTILL | THE

DEMISE OF GEORGE III . 1820 | REAPPOINTED BY GEORGE IV . ON | HIS ACCESSION | AND CREATED VISC . ENCOMBE | EARL OF ELDON 1821

Bronze, struck, 48 mm.

1966.137.274

Engraved in Rome on Scott's resignation of the lord chancellorship.

Bibl.: Forrer 6, p. 309.

RUSSIA

JOHANN GEORG WAECHTER
(1724–97)

Born in Heidelberg, Waechter was active in Russia as an engraver at the mint of Saint Petersburg from 1741, working for the Empresses Elizabeth and Catherine II.

See Forrer 6, p. 339; Thieme-Becker 35, p. 16.

JOHANN BALTHASAR GASS
(1730–1813)

Of German or Swiss origin, Gass began work at the Saint Petersburg mint in 1768 as assistant engraver. He was chief engraver from 1772 until 1797, when he resigned due to bad health.

See Forrer 2, p. 205; 7, p. 341; Thieme-Becker 13, p. 232.

Johann Georg Waechter/Johann Balthasar Gass

352 J. W. von SCHLATTER (1708–68), director of the Saint Petersburg Mint   1768

Obv. Bust to right. Around, I · W · A · SCHLATTER PRES · ET CONSILIAR · INTIMVS · ; below, I · G · W · F ·

Rev. Woman in classicizing costume seated among tools used in minting coins, holding a lamp. Around, ROSSICAM REM MONETARIAM PERFECIT · ; Lower right, G; in exergue, P · O · M · NATO 19 · FEBR · 1708 | DECESSO 23 · IAN · 1768 | IO · A S · F […] M · F · C ·

Bronze, struck, 53 mm.

1966.131.50

Bibl.: Forrer 6, p. 339 (obv.); 2, p. 205 (rev.).

SCANDINAVIA

ANTON MEYBUSCH
(ca. 1645–1702)

Of German or Dutch origin, Meybusch was trained in Stockholm or Copenhagen. Beginning in 1667 he worked for the courts at Copenhagen and Stockholm until his death, except for the five years from 1685–90 when he was in Paris as a *médailleur du roi de France*.

See Forrer 4, pp. 52–55; I. Buhl in Thieme-Becker 24, p. 460.

353 LEOPOLD I (1640–1705), Holy Roman Emperor, 1658   1683

Obv. Bust to right, laureate, in cuirass and cloak. Around, * LEOPOLDUS · I · D : G : ROM : IMP : SEMP : AUG : TURCARUM · VICTOR * ; below, ANTON · MEYBUSCH · FECIT

Rev. Scene of battle with Turks in flight from troops bearing standard of Holy Roman Emperor; tents and city behind; winged Victory blowing trumpet above. Around, URBEM · SERVASTIS · ET ORBEM; in cartouche, VIENNA · AUSTRIÆ · A · TURCIS · | OPPUGNARI · CÆPTA · D : 14 · IULII | LIBERATA · D : 12 · SEPT : Aō1683 · ; below, ANT . MEYB; on rim, illegible legend

Bronze, struck, 55 mm.

1966.131.45

Commemorates victory over Turks at Vienna.

354 CHARLES X GUSTAVUS (1622–60), King of Sweden, 1654, and HEDVIG LEONORA

Obv. Bust of Charles to right, in helmet, laureate. Around, CAROLVS · GVSTA · D · G · SVE · GOT · WAN · REX · ; below, Meijbusch · fec :

Rev. Bust of Hedvig Leonora to left. Around, HEDEWIG · ELEONORA · DEI · GRATIA · REGINA · SVEC ·

Gilt bronze, 51 mm. Ring at top

1966.144

Bibl.: Forrer 4, p. 54 (notes several varieties); B. E. Hildebrand, *Sveriges och svenska konungahusets minnespenningar, praktmynt och belöningsmedaljer* 1, Stockholm 1874, p. 363, no. 58 (type).

SPAIN

———

SEVENTEENTH CENTURY
UNATTRIBUTED

355 CHARLES II (1661–1700), King of Spain, Naples and Sicily, 1665 1679

Obv. Half-length figure, three-quarters to left, with scepter, wearing the Order of the Golden Fleece. Around, + CARLOS · II · DEI · GRATIA · REY · DE · LASPAÑAS · Y · DELAS · YNDIAS · 1679

Rev. Saint James riding a rearing horse. Around, + SANTIAGO · PATRON · DE · SPAÑA · ORA · PRO · NOBIS · 1679

Bronze, 81 mm.

1966.107.18

Charles' mother Mariana of Austria ruled as regent for him until his brother John of Austria overthrew her in 1677 and put her in exile. At John's death in 1679 she returned and Charles came to power.

Bibl.: De Caro Balbi, p. 25, fig. 20 (as by J. B. Fischer von Erlach?).

TOMAS FRANCISCO PRIETO
(1716–82)

Spanish medalist and line engraver, a student of Lorenzo Montemán. In 1747 he was appointed engraver at the mint of Madrid; he was made chief engraver in 1752. From 1759 he directed the entire Spanish medal and coin production.

See Forrer 4, p. 690; 8, p. 146; Thieme-Becker 27, p. 399.

356 CHARLES III (1716–88), King of Spain, 1759; Marriage of Charles IV, Infante of Spain, to Maria Luisa De Bourbon of Parma 1765

Obv. Bust of Charles to right. Around, CAROLVS · III · PARENS · OPTIMVS; below, T · PRIETO

Rev. Busts of Charles and Maria Luisa jugate to right. Around, PVBLICAE · FELICIT · PIGNVS; on truncation, T · P · ; in exergue, ALOISIA · PHILIP · INF · HISP · | PARM · DVC · FIL · CAROL · | PRINCIP · NVPTA · | M · DCC · LXV ·

Bronze, struck, 49 mm.

1966.131.52

Bibl.: Forrer 8, p. 146; Houston, no. 381; Vives, no. 45, pl. 4,1.

MEXICO

———

PEDRO JUAN MARIA DE GUERRERO

Medalist and coin engraver in Mexico under Ferdinand VII of Spain. Guerrero was active from ca. 1800 until the fall of Augustin, first emperor of Mexico.

See Forrer 2, pp. 337–38; 7, p. 404.

357 FERDINAND VII (1784–1833), King of Spain, 1808 1809

Obv. Bust to left, in military uniform. Around, FERDIN · VII HISPAN · REX INDIARVMQVE IMPERATOR · ; below, J. Guerrero

Rev. Female figure holding shield with portrait inscribed around, FERDIN · VII · CATHOL · , strides over Discord behind a dog toward a round temple on a hill. On rocks in left foreground, inscribed, Guerrera | [illegible] | 4 (?) Medalla; around, FIDELITAS DOLI VICTRIX · ; in exergue, [REGE] A GALL . PERFID . CAPTO | [MEX] TRIDENT SEMIN . | MDCCCIX

Gilt bronze, struck, 46 mm. Top extends with ribbon, wheat stalks and loop for hanging. Widest point, 54 mm.

1966.137.256

The Seminario Tridentino of Mexico to the Captive King of Spain. In 1808 Ferdinand was forced by Napoleon to renounce his throne in favor of Charles IV, who resigned his rights to Napoleon, who gave the Spanish throne to Joseph Bonaparte. Ferdinand was imprisoned in France from 1808–14. Throughout the Spanish Empire his name was a rallying cry of revolutionaries. When he was restored in 1814, however, he proved himself a reactionary, and during his later reign, the Spanish colonies in North and South America were lost through the same rebellions that had supported him during his early captivity.

Bibl.: Forrer 2, p. 337; Vives, no. 280, pl. 10,5.

CATALOGUE OF THE
EXHIBITION OF PLAQUETTES

INTRODUCTION

THE plaquette as an independent and identifiable art object developed in Italy during the fifteenth century. Normally uniface, Italian plaquettes were cast in bronze or lead from a specially prepared model or were aftercasts of engraved gems; besides these, there were numerous copies and free reproductions after antique compositions. Portrayed on these plaquettes were mythological or historical scenes, events from the Bible, legends of saints, and allegories.

At times Italian artists regarded the small reliefs as independent art objects and signed them, but for a great proportion of plaquettes the name of the artist is unknown. In Italy the greatest number of plaquettes were produced by bronze artists, and, perhaps as a result, Italian plaquettes generally are cast in bronze. Very important sculptors, such as Donatello, Riccio, Moderno (no. 358), and Jacopo Sansovino, have produced small reliefs, but medalists and goldsmiths also worked in this field. Examples are Cristoforo Caradosso, Cristofore di Geremia, Gianfrancesco Enzola and, moreover, Valerio Belli and Giovanni Bernardi da Castelbolognese, who are both especially famous as gem engravers. In the cases of Belli and Bernardi, most of the time a stone engraving was the primary work, which was then cast in bronze. Generally, however, Italian artists preferred wax *modellos*. Italian plaquettes were certainly used as decorative elements on different sorts of applied art objects—bells, arms, and many kinds of furniture and religious objects—but frequently they were collected for their own sake.

Plaquettes began to appear north of the Alps at the beginning of the sixteenth century, first in Germany and shortly thereafter in the Low Countries. The themes covered by northern plaquettes were much the same as those in Italy. North of the Alps plaquettes were predominantly treated as utilitarian objects serving as working models for goldsmiths and artisans in many fields. The northern Renaissance plaquette is dependent upon the graphic arts for formal prototypes and was utilized as decoration for furniture and vessels.

Relatively few names of artists who created plaquettes in the North are known—the most important among them being Peter Flötner of Nuremberg—and not many of these artists so far recognized can be connected securely with existing reliefs. Moreover, only a few goldsmiths such as Wenzel Jamnitzer or the van Vianen brothers developed their own designs as well as doing their own modeling. From the later Middle Ages onward, goldsmiths were not considered so much as creative inventors as they were salesmen, workshop owners or managers and master craftsmen. Generally a plaquette is an anonymous product; composition and the translation into relief are the result of the labors of a number of specialized craftsmen whose names were recorded only by chance. The themes and compositions of these plaquettes were practically always determined by prints or book illustrations. Since the artisans who created plaquettes drew upon outside sources for their reliefs, their personal creative achievement must be judged by the skill by which they compiled their various models, often from differing artistic circles.

After the design of the plaquette was determined, it was then carved in wood, stone or slate or else modeled in wax or plaster. A mold was made from the model, allowing a number of cast lead or bronze reproductions. These replicas were then put on the market and acquired by artisans of all kinds—goldsmiths, founders of bronze or pewter, potters, ivory carvers, even cabinetmakers and an occasional sculptor—to be used as prototypes or models from which to work.

Plaquettes could be modeled by a sculptor or an artisan without guild affiliations. They could, as well, be created by a goldsmith or prepared by a so-called *Patronenmacher* who could act to some extent as a designer in a large goldsmith's workshop.[1] The modeled

[1] Th. Hampe, *Nürnberger Ratsverlässe über Kunst und Künstler im Zeitalter der Spätgotik und Renaissance* II, Wien/Leipzig, 1904, p. 8, no. 59: "... Das hinfüro kein maister in seiner furderung mehr nit dann 4 gesellen und 2 lehrjungen bei und nebeneinander halten, do aber einer eins gesellen zum possirn oder patronmachen notdürftig, der solt denselben nicht zu den 4 gesellen in die werckstat, sonder in ein besunder stüblein setzen. Und do ein meister von eim potentaten so ein groses werck, das er mit den 4 gesellen nit vollbringen kont, solt in uf erkantnus ains e. rats dern mehr nach

plaquette was not always the starting point for replication, since copies or aftercasts were often made from embossed silver works (cf. no. 384). These casts in turn served as models or prototypes for other plaquettes.

Italian plaquettes were generally cast in bronze, while those produced in Germany and the Netherlands were more commonly of lead, which has a lower melting point. While the *ciré perdu* (lost wax) process could be used for casting plaquettes, a far more common practice was for a cast to be made in a sand mold from an impression of the original model.[2] One of the advantages of lead was that its softness made it possible for it to be easily struck in a die, as well as being heated and cast in a mold.

During the Renaissance, no distinction was made between *Bleie* (leads) and the *Patronen* (models). The designation *plaquette* was unknown and one finds the term *Patrone* (or modello) used for productions of all kinds. *Patrone*[3] designates a relief cast in bronze, brass or iron (and later pewter), either raised (positive) or sunken (negative). The sunken, negative relief is also called a matrix. Over the raised, positive form or into the sunken one a thin metal sheet is chased. The most significant example of this technique of embossing reliefs over bronze patterns is the Silver Altar in the chapel of the Jagellons in Cracow.[4] The designs were developed by Hans Dürer and translated into boxwood reliefs by Peter Flötner. From these models, brass patrices were cast by Pankraz Labenwolf, on which—according

to Neudorffer—the goldsmith Melchior Bair formed and chased sheets of silver.[5]

Plaquettes could be in use for an exceptionally long time; like tools or other objects in a workshop inventory they were often sold or bequeathed. Since goldsmiths could have their drawings made by painters or have models carved by wood carvers, the plaquette maker is an artist who as a type cannot be rigidly defined. If the goldsmiths were members of a craft guild, and basically only privileged court goldsmiths were exempt, they had to submit to strict regulations. The regulations for goldsmiths allowed only a limited number of collaborators to the owner of a workshop. For example, in 1572 no master in Nuremberg could keep more than a total of four journeymen and two apprentices. Only when a master received a royal commission for a work which he could not complete with four journeymen would he be granted special permission from the council to employ more journeymen on a short-term basis.[6] However, for the production of models the master goldsmith was permitted to employ an additional journeyman, who would occupy a special room. He produced only the sculptural models and a special room had to be available to him.[7] The makers of the *Patronen* sometimes belonged to the guild of coppersmiths, but they could also work without belonging to a guild.

Protection of designs and ideas was largely unknown during the Middle Ages and the Renaissance. The concept of copyright protection hardly existed, especially in the field of decorative arts. On the contrary, print makers and plaquette makers strove to create prototypes or mod-

---

gelegenheit zugelassen werden..." (Henceforth no master will be permitted to keep for his assistance more than four journeymen and two apprentices working in the same place. However, when another journeyman is necessary [for striking dies?] or making *patronen*, he must be kept apart from the four journeymen in the workshop, in a room to himself. And when a master receives such a large commission from a sovereign that he cannot complete it with his four journeymen he will be granted permission by the council to use more for that occasion...).

[2] For further information concerning the different techniques of casting see H. R. Weihrauch, *Europäische Bronzestatuetten 15.–18. Jahrhundert* (Braunschweig, 1967), pp. 15 ff.

[3] These terms were already defined by G. Habich, "Treibarbeiten," *Münchner Jahrbuch der Bildenden Kunst*, N. F. IV (1927), pp. 334–343.

[4] Cracow (Poland) Cathedral, Sigismund Chapel, Silver Altar, 1531–1538. See Heinrich Kohlhaussen, *Nürnberger Goldschmiedekunst des Mittelalters und der Dürerzeit 1240 bis 1540*, Berlin 1968, S.455, Nr.458.

[5] Johann Neudörfer's *Nachrichten von Künstlern und Werkleuten*, Nürnberg 1547, hrg. von W. K. Lochner, Wien 1875, S.125: "Dieser Bayr ist im Treiben, Reissen und grossen Werken von Silber zu machen berühmt. Er machet dem König in Polen eine ganz silberne Altartafel, die wog viel Mark. Zu solcher Tafel machet Peter Flötner die Patron und Figuren von Holz, aber Pancraz Labenwolf goss dieselben hölzernen Patronen von Messing, über diese messingene Tafeln wurden die silbernen Platten eingesenkt und getrieben..." (This Bayr was famous in embossing, engraving and doing big works in silver. He made for the King in Poland an Altarpiece full of silver, which has the weight of many marks. For these sheets Peter Flötner did the patron and figures in wood, but Pancraz Labenwolf cast these wooden Patronen of brass, on these brass sheets the silver sheets where fixed and embossed...).

[6] Cf. note 1.

[7] Cf. note 1.

els for a widespread circle of imitators. Imitation, repetition or transformation were scarcely objected to, since these artists were rarely concerned with inventing something truly individual in terms of composition or theme. Without qualm, paintings, reliefs, prints, drawings, and occasionally sculptures and goldsmith works, too, were more-or-less faithfully copied or adapted to fit specific uses. In the case of large commissions, other less busy workshops would participate for a while, resulting in the further dissemination of models and designs. Frequently, too, the workshop of a goldsmith or that of a bronze or pewter caster would be sold, mortgaged, or bequeathed either in its entirety or in part.

From the sixteenth century on, plaquettes were also valued as collector's items. This can be documented by various old collections which have been handed down, still partially intact, or can be traced in old inventories. One of the most important extant collections of goldsmith models, plaquettes, and designs for goldsmith work is the Amerbach collection in Basel. This *Kunstkabinett* was brought together by three generations,[8] but only Basilius Amerbach (1533–1591) saw himself as a collector. At the urging of the burgomaster Wettstein, the collection was acquired in 1661 by the city council and the University of Basel, and today its contents are in the Historical Museum and Print Collection there. The Nuremberg patrician family Geuder und Behaim also possessed a considerable collection of woodcuts, engravings, and plaquettes, mainly assembled by Paulus Behaim the Elder (1557–1621) and his son of the same name (1592–1637). An inventory made in 1624 constitutes an important source for the knowledge of southern German plaquettes, even though the representations are only briefly described and the whereabouts of the plaquettes are uncertain.[9]

The cisalpine plaquette originated in the early sixteenth century, at a time when nobility and patricians switched from wooden dishes and cutlery to silver tableware; this change produced a variety of utensils which could be richly decorated. Dishes, bowls and cups began to be produced in sets and decorated in relief, stimulating the demand for relief models. The invention of book printing, too, required the quantity production of decorated book covers; small altars for private devotion as well as jewelry boxes and toilet utensils were decorated with silver panels. It is in this context that the plaquette made its debut with its principal master, the Nuremberg carver Peter Flötner (nos. 370–372), who helped form the Early Renaissance style in Germany. Major centers of production were established in Nuremberg and Augsburg in the sixteenth century.

During the second half of the sixteenth century Nuremberg still led in the production of plaquettes and medals. The tradition so brilliantly initiated by Flötner was continued by Wenzel Jamnitzer and his workshop, as well as by his son Hans Jamnitzer. By this time the significant artists were no longer sculptors or bronze casters, as for example, Georg Labenwolf (see no. 374), but rather goldsmiths. While Flötner created relief images of small format which could be and were reproduced in practically all branches of the decorative arts, the models preserved from Wenzel Jamnitzer's workshop were almost exclusively used for works done in gold or bronze. Unfortunately, no models for the plaquettes produced by this workshop have been preserved. We do know that stone and wood models were made primarily during the first half of that century, while later plaster and wax were used which were less expensive and could be more easily executed. The master H. G., whom scholarship has identified as Hans Gamnitzer (Jamnitzer), Wenzel's son, specialized in the creation of rondels destined as decorations for the central field of silver bowls, the *Schalenboden,* as did some other goldsmiths in Nuremberg and Augsburg. At the same time as the plaquette, the medal made its arrival in Germany from Italy. Frequently plaquette makers also produced medals. The first generation preferred stone from Kehlheim and boxwood as material for models. A few stone reliefs by Flötner still exist, and the masterful execution of these small format pieces make them jewels of German Renaissance art. They clearly show a preference for narration, an "inclination to spin a fable." Often a theme is depicted in several scenes, as a

[8] Johannes Amerbach (came to Basel from Franconia in 1477, died there in 1514); Bonifazius, his youngest son (1495–1562); and his grandson, Basilius.

[9] The plaquettes in this collection were published by F. F. Leitschuh, *Flötner-Studien,* Strasbourg, 1904.

sequential or supplementary pictorial sequence. Typical of almost all Renaissance plaquettes with figural scenes is that they have didactic, religious, moral, allegorical, or symbolic (pictorial) content. Satire is rare. In this area, too, Flötner's deft pictorial language remains unmatched.

Towards the end of the sixteenth century the art of the Augsburg goldsmiths became increasingly important. At the same time Augsburg gradually took the lead in the production of reliefs. The most important artists at the end of the sixteenth and the beginning of the seventeenth century are the Lenckers, Christoph and his son Zacharias, Matthias Wallbaum (nos. 383, 384), Paul Hübner[10] and Hans Jakob Bayr (no. 385). Wallbaum, the Lenckers and some of the other Augsburg artists occasionally used the same plaquettes, which makes it difficult to determine authorship. These workshops were very productive, especially Wallbaum's workshop in which small house altars, writing cases and jewel boxes were made in large numbers. For such productions relief decoration from the workshop's repertoire were constantly reused. The silver reliefs so produced were mounted on ebony casings. Of interest in this respect is the sequence of plaquettes depicting Passion Scenes (no. 384), which are casts from the silver panels of the altar in the Benedictine monastery in Lambach, Austria. We can determine their source because the bronze plates reproduce the hallmark of the city of Augsburg and the master stamp of Wallbaum. Hallmarks warrant the fineness of the silver and they had to be stamped on every detachable part of a silver piece after its completion. But they have no reason to be on a bronze piece. The inclusion of such stamps on a cast, as well as the impression of the mounting holes, are obvious characteristics of secondary casts. Besides the works from Wallbaum and Lencker workshops, Augsburg plaquette production of the early seventeenth century includes bowl decorations, outstanding in com-

position as well as in execution, which have tentatively been attributed to Hans Jakob Bayr. Some, such as the Rape of the Sabine Women (no. 385), are based on designs by Hans Rottenhammer, one of the most important painters of this period. Rottenhammer repeatedly made designs for decorative arts.[11] He and Hans Jakob Bayr were closely acquainted. Their contemporary, the art expert Philipp Hainhofer, considered Bayr as one of the four best goldsmiths in Augsburg, and informs us that Bayr and Rottenhammer were drinking companions.[12] But such collaboration between painter and goldsmith was not the rule. Generally, reliefs were made after prints. Whereas in Nuremberg, primarily prints by Nuremberg artists were transformed into reliefs, Augsburg was more open-minded. In that city, the designs used for models encompassed prints by Nuremberg artists, and Netherlandish artists, as well as prints by Tobias Stimmer, Bernard Salomon, and Etienne Delaune.[13] Compositions by Italian artists were popular, especially as reproduced in the engravings made by the various members of the Sadeler family. The Sadelers copied the works of the most important Italian, Netherlandish, and German painters and print makers.

During the last quarter of the sixteenth century the Wittelsbach court in Munich also increased in importance both in regard to commissioning and collecting. Maximilian I (1597–1657, Duke of Bavaria; Elector from 1623), in particular, drew a number of important artists, sculptors, painters, bronze casters and goldsmiths to his court. Among these was the young Paulus van Vianen (who by privilege of the Wittelsbach court was exempted from his master's exam) and Alessandro Abondio. Van Vianen was one of the truly great master goldsmiths and a member of an important Netherlandish goldsmith family. In addition to Abondio and van Vianen, the painters Hans van Aachen and Christoph Schwarz, along with members of the Sadeler family, were in Munich from time to time.

Around 1600 Prague was one of the most important

[10] O. von Falke, "Die Bleiplaketten des Paul Hübner," *Berliner Museen: Berichte aus den preussischen Kunstsammlungen*, 48, 1927, p. 2 ff, compiled a suggested *oeuvre* of plaquettes by Hübner which are stylistically incompatible. I. Weber, "Bildvorlagen für Silberreliefs an Arbeiten von Paul Hübner und Kornelius Erb, Heute im Palazzo Pitti und im Britischen Museum," *Mitteilungen des Kunsthistorischen Institutes in Florenz*, 14, III, 1970, p. 352 doubts that Paul Hübner himself actually produced any plaquettes.

[11] O. Doering, "Des Augsburger Patriciers Philipp Hainhofer Beziehungen zum Herzog Philipp II. von Pommer-Stettin," *Quellenschriften*, N. F. VI (Vienna, 1896), p. 48.

[12] I. Weber, "Rottenhammer-Entwurf für ein Goldschmiederelief," *Pantheon* XXVII, 4 (1969), p. 330.

[13] See Weber, "Bildvorlagen für Silberreliefs," p. 329 ff.

artistic centers in Europe, because it was the residence of the Holy Roman Emperor Rudolf II. He drew the best artists of his time to his court or gave commissions to them. The conception of the court art of Prague paralleled that of the international style around 1600, nourished by the mainstreams of artistic creation in Italy, France, the Netherlands and the art of the German lands. Court artists were not subject to craft guild regulations; they frequently changed patrons and locations. Paulus van Vianen, for example, also worked for the Prague court and some of his plaquettes have been preserved.

The serious production of plaquettes in the Netherlands and in France developed during the last third of the sixteenth century. While primarily models for goldsmiths and pewter casters, these plaquettes (or the graphic designs made for them) were also used by the enamel painters of Limoges and the ceramicist Palissy. The expulsion of religious dissidents from France and the southern Netherlands also brought artists to Germany. One of the most influential of them was Etienne Delaune, a Huguenot from Paris, who worked primarily in Augsburg and Strasbourg during the last ten years of his life. His prints had a decisive influence on the decorative arts in southern Germany as well as in France. François Briot, one of the most outstanding pewter casters of the Renaissance, made casts after Delaune's engravings. Briot's reliefs were already much appreciated by his contemporaries and they were often copied. The Nuremberg pewter casters Jacob Koch II and Caspar Enderlein, in particular, based their extensive production essentially on the exploitation and replication of Briot's compositions (see no. 387).

At the end of the sixteenth century an artistically extremely fruitful period began in Holland. The Netherlands became an important counterweight to southern German goldsmith artistry. The most important representatives were the brothers Adam and Paulus van Vianen. Paulus, however, worked primarily in Germany and in Prague. The two Vianen belong to those few goldsmiths whose works are largely based on their own designs. We have numerous drawings by them; *Patronen,* too, have been preserved. The works by these brothers were almost exclusively embossed. The preserved plaquettes are mostly casts after embossed silver reliefs. Arent van Bolten (see no. 397), the master AVB, also belongs to those goldsmiths who executed their own designs, models, silver, and plaquettes. The reliefs by Arent van Bolten have unmistakable individual traits. Typical are the thick-set figures, rendered with lowered heads in profile or seen from the back, totally absorbed in their activity or the depicted action, permitting the viewer no contact with them. Whereas the brothers van Vianen embossed their silver panels in soft, painterly representations with unmatched mastery, Arent van Bolten's works are more sculptural.

Among the southern Netherlandish artists François du Quesnoy, in particular, (no. 406) succeeded in finding a style of his own and in forming a school. The Italian influence is unmistakable. During the sixteenth century Spain had practically no plaquette production of its own, and only to a very limited degree during the seventeenth century. Most of the reliefs attributed to Spain (cf. nos. 410–416) do not have the character of models and functioned instead as small devotional images. Spain was touched by the various kinds of European plaquette production, but it exerted no influence.

INGRID WEBER

Translated from the German by R. V. West

BIBLIOGRAPHY

AMP	*Archiv für Medaillen- und Plaketten-Kunde* (periodical), vols. 1–5 (1913–14, 1920–26).
Bange	E. F. Bange, *Staatliche Museen zu Berlin: Die Italienischen Bronzen der Renaissance und des Barock, zweiter Teil: Reliefs und Plaketten,* Berlin 1922.
Bange, *D.M.*	E. F. Bange, *Staatliche Museen zu Berlin: Die Bildwerke des Deutschen Museums, II: Die Bildwerke in Bronze und in anderen Metallen,* Berlin, Leipzig 1923.
Bardini	Sale Catalog, Bardini Collection, Christie, London, 27 May 1902.
Braun	E. W. Braun, *Die deutschen Renaissanceplaketten der Sammlung Alfred Walcher, Ritter von Molthein in Wien,* Vienna, Anton Schroll, 1918.
Braun-*Span.*	E. W. Braun, "Über eine Gruppe spanischer Spätrenaissance-Plaketten," *AMP* 3 (1921/22), p. 15ff.
DeCoo	Joz. DeCoo, Museum Mayer van den Bergh, Cat. 2. Beeldhouwkunst, Plaketten, Antiek, Antwerp 1969.
Harvard	Charles L. Kuhn, *German and Netherlandish Sculpture, 1280–1800—The Harvard Collections,* Cambridge (Mass.) 1965.
Heinrici	Sale Catalog, Heinrici Collection, Cahn, Frankfurt am Main, 7 December 1920.
Houston	J. Fischer, *Sculpture in Miniature: The Andrew S. Ciechanowiecki Collection of Gilt and Gold Medals and Plaquettes,* The Museum of Fine Arts, Houston, Texas, 1970.
Imbert	E. Imbert and G. Morazzoni, *Le Placchette italiane,* Milan 1941.
Lange	Konrad Lange, *Peter Flötner,* Berlin 1897.
Leitschuh	Franz F. Leitschuh, *Flötner-Studien,* Strasbourg 1904.
Löbbecke	Sale Catalog, Arthur Löbbecke Collection, Hirsch, Munich, 26 November 1908.
MacLagan	E. MacLagan, *Victoria and Albert Museum. Catalogue of Italian Plaquettes,* London 1924.
Middeldorf-Imbert	U. Middeldorf, "The Imbert Collection, Book Review," *Art Bulletin,* vol. 30, no. 2 (1948), pp. 151–56.
Molinier	E. Molinier, *Les Plaquettes: Catalogue raisonné,* 2 vols., 1886.
Molthein	Sale Catalog, Walcher von Molthein Collection, Helbing, Munich, 17–18 May 1926 (Max Bernhart, ed.).
Morgenroth	U. Middeldorf and O. Goetz, *Medals and Plaquettes from the Sigmund Morgenroth Collection,* Chicago 1944.
von Parpart	Sale Catalog, von Parpart Collection, Lepke, Berlin 1913.
Pechstein	K. Pechstein, *Bronzen and Plaketten vom ausgehenden 15. Jahrhunderts bis zur Mitte des 17. Jahrhunderts,* Berlin 1968.
Planiscig	L. Planiscig, *Kunsthistorische Museen in Wien. Die Bronzeplastiken,* Vienna 1924.
Planiscig-*Este*	L. Planiscig, *Vienna, Kunsthistorisches Museum: Die Estensische Kunstsammlung, Band 1: Skulpturen und Plastiken des Mittelalters und der Renaissance,* Vienna 1919.
Pope-Hennessy	John Pope-Hennessy, *Renaissance bronzes from the Samuel H. Kress Collection—Reliefs, Plaquettes, Statuettes, Utensils and Mortars,* London 1965.
Rosenheim	Sale Catalog, Max and Maurice Rosenheim Collection, Sotheby, London, 30 April–4 May 1923.
Salton	*The Salton Collection, Renaissance and Baroque Medals and Plaquettes* (second edition), Bowdoin College Museum of Art, Brunswick, Maine, 1969.
Weber	I. Weber, *Deutsche, Niederländische und Französische Renaissanceplaketten,* Munich 1975.

CATALOGUE

ITALIAN

MODERNO or AFTER MODERNO
Late Fifteenth or Early Sixteenth Century

Moderno is a pseudonym for an Italian goldsmith and seal cutter who was active at the end of the fifteenth and beginning of the sixteenth centuries and belongs among the most important of Italian plaquette artists. There exists little agreement on the identity of the artist or the extent of his works—that is, the attributed works (see the detailed discussion in Pope-Hennessy, p. 42).

358 HERCULES AND THE NEMEAN LION

Hercules stands facing left, head tilted forward and wrestling the lion which he has lifted off the ground. To right Hercules' club leans against edge and a bow and quiver hang from dry tree. Narrow double border.

Bronze, 75 x 56 mm.

1967.20.19

This plaquette belongs to a series depicting the exploits of Hercules. This view disagrees with that of Bange, who suggested that Mars and Victory (Bange, no. 466) belongs to the same series. Pope-Hennessy (no. 161) gives a description of the main variants. According to Leeuwenberg and Halsema-Kubes the round version (Kress, no. 161) is the first. This version is thought by Molinier (no. 198) to have been inspired by a coin of Heraclea. Leeuwenberg and Halsema-Kubes think the present version is done after Moderno. The plaquette is found as part of the decoration on a box in the Musée des Arts Decoratifs, Paris 1546.

Other specimens: (bronze) Amsterdam, Rijksmuseum; Berlin, Staatliche Museen; London, Victoria and Albert Museum; Santa Barbara, University Art Gallery, Morgenroth Collection; Washington, National Gallery of Art (Kress Collection); Vienna, Kunsthistorisches Museum.

Bibl.: Molinier, no. 198; Bange, no. 474; MacLagan, p. 35, no. 316–1889; Planiscig, no. 414; *Morgenroth,* no. 245; Pope-Hennessy, no. 161 (variant ii); Leeuwenberg, Jaap and Halsema-Kubes, Willy, *Beeldhouwkunst in het Rijksmuseum,* Catalogue, Amsterdam 1973, no. 712. Auction catalog: Löbbecke, no. 708, pl. 38.

VENETIAN
Late Sixteenth Century

359 MADONNA OF LORETO

The Madonna, wearing long flowing robes, her feet resting on clouds, sits on the roof of a church which is seen laterally and rests on waves. Her knees are turned to the left; she looks down to the right, where a child rises from behind the church roof and holds a wreath up to her. With her right arm, she holds her mantle out around the Christ Child's shoulder. The Christ Child stands frontally on a pillow on her right knee and points to the other child with his left hand.

Bronze, 98 x 65 mm. Hole at top.

1967.20.79

There are several different versions of the Madonna of Loreto. An earlier one, with another type of the Madonna and without the child with the wreath, but including clouds and heads of angels on the floor, which is in Berlin, Staatliche Museen (Bange, no. 943) is attributed to the style of Sansovino. There are also two variants of this type, one in the Museo Civico in Brescia, F. Rossi, *Placchette Sec. XV–XIX* (Musei Civici di Brescia, Cataloghi 1), Vicenza 1974, no. 117, pl. 63 and another illustrated in Löbbecke, no. 838. Still another variant in Vienna, Kunsthistorisches Museum, shows a standing Madonna (Planiscig-*Este.,* no. 430).

NORTH ITALIAN
End of the Sixteenth Century

360 THE FLAGELLATION

Christ, his left foot forward, bound to a half column, is being beaten. The flagellator at left is frontal, that to the right is seen from behind, and a third is visible behind Christ. Two other men stand at left and right. Rods and whip in foreground. Architectural background; patterned floor.

Lead, oval, 113 x 93 mm. Hole at top.

1967.11.6

This work is based on an etching by Egidius Sadeler after Cavaliere d'Arpino (L. Bruhns, *Würzburger Bildhauer der Renaissance und des werdenden Barocks, 1540–1650,* Munich 1923, pl. 76). The following works reveal more elaborate forms: no. 416 and a reversed bronze relief in Prague, Kunstgewerbemuseum (Inv. no. 11 923, 168 x 141 mm.). The artist is influenced by the circle of Giovanni da Bologna (cf., i.e., the Flagellation for the tomb chapel of Luca Grimaldi in Genoa 1579–85 [Elisabeth Dhanens, *Jean Boulogne, Giovanni Bologna Fiammingo,* Brussels 1956, fig. 141]). Another specimen: (lead) New York, Coll. Michael Hall, Esq. (sharper).

ITALIAN
Sixteenth Century

361 MADONNA AND CHILD WITH SAINT JOHN

The Madonna, wearing richly decorated robes, sits facing three-quarters to right. On her left leg she holds the standing nude Christ Child. At lower left the young nude Saint John, holding a cross, stands cross-legged and looks upward. Architectural background.

Bronze, traces of gilt, 134 x 89 mm.

1967.20.36

This relief is said by Molinier to be Venetian, by Bange and Braun to be in the manner of Sansovino. Middeldorf called it Florentine and wrote "the motif, in the last analysis, stems from Donatello and Luca della Robbia." Surely the artist was influenced by Sansovino, but not so much that it can be said that he worked in his manner.

Other specimens: (bronze) Berlin, Staatliche Museen; Venice, Museo Correr.

Bibl.: Molinier, no. 431; Braun, *Kunst und Kunsthandwerk,* 1911, p. 406; Bange, no. 946; Imbert, no. 24, pl. 5,1; Middeldorf-Imbert, p. 152. Auction catalogs: Löbbecke, no. 865; Molthein, no. 93.

ITALIAN
Second Half of the Sixteenth Century

362 SAINT SIMON

A bust of the bearded, bald apostle turned three-quarters left. Neck partly bare. In the upper corners, incised, S SI. Narrow raised border.

Bronze, 41 x 41 mm.

1967.11.7

Other specimens: (bronze) Berlin, Staatliche Museen; Munich, Staatliche Münzsammlung; Oxford, Ashmolean Museum.

Bibl.: Bange, p. 125, no. 956, pl. 58. Auction catalogs: Bardini, pl. 10,353; Löbbecke, no. 841, pl. 40.

ITALIAN
Late Sixteenth Century (?)

363 PIETA

At the foot of a cross, slightly to left, the seated Madonna holds the dead Christ across her lap. At right, the Magdalen kneels, her head resting on her hand. Elaborate frame of scroll caryatids supporting cornice inscribed, · HVIVS · LANGVORE · SANATI · SV̄; base inscribed, · IO · ANTONIVS · PETRASANTA ·

Bronze, traces of silvering, 130 x 99 mm. Reverse surface indicates former use as a pax.

1967.20.44

This relief is difficult to date. The proportions of the figures are awkward. They have far too large hands and the Magdalen seems to be larger in size and younger in dress and style than the others. Middeldorf and Goetz mention another pax in the museum of the Cathedral of Pienza with a different frame. The frame of our pax is used also for a relief of Christ and the Apostles in Berlin (Bange, no. 1062); here the frame is organic but not in the case of the pax, for Magdalen and one foot of Christ are cut and the heads of the scroll caryatids are placed awkwardly beside the arms of the cross. This composition seems therefore not to be the original one; moreover, it should be mentioned that the frame of our pax shows the same damage as the frame of the pax in Berlin.

Other specimen: (bronze) Santa Barbara, University Art Gallery, Morgenroth Collection.

Bibl.: Molinier 2, no. 564 (without frame); *Morgenroth,* no. 310.

ITALIAN
Late Sixteenth Century

364 ASSUMPTION OF THE VIRGIN MARY

The Virgin Mary on a half moon, above her head two angels holding a crown. Mary is draped in a long cloak with hands crossed at her chest and supported by four angels. Elaborate frame with rondel above with head of Christ, candelabra, columns at the sides, rosettes, volutes, and a putto head below.

Bronze, traces of gilt, 173 x 115 mm. The frame is damaged at top.

1967.20.54

NORTH ITALIAN(?)
Late Sixteenth Century or Later

365 VENUS AND PUTTO (CUPID?)

Bust of Venus, with head three-quarters to left, looks toward a putto who, with his right hand on her shoulder, looks at her from behind. She wears a hairband with one flower at the top, a cloak over her head and shoulders, and a flower hanging from one of two strands of beads. Stippled background. Around, VE NVS.

Bronze, dia. 76 mm.

1967.20.60

NORTH ITALIAN
Sixteenth or Seventeenth Century

366 THE VIRGIN IMMACULATE

The Virgin, clothed in long robes, stands frontally on a half moon. She wears a large crown and is surrounded by an aureole. Her left hand is at her chest; her right hand is open at her side.

Bronze, gilt, appliqué, 95 x 59 mm. Loop attached at top.

1967.11.1

ITALIAN
Sixteenth or Seventeenth Century

367 SAINT JOHN THE EVANGELIST

Saint John, seated reclining in a landscape, holds an open book in his right hand and leans forward toward an eagle which sits, wings extended, at John's feet to the left.

Bronze, elliptical, 46 x 59 mm. Hole at top.

1967.20.90

ITALIAN
Late Seventeenth Century

368 ANNUNCIATION

The Virgin at lower right kneels facing left and leans her crossed arms on a prie-dieu. She looks up at an angel who flies toward her on clouds, holding lilies in its right hand and gesturing to her with its left. Above the angel a dove descends on long rays. At upper right, a curtain drawn back. Incised on frame, ARCI CONFRATERNITA DELLA S.Sᴬ ANNUNCIATA

Bronze, silvered, appliqué. Irregular oval frame, 120 x 97 mm. Holes on edge of frame in eight groups of three each.

1967.20.86

ITALIAN(?)

369 ASCENSION OF CHRIST

Christ, frontal, with halo, and arms extended at his waist, encircled by a ring of clouds, floats above a small mound on top of which are two footprints. He is flanked by two male figures who look up at him with arms extended toward center. Beaded and molded frame. Above, Phoenix in flames.

Bronze, 134 x 88 mm. Reverse fixtures indicate former use as a pax.

1967.20.38

Location and date are uncertain.

GERMAN
PETER FLÖTNER (ca. 1485–1546)

Flötner, born presumably about 1485 in Thurgau, Switzerland, became a citizen of Nuremberg on 8 August 1523, having apparently come there from Ansbach. He died on 23 November 1546, in Nuremberg. Flötner cut reliefs in stone and wood, designed architectural details, fountains, furniture, vessels, decorative compositions, and ornaments. Many of his sketches, like his illustrations and broadsides, were published as woodcuts. Architectural works and one sculpture are preserved and certified. Flötner, one of the most many-sided artists of the Renaissance, belonged to no guild. It is assumed that he had a period of training in Augsburg and a sojourn in Italy. His sketches and models were used by goldsmiths and artisans of almost every sort until well into the seventeenth century.

Series: NEW TESTAMENT SUBJECTS

370 CHRIST AND THE SAMARITAN WOMAN, ca. 1530–35

Christ, seated on a rock by a well, turns with outstretched

arm toward the Samaritan woman, left, who bends over the well holding a rope attached to a pail. An ewer stands nearby. Far right, a group of persons appears from the woods. Behind, a forested mountain landscape with buildings.

Lead, 55 x 111 mm.

1967.11.2

This plaquette is among a number from the artist's early period which Bange ("Zur Datierung von Peter Flötners Plakettenwerk," *AMP* 3 [1921/22], p. 46ff.) dates before 1537. Braun (p. 29, no. 6) believes that the composition was taken a second time by Flötner in a smaller scale to illustrate the Rivius (see Book 3, 1558 edition, p. 13). The plaquette was intended as furniture appliqué and used for a small case in bronze (see Lange, p. 145ff. and pl. 6, no. 9). The composition can be found on a ceremonial cup ("Prunkpokal") by the Augsburg monogrammist LS from ca. 1570–80 (Munich, *Schatzkammer der Residenz*, 1964 Catalogue, no. 576); on Sieburger flagons ("Schnellen") (M. L. Solon, *The Ancient Art: Stoneware*, London 1892, p. 99); and on a medal from Kremnitz of 1554 (Braun, no. 6).

Other specimens: (lead) Antwerp, Museum Mayer van den Bergh; Cologne, Kunstgewerbemuseum (Clemens Collection); London, British Museum; Munich, Bayerisches Nationalmuseum; Santa Barbara, University Art Gallery, Morgenroth Collection; (bronze) London, British Museum (late, feeble cast); New York, Metropolitan Museum (gilt, reworked cast with variations and inscription).

Bibl.: Lange, no. 9, p. 124, pl. 6; Leitschuh, no. 32, pl. 4; Braun, no. 6, pl. 3; Bange, *D.M.*, p. 77, no. 2341; *Morgenroth*, no. 358, pl. 26; Clemens Collection, no. 213; DeCoo, no. 2377; Weber, no. 34,2. Auction catalogs: Löbbecke 1908, no. 876, pl. 42; Molthein, no. 196.

Provenance: Schreiber Collection.

371   TEMPTATION OF FAITH, ca. 1535–40

In front of a mountainous landscape near a church with chapel, Faith sits with bare chest and bent head, raising her left arm; a cross lies before her. Four monsters are tempting her. At the right one of them, a man with glasses wearing a hooded robe, bows from a hole in a tree and holds out a sausage to her. Further right another, a bird with a mask wearing a cowl and slippers, appears from a small door in a wall. On its back rides a monk, his body clothed in a barrel and wearing scapulary and cappa. He holds a book in his left hand and the bird's neck in his right. To Faith's left another, a bitch

with woman's head wearing a woman's cap, holds an article of clothing. At the left, the fourth monster, a bird(?) having hen's legs and a human head with cockscomb, stretches two wings in the air behind. Left background, a bridge connecting two parts of a burning city.

Bronze, aftercast, 96 x 107 mm.

1967.11.28

This plaquette is known as the Great Temptation of Faith, as opposed to another, the Small Temptation of Faith. Weber (no. 37) has corrected the name of the smaller temptation to the Temptation of Patience. This plaquette is dated by Bange (*AMP* [1921/22], p. 46ff.) in the early period of Flötner—that is, before 1537, but it probably was done in the late 1530s. In a recent publication by Edward Lucie-Smith and Aline Jacquiot (*The Waking Dream: Fantasy and the Surreal in Graphic Art, 1450–1900*, New York 1975, p. 24, no. 51, illus.) there appears an illustration of a woodcut in reverse after the same subject. It is given no attribution or provenance, but appears to be a study for or copy after the plaquette. The woodcut also contains more detail.

Other specimens: (lead) Antwerp, Museum Mayer van den Bergh; Berlin, Staatliche Museen (lost); London, British Museum; Munich, Bayerisches Nationalmuseum; Nuremberg, Germanisches Nationalmuseum; (bronze) Munich, Staatliche Münzsammlung (gilt); Paris, Bibliotheque Nationale; Paris, Ecole des Beaux-Arts (Coll. Wasset); Prague, Kunstgewerbemuseum.

Bibl.: Lange, no. 115, p. 131; Leitschuh, p. 19, no. 85, pl. 8; Bange, *D.M.*, p. 79, no. 5689, pl. 6; DeCoo, no. 2382; Weber, no. 38. Auction catalogs: Löbbecke, no. 890, pl. 43; Heinrici, no. 158, pl. 19; Rosenheim, no. 764,2.

GERMAN (AFTER FLÖTNER)
after 1550

372   PAGAN KING IN A SCROLL ORNAMENT FRAME

A bearded king in armor, cape, and crown with fillet leans on a spear before a landscape with buildings; in his right hand he holds a saber. Around, scroll ornament with putti, a satyr, a satyr mask, and flowers.

Bronze, dark patina, buckle-shaped, rounded below, 122 x 80 mm. Late cast from an example with pitted surface; two holes in upper portion.

1967.11.4

The depiction of the king is based on the *Unknown*

King from the series *Die zwölf ältesten deutschen Könige* by Peter Flötner (Weber, no. 46, 13).

Other specimens: (bronze) Florence, Museo Nazionale, Carrand Collection; Santa Barbara, University Art Gallery, Morgenroth Collection.

Bibl.: Morgenroth, no. 379, pl. 27; Imbert, no. 68, pl. 11,3 (as Venetian, sixteenth century); Middeldorf-Imbert, p. 154. Auction catalog: Molthein, no. 200.

WORKSHOP OF PANKRAZ LABENWOLF

Pankraz Labenwolf, born in 1492, belonged to a renowned Nuremberg family of bronze casters. He died in 1563. His work shows a close relationship to that of the Vischers, in whose workshop he had his training. In 1519 he became master; in 1523 he had his own workshop; and in 1537 the city council allowed him to build a foundry. In his workshop, in addition to important bronze works, stencils were also made—that is, models for the chased patterns of goldsmiths. It is assumed that Labenwolf made casts only after the sketches and models of other artists, as, for example, is proved in the case of the silver altar of Cracow. The relationship to Peter Flötner is close. The "Meister des Nürnberger Rathausputto," whose name is unknown, made the wooden model (Nuremberg, Germanisches Museum) for the crowning figures of the columns of the fountain in the courtyard of the Nuremberg Town Hall, cast in 1557.

Series: PUTTI AS MUSES

373 EUTERPE, ca. 1545

A nude putto walks to the left playing a shawm; an organ in right background.

Bronze, 48 x 32 mm. Considerably cut.

1967.11.3

The series of putti as muses has been attributed to Peter Flötner. This author attributes it to the workshop of Pankraz Labenwolf, for instance, to a man like *Meister des Nürnberger Rathausputto,* since seven putti are simplified copies of the series of nine female muses of Flötner (Weber, no. 58). In addition, the figures in other examples in the series are inscribed, which is not customary for Flötner. The inscriptions are awkwardly placed on the picture and show errors.

Bibl.: Lange, no. 31, p. 125, pl. 8; Leitschuh, no. 116, pl. 17; Weber, I, "Bemerkungen zum Plakettenwerk von Peter Flötner," *Pantheon* 28, 6 (1970), p. 521ff.; Weber,

no. 71,2. Auction catalogs: Bardini, pl. 9,235; Löbbecke, no. 885, pl. 43; Riechmann & Co., Halle/S., 23–24 February 1921, no. 876, pl. 12; Rosenheim, no. 756, 2–3.

GEORG LABENWOLF (d. 1585)

Bronze caster, born in Nuremberg, active 1559–63 in Neuburg on the Danube, took over the Nuremberg workshop of his father Pankraz in 1563. He died in Nuremberg in 1585.

374 RABBIT HUNT, Third Quarter of the Sixteenth Century

At the left three hunters stand around a tree. One carries a spear in his right hand and holds a dog; the others strike with clubs a rabbit who is being chased by two other dogs. Two hunters on horseback follow these dogs from the right. All the hunters wear baggy pants, short jackets, caps and swords at their belts.

Bronze, presumably a cast from an electrotype of another specimen, 69 x 217 mm. Four holes at the corners.

1967.14.9

Bange attributes this work to a follower of the Nuremberg bronze caster Pankraz Labenwolf, perhaps his son Georg. He refers to the statuette of a hunter kneeling to shoot in the O. Bondy Collection, Vienna (E. W. Braun, "Nürnberger Bronzestatuetten aus der Werkstätte von Georg Labenwolf," *Kunst und Kunsthandwerk* 23 [1920], p. 129ff., fig. f. 1f.).

Other specimens: Berlin, Staatliche Museen (lost); Florence, Museo Nazionale (Carrand Collection); New York, Metropolitan Museum.

Bibl.: Bange *D.M.,* p. 114, no. 8309; Weber, no. 292.

GERMAN
Middle of the Sixteenth Century

375 THE JUDGMENT OF PARIS

To the right, Paris in armor, his helmet beside him, sitting under a tree to which his horse is tied; a bird on a branch. Before him, Mercury, also in armor, indicating the three goddesses, Juno, Minerva, and Venus, nude, with his caduceus; two are seen from the front, one from the back. Before Venus lies an apple. Left, above, Eros in the clouds shoots an arrow at Paris.

Bronze, green patina, dia. 73 mm. Cast from a reworked model; some details from the original are illegible.

1967.11.13

This depiction goes back to a woodcut attributed to Jörg Breu the Younger and dated to 1535 (H. Röttinger, "Das Holzschnittwerk Jörg Breu's d.J.," *Mitteilungen des Vereins für vervielfältigende Kunst* [1909], no. 56; M. Geisberg, Bilderkatalog zu: "Der deutsche Einblattholzschnitt in der ersten Hälfte des XVI. Jahrhunderts," Munich 1930, no. 400). On its part, Breu's conception is influenced by the numerous representations of this scene by Lucas Cranach the Elder. Possibly stimulated by Breu's composition is a drawing by Erhardt Schön, dated 1536, which closely resembles the plaquette depiction (Berlin, Staatliche Museen, Kat. E. Bock, *Die Zeichnungen alter Meister* 1, 1921, p. 77, no. 919, pl. 109), as well as one seen on a medallion in a study for a tankard by Hans Brosamer (A. Frisch, *Hans Brosamers Kunstbuechlein,* Berlin 1878, Bl. 13v). A larger boxwood medallion (dia. 82 mm., Berlin, Staatliche Museen) and an ivory replica (77 x 75 mm., Munich, Bayerisches Nationalmuseum) were dated around 1550, both by Bange (Berlin, Deutsches Museum 4, Kat. Bange, 1930, p. 74f., no. 829) and R. Berliner (Munich, Bayerisches Nationalmuseum 13, 4, Kat. Berliner, 1926, no. 86, pl. 34). The composition exists in some variants, both as a plaquette and as a boxwood relief (Weber, nos. 201–03).

Other specimens: (bronze) Florence, Museo Nazionale (gilt); Munich, Bayerisches Nationalmuseum (gilt, chased); Opava (Czechoslovakia), Museum.

Bibl.: Weber, no. 201.

SOUTH GERMAN
After the Middle of the Sixteenth Century

376 DANCING PEASANT COUPLE

A peasant couple holding hands stepping to the right; the man with a knife in his belt and a feathered cap. Background, left, a tree; continuous wreathed border broken by four bands.

Bronze, gilt, dia. 36 mm. Gilding worn; three holes in edge.

1967.11.20

Based on *Des Jahres Ende* from the series "Das Bauernfest oder die zwölf Monate," engraved by Hans Sebald Beham in 1546 (Bartsch, Adam, *Le Peintre Graveur* 8, no. 160; Hollstein, F. W. H., *German Engravings, Etchings, and Woodcuts, 1400–1700,* 3, Amsterdam,

n.d., p. 98ff.). Four further depictions from this series are known. Some compositions from the plaquettes occur on pieces for draughts (see Bayerisches Nationalmuseum, Catalog 14, Georg Himmelheber, Spiele Munich, 1972, nos. 156–58).

Other specimen: (bronze, gilt) Berlin, Staatliche Museen (lost).

Bibl.: Bange, *D.M.,* p. 105, no. 7088, pl. 20; Weber, no. 209, 5.

SOUTH GERMAN
Second Third of the Sixteenth Century

377 ALLEGORY OF UNITY

Left, the figure of a father on a bench raised by three steps on a two-stage platform breaks a rod in two. Before him, a figure breaks a single rod while another figure attempts to break a bound bundle of rods at the foot of the platform. To the right stand the sons observing the demonstration of the strength of unity. In the background a columned arcade.

Lead, semicircular top, 53 x 39 mm.

1967.11.8

This scene represents an antique fable, "The Father and the Rods," transmitted by Babrius (*Babrius Fabeln,* translated by Hertzberg, Halle/S., 1846, p. 24. Dr. Friedrich Kobler, Munich, is to be thanked for pointing out the literary source.). Stylistically, the plaquette is related to the series of scenes of justice based upon the *Gesta Romanorum,* attributed to the workshop of the so-called Blattfriesmeister (Weber, no. 82).

Bibl.: Weber, no. 181.

SOUTH GERMAN
Last Quarter of the Sixteenth Century

378 CRUCIFIXION

Christ on the cross, which stands above a skull and bones, is mourned by Mary at left with outstretched hands and John on the right with hands clasped. Both have halos and look at each other. Two angels hover under Christ's arms, catching his blood in goblets. At the top of the cross, an inscription tablet.

Bronze, aftercast, molded frame, 110 x 83 mm. Hole at top.

1967.20.50

Bange and Middeldorf view this as a German work from the middle of the sixteenth century. Middeldorf rejects the thesis of Morazzoni, who calls it "maniera del Sansovino." Braun has attributed an altar, formerly in Vienna, Auspitz Collection, which shows this Mary transformed to Hilaria with a palm branch in the right wing, to the so-called Augsburg plaquette workshop. Braun dates the works from this shop—certainly too early—to the middle of the sixteenth century. The use of this relief on the Liber Aureus from Pfäfers of 1590 (St. Gallen, Staatsarchiv Pfäferser Archiv; D. F. Rittmeyer, "Der Kirchenschatz des einstigen Klosters Pfäfers und die Kirchenschätze in Sarganserland," 85. *Neujahrsblatt,* Historischer Verein St. Gallen, 1945, p. 18, pl. 2, fig. 5) gives a "terminus ante quem"; that is, the group must date from the last quarter of the sixteenth century. The plaquette was attached either in rectangular or rounded form to numerous bells, which are dated from 1592 to 1779 (S. Thurm, *Deutscher Glockenalas, Württemberg und Hohenzollern,* Berlin/München 1959, no. 633b, fig. 77a; Bayerisch-Schwaben 1967, no. 408, fig. 127, no. 754; 294; 948 and 972a, fig. 177; Mittelfranken 1973, no. 672).

Other specimens: (lead) Nuremberg, Germanisches Nationalmuseum; Stuttgart, Württembergisches Landesmuseum (partly rounded off at top); (bronze) Berlin, Staatliche Museen; London, Victoria and Albert Museum; Munich, Bayerisches Nationalmuseum; Madrid, Lazaro Collection. In addition, the flanking figures also exist independently.

Bibl.: Molinier, no. 694; Braun, E. W., "Aus der Slg deutscher Renaissanceplaketten in BNM," *AMP* 2 (1920/21), p. 83f.; Bange, *D.M.,* p. 104, no. 1475, pl. 19; *La Coll. Lazaro de Madrid* 2, Madrid 1927, p. 276, no. 782; Imbert, no. 27, pl. 5,5; Middeldorf-Imbert, p. 152; Weber, no. 381,1. Auction catalogs: Heinrici, no. 170, pl. 16; Cahn, Frankfurt/M., 2 March 1926, no. 1728, pl. 27.

ANTONIO ABONDIO
(1538?–91)

Abondio was apparently born in Riva in 1538 and died on 3 May 1591, in Vienna. This medalist and wax embosser worked 1565–66 in Innsbruck for Ferdinand II and on 1 June 1566 became Imperial "Konterfetter" in the service of Maximilian II. From 1576 active for Rudolph II, Abondio settled in Prague in 1580. Journeys took him to the Netherlands (1566), Pressburg (1569), Munich and Augsburg (1572), Graz (1575), Italy

(1585), and Lyons (1588–89). He was the father of Alessandro Abondio, born about 1570, who was court sculptor of Rudolph II from 1606 to 1612 in Vienna, Prague, and Innsbruck. From 1632 to 1645 he was active in the service of Elector Maximilian I of Bavaria. He died in 1648.

379 TOILET OF VENUS, ca. 1587

A bust of Venus, her head turned slightly to the left, her breasts exposed and a pearl earring in her left ear. Behind, a servant holds a braid by a cloth out to the right; a second servant on the left, partly cut off by the border, combs her hair. At the right, Amor embraces the goddess and raises a mirror with his left hand. Above, the artist's monogram, AN AB (superimposed).

Lead, oval, 93 x 72 mm.

1967.20.42

An example at the National Museum in Budapest is dated 1587. A detail in gilt gypsum depicting Venus and Amor can be found on a cabinet of Rudolf the Second at the Kunsthistorisches Museum in Vienna (Habich, G., *Schaumünzen* 2, 2, p. 485, fig. 503a); a lead cast in Nuremberg, Germanisches Museum (Fiala, E., *Antonio Abondio,* Prague 1909, no. 87, pl. 9, 4). Habich (*Ibid.,* p. 507) mentions a variation: an oval model (in stone?—ex coll. Felix: Felix Collection, Catalogue Heberle, Cologne 1896, no. 910) as an imitation dating from the seventeenth century. A drawing by Paul Zeggin, done in 1618, is in Munich at the Graphisches Sammlung (Nagler, G. K., *Kunstlerlexikon* 22, 1852, p. 280; same author, *Die Monogrammisten,* Munich 1858, 4, no. 3416).

Other specimens: (lead) Basel, Historisches Museum; Budapest, National Museum; Hamburg, Museum für Kunst und Gewerbe; London, Victoria and Albert Museum; Munich, Bayerisches Nationalmuseum; Nuremberg, Germanisches Nationalmuseum; Prague, Kunstgewerbemuseum; Stuttgart, Württembergisches Landesmuseum; Vienna, Kunsthistorisches Museum; (bronze) Basel, Historisches Museum.

Bibl.: Molinier, no. 355; Fiala, E., *Antonio Abondio,* Prague 1909, p. 47, no. 86, pl. 9,3; Planiscig, no. 459; MacLagan, p. 45, no. 5412–1859, pl. 12; Weber, no. 650. Auction catalogs: Frank Collection, Cubasch, Vienna, 18 January 1904, no. 956; Riechmann & Co., Halle/S., Catalog 6, 12 March 1913, no. 434, pl. 16; Cahn, Frankfurt/M., Catalogue 37, 7–9 March 1918, no. 69; Riechmann & Co., Halle/S., Catalog 17, 22–23 February 1921, no. 789, pl. 10; Collection Lanna II, Lepke, Berlin, 21–23 March 1911, no. 304, pl. 25.

ANTONIO ABONDIO
(Follower of?)

380 PIETA WITH ANGELS, ca. 1600

In a landscape, Mary sits under the cross holding before her Christ's body, which lies on a cloth held by two angels.

A. Bronze, cast from a reworked model, 80 x 58 mm. Cut at left.

1967.32.2

B. Bronze, silvered, reworked, 81 x 64 mm. Edges damaged, traces of fastenings on the reverse.

1967.20.51

Bange and Frederiks (*Dutch Silver* 1, The Hague, 1952, no. 117d) compare this lamentation to the series of passion scenes by Arent van Bolten (see no. 397). Composition is based on an Italian model and exists in several variations. The model could either belong to the circle of or, better, to a follower of the Abondio workshop.

Other specimens: (lead) Cologne, Kunstgewerbemuseum; (bronze) Baltimore, Walters Art Gallery; Basel, Historisches Museum; Berlin, Staatliche Museen; Rome, Palazzo Venezia; (silver) Brescia, Museo Civico.

Bibl.: Rizzini, *Illustrazione dei civici di Brescia*, Brescia 1889, no. 257; Bange, *D.M.*, p. 132, no. 5955, pl. 30; Weber, no. 658.

ANTONIO ABONDIO
(Circle of?)
Munich, ca. 1600

381 PIETA WITH ANGELS

Mary sits at the foot of the cross holding Christ's body across her lap, her arms encircling him, and holds both of his arms with her hands. Angels at right and left each hold one of Christ's arms. Landscape behind.

Bronze, dia. 78 mm.

1967.20.92

This type has its origins in Italy (compare, for example, Bange, no. 945, pl. 97). Many variations exist (see nos. 380A,B above), each differing only slightly from the others. A stylistic relation to the work of Antonio Abondio, for example the Venus (F. Dworschak, *Antonio Abondio*, Trento 1958, p. 111) suggests an origin in the circle or imitators of Abondio.

Other specimens: Basel, Historisches Museum; Berlin,

Staatliche Museen; Munich, Bayerisches Nationalmuseum.

Bibl.: Molinier, no. 565; Bange, *D.M.*, p. 137, no. 1476, pl. 34; Weber, no. 662. Auction catalogs: Faure Coll., 22–23 September 1913, Hamburger, Frankfurt/M., no. 693, pl. 20; von Parpart, no. 728; Cahn, Frankfurt/M., 23 October 1912, no. 132.

JAKOB KROMER
(Attributed to)

Goldsmith in Überlingen, was guild master in 1601. On 5 January 1611, because of his advanced age, he was admitted into the Überlingen hospital. In 1575–76 he was active for the Fürstenberger family, and from 1584 until 1599 for the cloister in Salem.

382 CHRIST SURROUNDED BY ANGELS, ca. 1600

Christ, half-length, is depicted in clouds, among which are the heads of eight angels. Over his garment, he wears a cloak clasped in front; he holds his right hand up in blessing and his left rests on an orb.

Bronze, gilt, 88 x 71 mm. Cast from model with rounded top; this specimen extends beyond the design on top and sides.

1967.11.16

The similarity between this plaquette and the God Surrounded by Angels, which G. Habich attributes to Jacob Kromer (*Schaumünzen* 2, 1, p. 449, fig. 464), suggests that the work was created in the same workshop. A variation by another artist was in the Molthein Collection (Molthein, no. 413, pl. 33). There is a lead specimen in the Bayerisches Nationalmuseum in Munich (with rounded top).

Bibl.: Weber, no. 471.

MATTHIAS WALLBAUM
(1554–1632)

Born 1554 in Kiel, Wallbaum is referred to from 1579 as a goldsmith apprentice in Augsburg. He became master there in 1590 and married. He died on 11 January 1632. Wallbaum was one of the most productive Augsburg goldsmiths of the late Renaissance. He undertook the management of a great workshop, in which were produced works from sketches and models of several of its members and also of artists who were active outside the workshop.

SOUTH GERMAN (AUGSBURG)
Circle of the Wallbaum Workshop
ca. 1600

383 Series: THE PASSION OF CHRIST

A. CHRIST BEFORE PILATE

In the middle stands Christ with bowed head, dressed in a loincloth, purple robe and crown of thorns, holding the mock scepter in his bound hands. On the right, Pilate sits on a throne under a canopy. Near him stands a bearded elder. To the left and behind Christ stand three armed men. In the background, an arcade.

Lead, oval, 57 x 43 mm.

1967.11.21

This plaquette and the next one, as well as Crucifixion and Resurrection scenes, belong to a Passion series. Despite different sizes and a disparity in style, the plaquettes can be assigned chiefly to the workshops of Augsburg goldsmiths, particularly Matthias Wallbaum. Habich ("Beiträge zu Antonio Abondio," *AMP* I [1913/14], p. 105) recognized that the Christ figure was derived from a medal by Abondio (Fiala, E., *Antonio Abondio,* Prague 1909, 4, 7) and on that basis attributed our plaquette to Abondio. What is more likely involved here are models of an Augsburg workshop drawn from graphic prototypes by artists of various regions. This plaquette was also employed on a gilt silver locket by Johann Belitz from 1620 (Museum für Kunsthandwerk, Frankfurt/M., Linel 801).

Other specimens: (lead) Berlin, Staatliche Museen; Munich, Bayerisches Nationalmuseum.

Bibl.: Bange, *D.M.,* p. 128, no. 8507, pl. 28 (as no. 5807); Weber, no. 400,1.

B. PIETA WITH PASSION SYMBOLS

Mary sits on a grassy mound beneath the cross, head bowed. She holds with both hands the body of Christ, which leans on her with outspread arms and sunken head. Hanging on or leaning against the cross are the Passion symbols: scourge, spear, tongs, crown of thorns, ladder, hammer, sponge and rod.

Lead, oval, 57 x 40 mm.

1967.11.9

This widespread Pieta type is of Italian origin. Bange gave this plaquette to an Italian artist, while recognizing its connection with the preceding one.

Other specimens: (lead) Munich, Bayerisches National-

museum; Munich, Staatliche Münzsammlung; (bronze) Berlin, Staatliche Museen (rectangular).

Bibl.: Bange, no. 1043, pl. 84; Weber, no. 400,3. Auction catalogs: Helbing, Munich, 20–22 December 1917, no. 449.

AUGSBURG
Circle of Matthias Wallbaum
Beginning of the Seventeenth Century

384 Series: EVENTS FROM THE LIFE OF CHRIST

A. ANNUNCIATION

An angel kneeling on a cloud and holding a lily sweeps down from upper left to Mary, who kneels at a prie-dieu and turns around in fright at the angel's appearance. The back of the prie-dieu shows an opened door. Above and behind the angel flies the dove of the Holy Spirit. At the left, a cat lies curled in front of a table on which is a breadbasket. Behind the Virgin, a canopied bed.

Bronze, 92 x 68 mm. Aftercast; there are faint impressions of two seals at the bottom.

1967.15.1

The series, comprising sixteen plaquettes, was complete in the Walcher von Molthein Collection (Braun, nos. 177–90, pls. 55–58; Molthein, nos. 420–35, pl. 32). Since a few examples show a view of the city of Augsburg (Rosenberg, *Die Goldschmiede Merkzeichen,* Aufl. 3, 1, no. 132) and the hallmark of Matthias Wallbaum (*Ibid.,* 1, no. 148), these must be casts after silver reliefs which were used in the Wallbaum workshop, for example, in the silver altar of the Monastery at Lambach (*Österreichische Kunsttopographie* 34, [1969], p. 152ff.). Braun, since he could not identify the master's mark, attributed the series to a "Master of the Passion." Bange (p. 121, no. 7651) and, later, Bernhart suggest more artists and various dates of origin. The wide variety of styles of the compositions derives perhaps from the use of designs from different periods and workshops.

Other specimens: (bronze) Rome, Palazzo Venezia; Rome, Vatican.

Bibl.: Braun, E. W., "Zur Ausstellung der Plaketten-sammlung Walcher von Molthein," *Kunst und Kunst-handwerk* 14 (1911), p. 411, fig. 11ff.; Braun, no. 177, pl. 55; Weber, no. 412,1. Auction catalogs: Heinrici, no. 177; Molthein, no. 420.

B. THE ADORATION OF THE MAGI

At the right in front of the stable sit Mary, with the

Christ Child on her lap, and Joseph, leaning on his staff. In front of the Holy Family, the three Magi with elaborate vessels. One, kneeling in the center, holds his gift out to the Child; the others stand at right and left. At right, a dog; at upper left, the Star of Bethlehem. Narrow border on left side.

Bronze, 94 x 71 mm. Below, two seals in the cast.

1967.15.2

Another specimen: (lead) Berlin, Staatliche Museen (lost).

Bibl.: Bange, *D.M.,* p. 140, no. 7650, pl. 25; Weber, no. 412,3. Auction catalogs: von Parpart, no. 704, pl. 16 (lead); Molthein, no. 422.

C. THE LAST SUPPER

Christ and the twelve apostles sit around a round table in a columned hall. Christ embraces John, who lies against his chest, and blesses with his left hand. In front of the table, a pitcher in a basin. On the right wall, a candelabra.

Bronze, 93 x 68 mm. Two hallmarks barely visible at bottom.

1967.15.4

Bibl.: Braun, no. 181, pl. 56; Weber, no. 412,6. Auction catalogs: Heinrici, no. 180; von Parpart, no. 708, pl. 16; Molthein, no. 425; Bange, *D.M.,* p. 136f.

D. CHRIST ON THE MOUNT OF OLIVES

In a landscape, Christ kneels at center rear on a rocky hill, looking toward an angel who holds a goblet and hovers in clouds at upper right. In the foreground three disciples lie sleeping—Peter at the left with a sword, John in the center, James at right in front of a tree. Narrow borders indicated.

Bronze, 97 x 69 mm. Two hallmarks visible at bottom.

1967.15.3

Other specimens: Munich, Bayerisches Nationalmuseum; Rome, Palazzo Venezia.

Bibl.: Braun, no. 182, pl. 56; Weber, no. 412,7. Auction catalogs: Riechmann & Co., Halle/S., cat. 18, 24–25 February 1921, no. 834, pl. 11; Molthein, no. 426.

E. CROWNING WITH THORNS

A man holding staves presses the crown of thorns onto the head of Christ, who sits on a pedestal facing half-right. Four other men mock him. In the left foreground

on the floor are a whip, rod, cane, and cloak; at the right a dog. Above, a curtain and an hourglass on the wall. Narrow borders.

Bronze, 98 x 75 mm. Two hallmarks at bottom.

1967.15.5

Other specimens: Augsburg, Städtische Kunstsammlungen; Frankfurt/M., Museum für Kunsthandwerk; Innsbruck, Ferdinandeum; Munich, Bayerisches Nationalmuseum; Santa Barbara, University Art Gallery, Morgenroth Collection.

Bibl.: Braun, no. 183, pl. 56; *Morgenroth,* no. 392, pl. 28; Weber, no. 412,9. Auction catalogs: von Parpart, no. 709; Heinrici, no. 181; Molthein, no. 427; Dirksen Coll., Lepke, Berlin, cat. 2042, 28 April 1931, no. 330, pl. 53.

F. CHRIST BEARING THE CROSS

In the left foreground Saint Veronica kneels and holds out her veil to Christ, who has collapsed under the cross. Two soldiers, one of them stepping on Christ, beat him with a whip and a rope, while Simon the Cyrenian takes up the base of the cross. Behind Veronica a man with a basket runs to the left. In the background, a city gate with portcullis, through which a group of soldiers, led by two cavalrymen, leaves the city.

Bronze, aftercast, 91 x 67 mm.

1967.15.7

Other specimens: (lead) Kafbeuren, Heimatmuseum; (bronze) Frankfurt/M., Museum für Kunsthandwerk; Leningrad, Hermitage.

Bibl.: Braun, no. 184, pl. 56; Weber, no. 412,11. Auction catalogs: von Parpart, no. 712/13, pl. 16; Molthein, no. 430.

G. ENTOMBMENT

Two men carry the body of Christ on a cloth toward an open tomb at lower left. At the right Mary Magdalene kneels next to her ointment jar and a small basin and anoints Christ's left hand. Behind Christ, the mourning Mary and John. In the background a landscape and houses; in the sky a half-moon. Narrow border.

Bronze, 96 x 70 mm. Two hallmarks at bottom.

1967.15.8

Another specimen: New York, Metropolitan Museum.

Bibl.: Braun, no. 186, pl. 57; Weber, no. 412,13. Auction catalogs: von Parpart, no. 716/17; Molthein, no. 432.

H. THE RESURRECTION OF CHRIST

Christ, wearing loincloth and cloak and holding the victory banner, floats in clouds above the open grave, the cover of which is held by two angels. Around the tomb, four soldiers, of whom two are seated and one tries to flee. Narrow border.

Bronze, 93 x 66 mm.

1967.11.5

The middle field of the Lambach Altar, a bronze plate in the Bayerisches Nationalmuseum (Inv. No. 70/57), and a few Augsburg and Nuremberg epitaphs are executed after the same design with the addition of two sleeping soldiers at the right.

Other specimens: Berlin, Staatliche Museen (lost); Leningrad, Hermitage; Santa Barbara, University Art Gallery, Morgenroth Collection.

Bibl.: Braun, no. 189, pl. 58; Bange, *D.M.,* p. 140, no. 1934, pl. 25; *Morgenroth,* no. 393, pl. 28; Weber, no. 412,14. Auction catalogs: von Parpart, no. 718/19; Heinrici, no. 183, pl. 11; Molthein, no. 433.

HANS JAKOB BAYR
(1574–1628)

Bayr, born 1574 in Augsburg, became master there and married in 1604. In 1616 he was "Vorgeher" of the goldsmiths' guild, in 1622 "Geschaumeister." He died in 1628. Few works of his are preserved. One of the most important, the monstrance made for the Cathedral of Eichstätt at the order of the Eichstätt Prince-bishop Johann Konrad von Gemmingen, is only known from a drawing after it. Bayr was a friend of Hans Rottenhammer, who made sketches for him.

ATTRIBUTED TO HANS JAKOB BAYR

385 RAPE OF THE SABINE WOMEN, ca. 1605–10

In a broad place, on the left of which stands a collonnade and a triumphal arch, the Roman warriors can be seen abducting the Sabine women. The Romans are in armor or nude or clad only in a cape and a helmet. In the right background, several riders with flags, lances and a standard; on the architecture at left, banners.

Bronze, reworked aftercast, dark patina, dia. 143 mm.

1967.11.17

This relief exists as a plaquette with two different border ornaments and as the bottom of a silver vessel, this last

in the Louvre, Paris. A drawing in the Uffizi, Florence, attributed to Hans Rottenhammer, can be considered the prototype (Ingrid Jost, "Drei unerkannte Rottenhammerzeichnungen in den Uffizien," *Orbis Artium,* Utrechtse Kunsthistorische Studien VII; Album Discipolorum Prof. J. G. Gelder, 1963, p. 74ff., fig. 5). The creation of the relief in the studio of Hans Jakob Bayr is possible.

Other specimens: (lead) Amsterdam, Rijksmuseum; (bronze) Opava (Czechoslovakia), Museum; Santa Barbara, University Art Gallery, Morgenroth Collection; Art Market.

Bibl.: Braun, no. 150, pl. 43; *Morgenroth,* no. 424; I. Weber, "Rottenhammer-Entwurf für ein Goldschmiederelief," *Pantheon* 27, 4 (1969), p. 328ff.; Weber, no. 781. Auction catalogs: Rosenheim, no. 792, pl. 40; Molthein, no. 527; Münzhandlung Basel, Basel, Catalog 2, 8 October 1934, no. 549, pl. 19.

SOUTH GERMAN(?)
ca. 1600

386 STANDING ELDER

Facing right, a bearded old man with close-fitting cap and cloak trimmed with fur leans on a staff.

Bronze, dark patina, cut-out silhouette, height 202 mm. Left foot and portion of base line broken off; eight holes.

1967.11.22

This figure is one of numerous related examples. It is not yet clear, however, exactly what personage is intended; perhaps an apostle or more likely a shepherd from an adoration scene is depicted.

CASPAR ENDERLEIN
(1560–1633)

Stone cutter and pewter caster, Enderlein was born in June 1560, in Basel and became a pupil of Hans Fridrich there in 1574. In 1583–84 he settled in Nuremberg and became apprentice to Melchior Koch III. In 1586 he passed the examination for master, under Jakob Koch II, married and became a citizen of Nuremberg. Enderlein was master of the guild from 1603 to 1606 and from 1613 to 1616. He died on 19 April 1633. He worked to a great extent after the models of François Briot, who, in turn, worked very much after the graphic models of Etienne Delaune. Enderlein made his models not, like

Briot, in copper, but in Solnhofner stone. This smooth limestone was preferred by the Nuremberg carvers of the Renaissance for their models.

First Quarter of the Seventeenth Century (After François Briot)

Series: THE FOUR WORLD-MONARCHS

387 ALEXANDER THE GREAT

The emperor sits in armor upon arms and trophies at a sea. At left, a four-headed dragon. The monarch holds the staff of command in his right hand, in his left a fluttering flag with the insignia of a ram. In the background, buildings on the shore; at left above, a wind-god in the clouds. Inscription below: ALEXANDER-MAGNVS.

Lead, 71 x 100 mm. Molded border, rounded tab at top with hole drilled through. Cast from the rim of a plate(?), with the border added, since the field is trapezoidal, the inscription cut, and the lower corners filled with ornamentation.

1967.11.10

The representations of this series are patterned after the so-called *Mars-Schüssel* of François Briot, produced around 1600 (Hans Demiani, *François Briot, Caspar Enderlein, und das Edelzinn*, Leipzig 1897, p. 50ff., pl. 24; Ulrich Haedeke, *Zinn*, Brunswick 1963, p. 166ff.). The series occurs on a butcher's guild tankard from Joachimsthal, in the Museum für Kunsthandwerk in Dresden, a work in pewter of the Joachimsthal metalsmith Christopher Dürr in 1565 (Haedeke, *Ibid.*, p. 239, fig. 201). The plaquettes were also aftercast by German metalsmiths for pewter sandvessels (Demiani, *op. cit.*, p. 55, pl. 13,3).

Other specimens: (lead) Nuremberg, Germanisches Nationalmuseum; Paris, Private Collection; Stuttgart, Württembergisches Landesmuseum; Posen, National Museum.

Bibl.: Neuerwerbungen des Germanischen Nationalmuseums, Nuremberg, 1970–71, p. 179ff.; Weber, no. 748, 3. Auction catalogs: Thewalt Coll., Lempertz, Cologne, 4–14 November 1903, no. 1216; Löbbecke, no. 923, pl. 46; Cat. 104, Dupriez, Brussels, 31 January 1912, no. 456.

SOUTH GERMAN (AUGSBURG?)
First Quarter of the Seventeenth Century

388 NOLI ME TANGERE

Left, underneath a tree, stands Christ with bared upper torso, hat and cape, supporting himself with his right hand on a spade. With his left hand he warns away Mary Magdalene, who kneels to the right. Between them, an ointment jar. In the background left, a balustrade; at the right, trees. A distant mountain landscape is indicated with houses and clouds. Narrow border strip.

Bronze, gilt, 83 x 64 mm. Hole at top; a surface crack (cast in) extends through the lower quarter.

1967.11.12

With the exception of an altered background, this composition follows the same graphic prototype as the relief by the Master DG, or DGI, in the Kunstgewerbemuseum, Berlin (Pechstein, no. 237). The modeling of our specimen is finer. Another variant of the relief, with a bronze frame, is in the Ciechanowiecki Collection, London (Houston, no. 447).

Bibl.: Weber, no. 783A.

SOUTH GERMAN
First Quarter of the Seventeenth Century

389 Series: TWENTY-FOUR SCENES FROM OVID'S METAMORPHOSES

A. PAN AND SYRINX (Met. 2, 697–705)

Syrinx, garments fluttering, flees into a stream filled with rushes, which are embraced by the pursuing Pan. On the left, a bridge and architecture; to right, reeds and a tree.

Bronze, gilt, 71 x 127 mm. Hole in area of reeds.

1967.16.10

This series of plaquettes was presumably mounted, perhaps on a cabinet. Besides those described here and below, other depictions from the series are known: Corinis Transformed into a Crow (Met. 2, 496–507) and Aeneas Rescuing Anchises from Troy (Met. 13, 623–25), which with other specimens from this series are mounted on a cabinet (now in the Bowdoin collections, Acc. no. 1972.70; see Weber, no. 860). A gilt copper relief, Daedalus and Icarus, also in the Bowdoin collections (Acc. no. 1970.28; 70 x 122 mm.; Weber, no. 861), could be modeled after a further example of the series. A later adaptation based on the series is a bronze relief, also from the Molinari Collection, Hercules Slaying Nessus (Met. 9, 125–30; Acc. no. 1967.16.9; 72 x 127 mm.). This specimen in galvanic gilding is perhaps based on an older prototype—Nessus is mistakenly depicted with a female head. Several of these motifs appear to derive from woodcut illustrations by Virgil Solis for

Ovid's *Metamorphosen,* printed in 1563 by Feyrabent in Frankfurt (see no. 389I). In turn, many of Solis's cuts appear to be direct copies of those attributed to Bernard Salomon, which first appeared in *La Metamorphose d'Ovide Figuree,* de Tournes, Lyons 1557 (see no. 389G).

Bibl.: Weber, no. 860,1.

B. THE FALL OF PHAETON (Met. 2, 304–24)

On the right, Jupiter in the clouds hurling a thunderbolt at the chariot which was taken from his father Phoebus by Phaeton, who falls into the River Edrinus with the horses and wreckage. Left, the sun; in the background, the shore with hills and houses.

Bronze, gilt, 72 x 126 mm. Hole at upper left.

1967.16.2

Another specimen: (bronze) Munich, Private Collection.

Bibl.: Weber, no. 860, 2.

C. THE HELIADES (Met. 2, 340–66)

The nude Heliades, sisters of Phaeton, stand in a forested river landscape before the sarcophagus of their brother; their upraised arms are being transformed into branches. On the right, one of the sisters is being embraced by her mother, Clymena. Also right, two swans on the river; on the far shore, a mountain.

Bronze, gilt, 72 x 129 mm.

1967.16.13

Another specimen: (bronze, gilt, cabinet-mounted) Bowdoin collections, Acc. no. 1972.70.

Bibl.: Weber, no. 860, 3.

D. JUPITER SEDUCES CALLISTO (Met. 2, 425–33)

In a glade, Jupiter in the guise of Diana embraces the struggling Callisto; near her lays her bow; to the left, two hounds; in the distance, a river.

Bronze, gilt, 74 x 129 mm.

1967.16.15

Another specimen: (bronze, gilt, cabinet-mounted) Bowdoin collections, Acc. no. 1972.70.

Bibl.: Weber, no. 860, 4.

E. JUNO TRANSFORMS CALLISTO INTO A BEAR (Met. 2, 475–84)

Juno, bosom bared and wielding a scepter, holds Callisto to the ground by her hair. Callisto raises her hands in supplication. To the right by a stream, Callisto transformed into a bear; in the background, left, of the wooded river landscape are high mountains and right, a building in the antique manner.

Bronze, gilt, 72 x 128 mm.

1967.16.6

Bibl.: Weber, no. 860, 5.

F. ARKAS KILLING CALLISTO AND THEIR APOTHEOSIS (Met. 2, 496–507)

Arkas, the son of Callisto, stands dressed as a hunter on the right, aiming an arrow at his mother who has been transformed into a bear. On the left, Arkas and Callisto, apotheosized, are in the clouds under the Zodiac; on the right, trees.

Bronze, gilt, 72 x 128 mm.

1967.16.17

Bibl.: Weber, no. 860, 6.

G. DIANA AND ACTAEON (Met. 3, 143–95)

At the left, Diana and three nymphs stand nude in a fountain pool, the water of which flows through the mouth of a mask into a stream. Actaeon approaches from the right, arms outstretched, with antlers sprouting from his head and followed by two dogs. In the background a large growth sprouts from stony ground; at the right, trees.

Bronze, reduced aftercast, gilt, 72 x 111 mm. The nymph on the left cut off in part.

1967.16.11

A horizontal adaptation of a composition which follows that of a woodcut illustration attributed to Bernard Salomon in *Les illustres observations antiques du seigneur Gabriel Symeon Florentin,* Lyons 1558, p. 97, which in turn first appeared among Salomon's illustrations to his 1557 Ovid (see no. 389A).

Another specimen: (bronze) Berlin, Kunstgewerbemuseum.

Bibl.: Berlin, Kunstgewerbemuseum, *Katalog Europäisches Kunsthandwerk,* 1970, no. 52; Weber, no. 860, 8.

H. THISBE AT THE GRAVE OF NINUS (Met. 4, 91–100)

Thisbe, center, sits on the sarcophagus of Ninus, dipping water from a stream from which a lion drinks. Above, the moon surrounded by stars; in the left background, a forest; at the right, Thisbe flees to a cave.

Bronze, gilt, 72 x 128 mm.

1967.16.12

Bibl.: Weber, no. 860, 9.

I. PYRAMUS AND THISBE (Met. 4, 162–63)

The dead Pyramus lies under some trees at left, while Thisbe behind him throws herself on a sword with up-raised arms. At the right, a fountain capped with the figure of a nude putto; above, the moon; in the background at left, the fleeing lion.

Bronze, gilt, 72 x 128 mm.

1967.16.18

The composition derives from a woodcut by Virgil Solis in *Joh. Posthii Tetrasticha in Ovidii Metam,* Feyrabent, Frankfurt, 1563 (see 389A). Braun considered the relief to be a Nuremberg work of the period 1565 to 1570; Bange and Bernhart on the other hand believed it to come from an Augsburg atelier at the beginning of the seventeenth century. The connection of this relief with the other examples from this series was unknown to the above writers.

Another specimen: (bronze, gilt) Baltimore (Maryland), Gordon Collection. There also exist reduced aftercasts in bronze of a mounted specimen formerly in the Staatliche Museen, Berlin. One of these is also in the Molinari Collection, in which the lion has been turned into a hare (Acc. no. 1967.14.7; 69 x 124 mm.).

Bibl.: Braun, no. 58, pl. 13; Bange, *D.M.,* p. 136ff., no. 8320; Weber, no. 860, 10. Auction catalog: Molthein, no. 374.

J. PERSEUS FREES ANDROMEDA (Met. 4, 669–733)

To the left, Andromeda standing nude, chained to a boulder. The sea monster guarding her emerges from the ocean on the right, while Perseus flies down upon it, sword raised, mounted upon Pegasus.

Bronze, gilt, 115 x 79 mm.

1967.20.45

Related to the composition in the 1563 edition of Ovid illustrated by Virgil Solis (p. 57, see no. 389I above). A stone relief with the composition reversed is in the Museo Correr, Venice.

Another specimen: (bronze) Berlin, Staatliche Museen (lost).

Bibl.: Molinier, no. 612; Bange, *D.M.,* p. 119, no. 1497, pl. 22; Weber, no. 860, 11.

K. THE RAPE OF PROSERPINA (Met. 5, 405–24)

Pluto, with the resisting Proserpina in his arms, drives his chariot drawn by four horses towards Hades, the gates of which are guarded by a seated music-making figure. From behind the chariot emerge two nymphs, with Cyane hanging to a wheel to prevent the abduction. In the background, a cliff formation.

Bronze, gilt, 74 x 179 mm.

1967.16.22

Bibl.: Weber, no. 860, 12.

L. THE ABDUCTION OF CEPHALUS (Met. 7, 700–04)

To the left, in a chariot framed by clouds, Aurora embraces Cephalus who stands before her. He holds a dog by a leash and has a hunting horn at his belt. Two other dogs are seen at the left in front of the chariot and to the right before some trees.

Bronze, gilt, 74 x 128 mm.

1967.16.4

Another specimen: (bronze, gilt, cabinet-mounted) Bowdoin collections, Acc. no. 1972.70.

Bibl.: Weber, no. 860, 13.

M. THE CALYDONIAN BOAR HUNT (Met. 8, 379–423)

Meleager spears the boar which Atalanta has just shot in the mouth with an arrow. A dog springs at the boar from the right. Behind Meleager, a tree; in the background, a forested hill.

Bronze, 155 x 115 mm. Hole at top.

1967.14.5

This depiction appears to be a cut-down version of a larger composition, since here only the head of the boar is included on the left. The higher quality of the modeling raises the question whether this relief properly belongs to this series. Certainly, however, the model for the relief originated in the same workshop in which the other reliefs were executed.

Bibl.: Weber, no. 860, 14.

N. THE BIRTH OF ADONIS (Met. 10, 502–16)

At the left, Myrrha, whose transformation into a tree is almost complete. From her trunk Lucina, kneeling, draws the infant Adonis. She is assisted by three naiads, one seen at the right arriving with a large basin. In the background, a forested river landscape.

Bronze, gilt, 71 x 128 mm.

1967.16.19

Bibl.: Weber, no. 860, 15.

O. VENUS AND ADONIS (Met. 10, 555–59)

Venus and Adonis sit in an embrace under a tree, somewhat to the left. Venus is nude, only her lap is covered. Adonis is attired as a hunter, with a small hunting horn at his belt. To the left, a dog; to the right, two others.

Bronze, gilt, 73 x 128 mm.

1967.16.1

Other specimens: (bronze, gilt) Berlin, Kunstgewerbemuseum; Molinari Collection, Acc. no. 1967.16.14 (this specimen is an aftercast, cut off on the right, gilding badly worn, 70 x 110 mm.).

Bibl.: Berlin, Kunstgewerbemuseum, *Katalog Europäisches Kunsthandwerk,* 1970, no. 52; Weber, no. 860, 16.

P. THE CONTEST BETWEEN ATALANTA AND HIPPOMENES (?) (Met. 10, 600–80)

Under some trees at the right runs a youth dressed in a costume in the antique manner and with a dog on a leash. He looks toward a woman, left, who stands with a dog at her feet.

Bronze, gilt, 177 x 121 mm.

1967.14.6

Although this relief departs from the customary format, it undoubtedly belongs to the series. As the relief Aeneas Rescuing Anchises from Troy (Bowdoin collections; see no. 389A above) proves, the series does include plaquettes of various sizes.

Bibl.: Weber, no. 860, 17.

Q. THE DEATH OF ADONIS (Met. 10, 710–16)

Adonis lies prostrate on the ground, dressed in an antique manner and with a small hunting horn at his side, being mauled by a boar; on each side, trees.

Bronze, gilt, 73 x 128 mm.

1967.16.7

Another specimen: (bronze, gilt, cabinet-mounted) Bowdoin collections, Acc. no. 1972.70.

Bibl.: Weber, no. 860, 18.

R. KING MIDAS RECEIVES SILENUS (Met. 11, 90–96)

To the left, King Midas with his scepter, dressed in robes and a turban, hurries toward Silenus, accompanied by two men. The drunken Silenus sits upon an ass led by five Phrygian peasants, one with a banner, another with a lance and a third with a jug. In the clouds, a goddess.

Bronze, gilt, 71 x 127 mm.

1967.16.8

Bibl.: Weber, no. 860, 19.

S. THE CONTEST BETWEEN APOLLO AND PAN (Met. 11, 153–79)

Tmolus, appointed judge of the contest, sits upon a grassy hill with the contestants facing each other before him. At the left, Apollo with his lyre; behind him, a maiden with a flute. At the right, Pan playing his pipes; behind him stand two satyrs and King Midas, who has sprouted ass's ears.

Bronze, gilt, 72 x 127 mm. Probably after a reworked model.

1967.16.21

Bibl.: Weber, no. 860, 20.

T. BATTLE OF THE LAPITHS AND CENTAURS (Met. 12, 223–460)

In the center, a Lapith swinging his club at two Centaurs at the left. Behind him, a Lapith in chase after a Centaur who is carrying off a woman. On the right, two fallen figures, a man sitting, and two warriors running; in the background, two trees.

Bronze, gilt, aftercast(?), 71 x 124 mm.

1967.16.3

Bibl.: Weber, no. 860, 21.

U. VULCAN FORGING THE WEAPONS OF ACHILLES (Met. 12, 614)

Vulcan sits on a bench in his smithy near an anvil forging Achilles's armor. Tools and a cuirass lay on the floor. At the right, Thetis is waiting for them; left, a furnace with objects among the flames.

Bronze, gilt, 73 x 127 mm.

1967.16.16

Another specimen: (bronze, gilt) Düsseldorf, Kunstmuseum.

Bibl.: Weber, no. 860, 22.

V. THE ABDUCTION OF HELENA (?) (Met. 12, 5, and 13, 200)

Two armored men carry the resisting Helena(?) toward a boat. At the right, a fallen warrior lies in front of a palace-like building; left, a large sailboat upon the high seas.

Bronze, gilt, 73 x 127 mm.

1967.16.5

The main motif is reminiscent of an engraving by Marcantonio Raimondi (Bartsch 209) which has influenced at least one other plaquette composition (Weber, no. 493) and an engraved onyx in the Kunsthistorisches Museum, Vienna (cf. Tietze-Conrat, E., "Die Erfindung im Relief," *Jahrbuch der Kunsthistorischen Sammlungen* 35, Vienna 1919, p. 141).

Bibl.: Weber, no. 860, 23.

W. VERTUMNUS AND POMONA (Met. 14, 654–80)

At the left, Vertumnus in the guise of an old woman, with a belted gown and covered head, holds a cane in his right hand and hands a flower to Pomona with the other. Pomona sits with bared breasts on a grassy bank, flowers in her left hand. Between them lies a dog; at the right, a trellis; in the background, trees and a mountain range.

Bronze, gilt, 71 x 127 mm.

1967.16.20

Bibl.: Weber, no. 860,25.

X. VENUS ANOINTS AENEAS A GOD (Met. 14, 585–608)

Above left, Venus, in the company of other deities, asks Jupiter, enthroned in the clouds with the eagle at his side, to take Aeneas into Olympus. In the foreground below, Venus in a sea chariot pulled by two swans anoints Aeneas, giving him immortality. Left, a neriad with two fish; behind her a dolphin; right, a music-making neriad.

Bronze, gilt, 73 x 128 mm.

1967.16.23

Bibl.: Weber, no. 860, 26.

SOUTH GERMAN
First Quarter of the Seventeenth Century

390 ADORATION OF THE CHRIST CHILD

The Christ Child, Mary and Joseph before a palace-like building. On the left, a shepherd kneeling and several women, some carrying baskets on their heads. To the left, a woman leading a child; with them a flutist. To the right, an ox and a donkey; in front, a lamb. Above, an angel with a scroll (banderol). Around, narrow border.

Bronze, gilt, chased, dia. 96 mm.

1967.20.46

The example in the Molthein Collection, which Braun and Bernhart considered a South German work of the late sixteenth century, is probably a reworked aftercast, as the architecture is not clearly articulated. Without doubt, the composition comes from the sixteenth century, and reveals Italian influence.

Bibl.: Braun, no. 168, pl. 49; Weber, no. 858. Auction catalogs: Molthein, no. 347, pl. 32; Cahn, Frankfurt/M., Catalog 59, 14 March 1928, no. 2292, pl. 39 (bronze, gilt).

SOUTH GERMAN
End of the Seventeenth Century

391A THE GATHERING OF THE MANNA

In the center, Moses, horned, in a robe and cape, points with his left hand to the heavens, from which the manna rains, and with his right to the manna on the ground. To the left kneels a bearded man; to the right a woman gathers manna into her apron, a child behind her. Another child with a staff runs to the left in the background.

Bronze, oval, concave, 37 x 40 mm.

1967.11.14A

On the basis of the left-handed orientation of the figures, the composition is without doubt a reversed version of an engraving or another relief.

391B CHRIST APPEARING TO A SAINT

On the left, a female saint in a habit, rosary in her right hand, kneeling in front of an altar on which stands a monstrance and candles. She looks at a vision of Christ, who appears in clouds above the altar, pointing to his burning heart. In front of the saint, a book.

Bronze, oval, concave, 42 x 38 mm.

1967.11.14B

This plaquette, as the previous one (no. 391A), with which it is stylistically related, was probably intended as decoration for a liturgical object.

SOUTH GERMAN OR AUSTRIAN
ca. 1700

392 TRIUMPH OF A PRINCESS

An elaborately dressed woman is seated in a small chariot drawn to right by two putti, one of which holds a flying bird on a ribbon; two putti blowing trumpets and one grasping a garland which hangs from the chariot walk beside and behind her. Above fly two putti, one carrying flowers, the other holding a crown over the woman's head. At left, a tree. Stippled background.

Bronze, 45 x 70 mm., rounded corners.

1967.20.78

This relief most probably represents the triumph of an historical personage. Such mythological glorifications are in accord with baroque cultural attitudes toward the ruling class. Possibly the relief originally served as the lid of a presentation box which, from the time of Louis XIV onwards, became the most favored mark of royal esteem. "Ambassadors, diplomats and members of the court were singled out by the presentation of these little cases, generally bearing the portrait of a sovereign. Their value varied according to the person being honored.... Royal betrothals were sealed with the exchange of such boxes...." (*Reallexikon zur Deutschen Kunstgeschichte* 4, Stuttgart 1958, col. 336.) The place of origin of this plaquette can possibly be more precisely ascertained upon the identification of the person it depicts.

GERMAN(?)
ca. 1700

393 THE REPENTANT MAGDALENE

The weeping Magdalene kneels in front of a table on which are books, a crucifix, a skull, a rosary and a jug, drying her eyes with a cloth. Over her, sunbeams break through the clouds. She is barefoot, wearing a full robe, a richly embroidered cape and a veil. Under the table, an open coffer with two necklaces; right, a decorated curtain.

Bronze, gilt, oval, 118 x 96 mm.

1967.20.83

As indicated by the groove around the edge of the plaquette, it was intended as a decorative applique.

FLEMISH OR GERMAN
Last Third of the Sixteenth Century

394 Series: EVENTS FROM THE OLD TESTAMENT
A. CAIN KILLING ABEL (Gen. 4:4–8)

In the foreground Cain has thrown Abel to the ground, grasps his garment and is about to strike him with the jaw-bone of an ass. In the background the two brothers kneel before their respective altars, Abel's burning at left, Cain's smoking at right. Landscape with rocks and trees behind; cartouche work at the borders.

Bronze, trapezoidal, 52 x 110 mm. Aftercast.

1967.14.1

Bibl.: Weber, no. 717,1.

B. JOSEPH BEING PULLED FROM THE WELL AND SOLD (Gen. 37:26–28)

Two of his brothers pull Joseph, seen from behind, out of a well with ropes. Two Midianites and two others stand behind at left. Trees at the sides and in background. Cartouche work at the borders.

Bronze, trapezoidal, 60 x 85 mm. Reworked aftercast.

1967.14.2

These works may be castings from plate rims. Besides these two, there exist scenes of Eleazer and Rebecca at the Well (bronze, 59 x 17 mm.; Parpart, no. 724, pl. 15) and Isaac Blessing Jacob (bronze, 60 x 83 mm.; *Morgenroth*, no. 399, pl. 27). The belief of Middeldorf and Goetz that the Isaac plaquette is "similar to a series from the Old Testament" (see Bange, *D.M.*, p. 114, nos. 5839–44, pl. 23) cannot be accepted.

Another specimen: New York, Coll. Michael Hall, Esq.

Bibl.: Weber, no. 717,3.

NETHERLANDISH
Last Quarter of the Sixteenth Century

Series: TRIUMPHAL PROCESSIONS OF HUMAN FORTUNES

395 TRIUMPH OF HUMILITY

On a cart drawn to the left by two horses (Modesty and Mansuetudo) and directed by an old man with a stick

(Methus), Humility sits, leaning forward, holding a split heart in her outstretched right hand and a winnowing shovel in her left. In front of the wagon walk Charity with three children and Faith with crossed arms, a cross in her right hand and a goblet with the Host in her left. Behind the horse walks Hope, shouldering an anchor on her right and holding a parrot in her left hand. A raised ground line rounded at both ends suggests an oval format.

Bronze, 63 x 118 mm.

1967.11.23

After an engraving in the series "Circulus Vicissitudines Rerum Humanorum" by Hieronymus Cock, after Martin van Heemskerk (Hollstein, *Dutch and Flemish Engravings, Etchings, and Woodcuts* 8, nos. 128–35). The engraving "Invidia" in that series is dated 1564, providing a "terminus post quem" for this series. Thirteen plaquettes from this series are now known. (Concerning these critical problems, see Weber, no. 678.) Other specimens in this series are most numerous.

Bibl.: Molinier, no. 663; Jacobsen, E., "Plaketten im Museo Correr zu Venedig," *Repertorium für Kunstwissenschaft* 16 (1893), p. 73; Leitschuh, no. 98, pl. 14 and p. 23, note 88; Braun, no. 108, pl. 23; Planiscig-*Este,* no. 460; Bange, *D.M.,* p. 133, no. 1489, pl. 30; S. Ricci, *Gustave Dreyfus Collection—Renaissance Reliefs and Plaquettes,* no. 427; *Morgenroth,* no. 405; Cott, *Renaissance Bronzes, Statuettes, Reliefs and Plaquettes, Medals and Coins from the Kress Collection,* National Gallery of Art, Washington 1951, p. 159; Pope-Hennessy, no. 454, fig. 460; *Harvard,* no. 46, pl. 38; Pechstein, no. 251; Weber, no. 678,6. Auction catalogs: Bardini, pl. 10, 179; Thewalt Collection, Lempertz, Cologne, 4–14 November 1903, no. 1188; Frank Coll., Cubasch, Vienna, 18 January 1904, no. 872; Gutekunst Coll., Hirsch, Munich, 7–8 November 1910, no. 377; Lanna Coll. II, Lepke, Berlin, 21–23 March 1911, no. 327, pl. 23; Faure Coll., Hamburger, Frankfurt/M., 22–23 September 1913, no. 723, pl. 22; Heinrici, no. 165, pl. 17; Molthein, no. 533; Gaettens Coll., Gaettens, Heidelberg, 1 April 1966, no. 152, pl. 19.

NETHERLANDISH OR SOUTH GERMAN(?)
Last Quarter of the Sixteenth Century

396 SAINT LUKE

The evangelist sits in a rocky landscape on the bull and

holds in his right hand an inkwell and a tablet on which he is writing. At left a wall and a bush; at right a tree.

Bronze, aftercast, dia. 77 mm. Hole at top. A smooth frame of the original was incompletely erased and is visible in the field.

1967.20.65

This plaquette is part of a series which exists with both smooth and pearled edges. Braun (nos. 146–49) thinks it a South German (possibly Nuremberg) work of the end of the sixteenth century, while Bange (nos. 980–82, pl. 82) and after him Bernhart (Molthein, nos. 118–21) consider the series Italian. The present author (Weber, "Fragen zum Oeuvre des Meister H. G.," p. 142ff.) surmises that the series was reproduced in a variety of different workshops. But she believes that its origin is in a South German workshop from the following of the Master H. G. or from a South Netherlandish shop from the Circle of the Master to whom she also attributes a Judgment of Solomon in the British Museum, London, among others.

Other specimens: (lead) London, British Museum; (bronze) Berlin, Staatliche Museen; Kassel, Staatliche Kunstsammlungen; Oxford, Ashmolean Museum (complete series).

Bibl.: Braun, no. 149, pl. 42; Bange, no. 982, pl. 82; I. Weber, "Fragen zum Oeuvre des Meister H. G.," *Münchner Jahrbuch der bildenden Kunst,* 3rd Ser., 22 (1971), pp. 133–45; Weber, no. 708,3. Auction catalog: Molthein, no. 121.

MONOGRAMMIST AVB
(Arent van Bolten)
(1573–ca. 1625)
First Quarter of the Seventeenth Century

The Monogrammist AVB is probably identical with Arent van Bolten, also called Arent van Bolten van Swol, who was born 1573 in Zwolle and died in the same place about 1625. He was jurist(?), model maker, and silversmith.

Series: THE PASSION OF CHRIST

397 CHRIST ON GETHSEMANE

Christ in prayer before altar-like stone, covered with a cloth on which are an open book and a chalice. Around, boulders and trees. Above, an angel holding a cross. In the foreground, a sleeping apostle; two others on the left, behind a boulder.

Bronze, gilt, 89 x 64 mm. Lower left corner broken off; hole at top.

1967.11.15

Four scenes are known from this series. The Lamentation (cf. no. 380) included by Frederiks (no. 117d) probably does not belong to the group.

Another specimen: (bronze) Cologne, Kunstgewerbemuseum.

Bibl.: Rudolf Verres, "Der Meister AV, ein holländischer Goldschmied des 17. Jahrhunderts," *Pantheon* 4 (1929), 413–16; Th. M. Duyvené de Wit-Klinkhamer, "Werk van den Zilversmid A. V. B.," *Oud-Holland* 63 (1948), p. 87; J. W. Frederiks, *Dutch Silver* I, The Hague, 1952, p. 189ff., no. 117, with illustrations; Weber, no. 954,1.

NETHERLANDISH
First Half of the Seventeenth Century

398 SCENE AT AN INN

At the right in front of a ladder, three men are seated at a table, under which a dog chews a bone. A fourth man stands behind, and a child stands at the left of the table drinking from a bowl. One of the seated men turns and talks to two older women on the left, one of whom holds an infant. Another child stands at the far left holding a walking stick. Interior of a rustic inn with rough floor. Raised border.

Bronze, 67 x 101 mm. Based probably on an oval or square precursor, as indicated by the unworked corners.

1967.14.10

This relief was probably thought of as a pendant to the Selling of Indulgences plaquette (Bange, *D.M.*, p. 131, no. 7965, pl. 29).

Bibl.: Weber, no. 1007,2. Auction catalog: Parpart, no. 748, pl. 17.

NETHERLANDISH(?)
ca. 1600

399 SCENE ON THE ROAD TO CALVARY (not illustrated)

Christ fallen to the ground under the cross, supporting himself on a large stone with his right hand. Saint

Veronica kneels in front of him with a kerchief. One soldier pulls at Christ's bonds, another strikes him. Following the group, a troop of soldiers with lances and a flag which, led by a mounted officer, appears from behind a hill.

Lead, 96 x 69 mm. Weak cast, some damage; several holes.

1967.14.15

Another specimen: (bronze) Cambridge (Mass.), Busch-Reisinger Museum (gilt).

Bibl.: Harvard, no. 41 (as South German, ca. 1550–75); Weber, no. 693.

FLEMISH(?)

400 BACCHANAL SCENE, ca. 1600

A nude, plump Bacchus sits above a group of five putti, who are making a goat jump through a hoop. He holds a bunch of grapes in his left hand and on his right arm a bowl, into which a satyr is pouring wine. Around this group are six satyrs in the background, one of whom is playing on a double flute (aulos). At the right, an almost nude woman holds a ring with both hands.

Bronze, black coating, dia. 131 mm. This cast is modeled after a damaged or modified cast, or replica (compare the arm of Bacchus or the arm of the putto front right, or the other limbs). Casting faults at lower right.

1967.20.62

There is a pendant to this relief which Pechstein (no. 266) calls the Wedding of Bacchus and Ariadne. There is no agreement concerning the attribution of the reliefs. Middeldorf and Goetz, and afterwards R. P. Ciardi, speak of an Italian master of the beginning of the seventeenth century. On the other hand, it is reported in the *Catalogue* of the Rijksmuseum in Amsterdam that the work is based on a drawing in the Albertina in Vienna, presumably by an unknown South Netherlandish master in the sixteenth century. Therefore the plaquette is attributed to a South Netherlandish master of the first quarter of the seventeenth century. In the auction catalog of the Gaettens Collection the plaquette is maintained to be a South German work made in the second half of the sixteenth century. Pechstein has attributed both reliefs to a "Netherlandish Romanist" of the end of the sixteenth century. An attribution to a South Netherlandish artist of ca. 1600 is the most credible.

Other specimens: (lead) Amsterdam, Rijksmuseum;

Paris, Bibliotheque Nationale, Cabinet des Medailles (later cast); (bronze) Berlin, Kunstgewerbemuseum; Gazzada, Cagnola Collection (two casts); New York, Coll. Michael Hall, Esq.; Opava (Czechoslovakia) Museum; Santa Barbara, University Art Gallery, Morgenroth Collection.

Bibl.: Morgenroth, no. 343; Amsterdam, Catalogus van Goud en Zilverwerken, Rijksmuseum, 1952, no. 464; R. P. Ciardi, *La Raccolta Cagnola dipinti e sculture,* 1965, no. 219; Pechstein, no. 267; Weber, no. 714, 2. Auction catalogs: Museo de la famille de Guide di Faenza, Sangiorgi, Rome, 21–27 April 1902, no. 364 (the Morgenroth specimen); Gaettens Collection, Gaettens, Heidelberg, 1 April 1966, no. 144 (the Berlin, Kunstgewerbemuseum specimen).

FLEMISH(?)
First Half of the Seventeenth Century

401 THE REPENTANT MAGDALENE

In front of a large tree, Mary Magdalene, wearing a cloak and dress and with dishevelled hair, kneels on a rock, looking upward. She holds an open book on her left arm; her right arm is on her breast. To the right a cross, pot, and skull. In the upper left corner, a vision of the Assumption of the Virgin surrounded by three angels in clouds.

Bronze, chased, a hole at top and screw through the right arm of the saint, 173 x 132 mm.

1967.17.3

The handling of the clothing and the tree are characteristic of Netherlandish work of the first half of the seventeenth century. The representation of the saint, on the other hand, is influenced by Italian works, so the work may be by a Flemish artist under the strong influence of Italian art.

Another specimen: art dealer, Rome, 1969 (the letters MAV are inscribed on the reverse of this specimen).

Bibl.: Weber, no. 1024.

FLEMISH OR NETHERLANDISH(?)
First Half of the Seventeenth Century

402 THE REPENTANT MAGDALENE

The saint sits among overgrown boulders, facing right. Her bosom is covered by the locks of her hair and her lap is covered with a robe. She holds a crucifix in her left hand and meditates upon a skull lying upon her knee. At the left, an ointment jar.

Bronze 147 x 120 mm.

1967.11.25

Italian influence is obvious.

Another specimen: New York, Coll. Michael Hall, Esq.

Bibl.: Weber, no. 1029.

NETHERLANDISH(?)
Second Quarter of the Seventeenth Century

403 MOSES AND THE BRAZEN SERPENT

In the middle stands the cross with the serpent. To the right, Moses gestures toward it with both arms while looking at a figure lying on the ground. To the left, a woman sits under a tree with right arm outstretched looking at the prophet; behind her another woman looks at the serpent. On the far right, a man's figure seen from the rear. Ridged frame.

Bronze, gilt, aftercast(?), oval, 106 x 90 mm. Four holes in frame.

1967.20.64

There exists a pendant to this plaquette depicting the Original Sin. A set in lead is in Nuremberg, the Germanische Nationalmuseum. In style they appear to be Netherlandish work done under Italian influence.

Bibl.: Weber, no. 1026, 2.

FLEMISH OR SOUTH GERMAN
Beginning of the Seventeenth Century

404A THE PENITENT SAINT PETER

Peter, wringing his hands in anguish, sits before a large boulder, while above him the cock crows. Behind him, a book leans against the rock; nearby hang the keys.

Bronze, rounded top, 144 x 100 mm. Hole at top.

1967.17.7

Italian influence can be noted.

Another specimen: London, Victoria and Albert Museum.

Bibl.: Braun, no. 199, pl. 65; Weber, no. 1023. Auction catalog: Molthein, no. 379, pl. 33.

404B THE PENITENT SAINT PETER

Same composition as no. 404A above.

Bronze aftercast, 145 x 117 mm. (without frame). Set into bronze frame.

1967.17.8

FLEMISH OR PRAGUE(?)
First Quarter of the Seventeenth Century

405 THE MOCKING OF CHRIST

To the right Christ sits wearing the mantle and carrying the scepter of his mocking. Four soldiers put the crown of thorns on his head with staves; a fifth kneels before him making a fist with his thumb between two fingers. At the left a bearded man with a staff converses with a beardless man who points to Christ. Further left, weapons, a shield, and helmet lean against a wall below a curtain. Behind, a group of onlookers standing next to a city wall on the right. Distant landscape; patterned floor.

Gilt bronze, bottom border intended for mounting, 128 x 160 mm.

1967.11.27

The influence of Giovanni da Bologna and Adriaen de Vries indicates that this work is by a Netherlandish artist working perhaps in Prague.

Bibl.: Weber, no. 980.

FLEMISH
Middle of the Seventeenth Century

406 SATYR AND PUTTI MILKING A GOAT

A satyr and two putti hold a goat in a forest setting, while a third putto milks it and another stands by. On the left a putto beating a drum, another blows a curved "lituus" or ram's horn.

Bronze, dark patina, aftercast, 68 x 94 mm.

1967.14.17

In composition and representation this relief is just like an ivory relief in the Victoria and Albert Museum, London (Inv. no. 1061), which is dependent on a drawing by Francois du Quesnoy, "Six Infants Playing with a Goat," in Vienna, the Albertina (Inv. no. 8446; see M. Fransolet, *Francois du Quesnoy sculpteur d'Urbain VIII, 1597–1643*, Brussels 1942, pl. 4,f.).

Another specimen: Santa Barbara, University Art Gallery, Morgenroth Collection.

Bibl.: Morgenroth, no. 427; Weber, no. 1016. Auction catalogs: Molthein, no. 556 (as French, middle of the sixteenth century); Cahn, Frankfurt/M., Catalog 59, 14 March 1928, no. 2269, pl. 34.

NETHERLANDISH, FLEMISH, OR FRENCH
End of the Seventeenth Century

Series: MYTHOLOGICAL LOVERS

407 HERCULES AND OMPHALE

The nude couple sit under a large tree in which three *amoretti* play. Hercules, with a distaff and spindle, leans toward Omphale, who holds a distaff in her left hand.

Bronze, dark patina, 84 x 106 mm. Hole at top.

1967.14.13

This series includes five representations of mythological lovers: Luna and Endymion, Hercules and Omphale, Mars and Venus, Jupiter and Io, and Venus and Adonis.

Other specimens: (bronze) Basel, Historisches Museum; Munich, Bayerisches Nationalmuseum; Vienna, Kunsthistorisches Museum.

Bibl.: Braun, E. W., *Die Bronzen der Sammlung Guido von Rho in Wien,* Vienna 1908, pl. 49,f.; Planiscig-*Este,* no. 436, pl. 27. Auction catalogs: Dupriez, Brussels, Catalog 112, 7 April 1913, no. 2977a; Dorotheum, Vienna, Catalog 339, 22–24 March 1923, pl. 48.

FLEMISH(?)
End of the Seventeenth Century(?)

408 BOAR ATTACKED BY DOGS

Running to the right, a wild boar is caught by three dogs; one attacks from the front, another behind, and the third atop the boar. Trees at each side.

Bronze, dark patina, oval, 51 x 70 mm.

1967.14.16

The ornamental treatment of the animals and trees is particularly noteworthy. From this treatment as well as the modeling of the figures the influence of an antique intaglio can be inferred, making dating and classification more difficult.

FLEMISH
Late Eighteenth Century

409 PUTTI WITH GOATS

In a field, before a large tree, a putto runs to the left with a kid in his arms, followed by a he-goat and another putto carrying a basket. Below, ground indicated by a strip. Ring at top.

Lead, traces of gilding, 82 x 64 mm.

1967.14.18

SPANISH
ca. 1600

410 MAN OF SORROWS

Christ in a loincloth is depicted in a frontal, three-quarter length pose with head bowed to the left. His hands are bound with a rope passed around his neck. Against his left arm is the mock scepter. Molded border with ring at top.

Bronze, traces of gilt and polychromy, 102 x 71 mm.

1967.18.6

Other specimens: (bronze) Munich, private collection; Stuttgart, Württembergisches Landesmuseum; (gilt, oval) Munich, Bayerisches Nationalmuseum; Paris, Musée Cluny.

Bibl.: Braun-*Span.,* p. 20, no. 18; Weber, no. 1039. Auction catalogs: Löbbecke, no. 849, pl. 40; Rosenheim, no. 747, pl. 34; Molthein, no. 175, pl. 12 (gilt).

SPANISH

411A THE PENITENT SAINT PETER, ca. 1600(?)

Saint Peter, depicted three-quarter length, wearing a belted garment and a cloak, clasps his hands and looks upward. In front and at right, a rock on which grows a grape vine. Two keys lie on the rock. At left, a cock crows on a column which has a line tied around it. Molded border.

Bronze, 103 x 71 mm. Ring at top broken off.

1967.18.5

Pechstein (nos. 259, 260) points to a related composition on an alabaster relief from Mecheln of the beginning of the seventeenth century and believes this plaquette, as well as no. 410 and the series no. 412 to be Netherlandish works of the second half of the sixteenth century.

Exactly those close ties demonstrated by Pechstein between Flanders and Spain in the sixteenth and seventeenth centuries could also speak for the works being Spanish. An Italian influence is discernible, but comparable Netherlandish works are missing. The question of dating remains open. Aftercasts exist from well into the twentieth century; all are bronze, some gilt.

Bibl.: Braun-*Span.,* p. 17, no. 5; Imbert, no. 215, pl. 45,1; Middeldorf-Imbert, p. 153 (under nos. 37–39); *Salton,* no. 185; Weber, no. 1043. Auction catalogs: Löbbecke, no. 854, pl. 41; Gutekunst Coll., Hirsch, Munich, 8 November 1910, no. 406; Molthein, no. 166, pl. 12; Basel, 1934, no. 494, pl. 16.

SPANISH
Seventeenth Century

411B THE PENITENT SAINT PETER

Same composition as the above (no. 411A), though in decorated frame with angels' heads in the corners. At top, incised: C A R R E R A .

Bronze, traces of gilding, 123 x 101 mm. The side border of the original plaquette still visible within the frame.

1967.18.4

It is uncertain to whom the inscription refers. For example, in the sixteenth and seventeenth centuries a family of painters named Carrera is documented in Italy and Spain (see Thieme-Becker 6, p. 69) and a seal engraver named Carrere was active in France in the 1590s (see Forrer 1, p. 215).

SPANISH(?)
Beginning of the Seventeenth Century

412 Series: THE SAINTS

A. SAINT SEBASTIAN

The saint stands, arms bound to a tree, pierced by seven arrows. To either side lie his armor and helmet; in the background, leafy trees.

Bronze, 102 x 71 mm. Molded border with ring at top.

1967.18.9

This relief and the four which follow belong to a series which consisted of thirteen or more plaquettes. Braun (*Span.,* p. 15ff.) also associated some plaquettes depicting events from the life of Christ and other depictions of saints (cf. nos. 410, 411) with this series, but it seems likely that actually two distinct series and some individual representations, which are related only indirectly to our group, are involved. Those plaquettes which show the entire figure of the saint, apart from the three-quarter length depiction of Saint Francis, are stylistically similar and can be differentiated from the heterogeneous reliefs showing the saints in half figure. These latter appear to be based on a variety of sources and modeled by more than one artist. The similarity of the framing of all the examples suggests the bringing together of various models into one workshop. Braun believed that the plaquettes were Spanish, referring to their common appearance in Spain and pointing out the initials SI (for San Jeronimo) on the plaquette of Saint Jerome. He dated one example (in the Museo Provincial de Antiquedales at Barcelona), a plaster cast, to the end of the sixteenth century. By extension the whole series can be so dated. Braun pointed out, however, that the plaquettes were commonly aftercast, so that a secure dating of an individual example is often impossible. Despite Italian influences that can be noted on the plaquettes, we concur with Braun's theory concerning their origin. It can be further supported by reference to the representation of two saints from Cordoba, Acisclus and Victoria (no. 412C). The signature G. L. on this plaquette is unknown. Unknown to Braun were the Adoration of the Kings (Historisches Museum, Basel) and the Saint Jerome (Cologne, Kunstgewerbemuseum), both marked RS on their hangers. Perhaps the marks refer to the caster. Other specimens in numerous collections.

Bibl.: Braun-*Span.*, p. 17, no. 4; Bange, no. 1055, pl. 85; *Morgenroth*, no. 354; Imbert, no. 217, pl. 45,3; Weber, no. 1041,1. Auction catalogs: Bardini, pl. 9,158; Heinrici, no. 114, pl. 15; Rosenheim, no. 745, pl. 34.

B. SAINT JEROME

The saint kneels, wearing a cloak and halo, holding a stone in his right hand, and looking toward a crucifix in his left. Clouds surround the cross. On a rock at the right, a skull and open book inscribed S I. Below, a lion's head. At the left, a tree, from which hangs the saint's hat.

Bronze, gilt, 103 x 72 mm. Molded border with ring at top.

1967.18.1

E. W. Braun owned a lead version painted in oils, the only lead specimen in a series known otherwise only in bronze. Other specimens in bronze are numerous.

Bibl.: Braun-*Span.*, p. 18, no. 6; Bange, no. 1054, pl. 85; *Morgenroth*, no. 353, pl. 25; Imbert, no. 216, pl. 45;

Weber, no. 1041,2. Auction catalogs: Bardini, pl. 10,310; Molthein, no. 167, pl. 12; Löbbecke Collection, Schulman, Amsterdam, 7 June 1929, no. 398, pl. 29.

C. SAINTS ACISCLUS AND VICTORIA (?)

The two saints stand on a patterned floor with a step behind them and to the left. Heavily draped and wearing laurel crowns and halos, each holds a palm in his right hand and a book in his left, Victoria on the left and Acisclus on the right. Between them above, rays breaking through clouds.

Bronze, gilt, chased, 102 x 71 mm. Molded border with ring at top.

1967.18.7

The initials G. L., which appear on the steps in the specimen presently in Basel at the Historisches Museum, are missing here. Braun believed that the figures were of two male saints, namely Gervasius and Protasius. Based on the attributes, the two would have to be the brother and sister, Acisclus and Victoria, the patron saints of Cordoba, which would indicate a Spanish origin (cf. the sculptures of the saints in the middle field of the main altar of the Church of Lanciego: Georg Weise, *Die Plastik der Renaissance und des Frühbarock im nördlichen Spanien*, II, Tübingen 1959, pp. 56–60, pl. 116).

Bibl.: Braun-*Span.*, p. 18, no. 9, pl. 6,1; Weber, no. 1043,3.

D. THE REPENTANT MAGDALENE

The saint sits in a landscape with her head bowed toward a crucifix held in both hands. On the right, an ointment jar stands near a tree stump upon which is a skull. A scourge hangs from a nearby bough. In the left background, buildings. Molded border with ring at top.

Bronze, 100 x 70 mm.

1967.18.2

This plaquette is known only in bronze examples. It belongs to the series of saints even though the saint is here depicted as a three-quarter seated figure. There is another specimen in the Molinari Collection, perhaps a later cast (Acc. no. 1967.18.3, bronze, 103 x 70 mm.).

Other specimens: Basel, Historisches Museum (gilt); Berlin, Staatliche Museen, Skulpturensammlung; London, British Museum; New York, Coll. Michael Hall, Esq.; New York, Metropolitan Museum; Paris, Musée Cluny (enameled).

Bibl.: Braun-*Span.,* p. 20, no. 16, pl. 4,4; Bange, no. 1060, pl. 85; Houston, no. 434; Weber, no. 1041,4. Auction catalog: Molthein, no. 173, pl. 12.

E. SAINT FRANCIS OF ASSISI

The saint, depicted three-quarter length, stands behind rocks with arms crossed on his breast, praying before a crucifix on rocks at left. He has a pointed beard and wears a monk's habit, with bare head. At the foot of the cross, a skull, an open book and a scourge.

Bronze, 100 x 71 mm. Molded border with ring at top.

Other specimens: London, British Museum; London, Victoria and Albert Museum; Paris, Louvre.

Bibl.: Braun-*Span.,* p. 20, no. 17; Weber, no. 1041,9. Auction catalog: Molthein, no. 174.

SPANISH
ca. 1600(?)

413 ADORATION OF THE CHRIST CHILD

On a mound, the infant Christ in swaddling clothes. Behind, Mary as *regina coeli* with folded hands. On the left, an old man, hat hanging behind him, holding his beard; on the right, a praying woman with veiled head. In the background, a landscape. Below, framed: ECCE · TV · PVLCHER · ES · DILEGETE · MI · ET | DECOR9 · LECIVT9 · NOSTER · FLORID · G[----].

Bronze, traces of gilding, 90 x 72 mm. Hole at top.

1967.17.1

Bibl.: Weber, no. 1046.

SPANISH(?)
First Half of the Seventeenth Century

414 THE REPENTANT MAGDALENE

The Magdalene with flowing hair, halo and richly decorated mantle, reading a book. On the left, a chalice and crucifix beneath clouds; on the right, a skull; behind at right, clouds and tree.

Bronze, gilt, chased, 108 x 150 mm.

1967.17.4

The stylistic origins of the relief are debatable. The handling of the clouds and the damask patterning of the clothing also make a South German origin possible.

415 THE ADORATION OF THE SHEPHERDS

In an open area with architectural elements around it, the manger with the Christ Child. On the left kneels Mary; behind the crib, a praying angel. On the right, two bareheaded shepherds, one holds a staff and his hat. Behind the shepherds, Joseph; nearby, an ox and a donkey. From the right a shepherd enters doffing his cap.

Bronze, gilt, chased, 94 x 90 mm. Hole at top.

1967.17.5

Provincial work, the attribution of which remains problematic.

SPANISH(?)
Seventeenth Century(?)

416 THE FLAGELLATION

Christ, bound to a half-column, is being whipped by three men. At the left, a fourth man bends to tie a bundle of scourges. At the sides and on a balcony, eleven spectators. Among these at the left probably stands the High Priest. At the right a man in a feathered headdress reaches out to Christ. Architectural setting with patterned floor.

Copper, gilt, chased, 185 x 148 mm.

1967.12

This composition is based on the same work as no. 360, although a few figures are added and some details changed. It is unclear, for example, why the man to the right wears a feathered headdress. Several details, for instance the headdress, make it possible that the relief was done in Spain. A silver gilt specimen at an art dealer's in Milan has different details and has been reworked by a goldsmith.

Bibl.: Weber, no. 1037.

FRENCH(?)
Beginning of the Seventeenth Century

417 THE CONVERSION OF SAINT PAUL

Paul is shown in form-fitting armor and cape, fallen onto rocky ground from his charger, seen behind him. In his right hand he holds a sword; his left arm is raised toward the figure of Christ, appearing in a radiant cloud nimbus with outstretched arms. To the right, a soldier seen from the rear holds both hands over his head. Behind him, seven mounted soldiers flee to the left; two look back over their shoulders, a third holds a shield over his head, and a fourth grips a lance with both hands. Two riders gallop to the right.

Bronze, oval, traces of gilt, 152 x 199 mm. Hole at top.

1967.20.61

Other specimens: (bronze) Düsseldorf, Kunstmuseum; Paris, Art Market; Würzburg, Art Market.

Bibl.: Weber, no. 1033. Auction catalogs: Dorotheum, Vienna, Catalog 339, 22–24 March 1923, no. 334, pl. 52; Dorotheum, Catalog 344, 2, 28 November 1923, no. 92, pl. 12.

FRENCH(?)
Middle of the Eighteenth Century

418 THE EDUCATION OF AMOR

The picture surface is divided into different sized fields by rocaille and flower tendrils. In the central field sit Venus, Amor, who is reading a book, and Mercury. At right, two putti with flower basket and garlands.

Bronze, 53 x 72 mm.

1967.20.97

FRENCH(?)
Second Half of the Eighteenth Century

419 MADONNA AND CHILD WITH THE INFANT SAINT JOHN

Mary, in belted gown, veil and sandals, seated on the grass with the infant Christ on her lap. To the left, Saint John kneeling with fruit in his cape, for which the Christ Child reaches. Mary holds some in her hands. The background is punched. Ring at top.

Bronze, oval, 107 x 79 mm.

1967.20.56

FRENCH(?)
End of the Eighteenth Century

420 A SATYR UNVEILING A SLEEPING BACCHANTE

At the right, on a stylized flowery hillock, lies a sleeping bacchante, a veil half-covering her body. To the right sits a goat-footed satyr crowned with vine leaves; he lifts one end of the veil. At his feet are bunches of grapes, a

bowl and an overturned vessel; at the feet of the bacchante, grapes and a tambourine.

Bronze, 41 x 77 mm.

1967.20.96

The relief shows Italian influence, but is possibly a French work.

JEAN PIERRE MONTAGNY
(1789–1862)

Montagny was born 31 July 1789, in Saint Etienne, the son of the engraver Clément Montagny the Elder. He died blind in 1862 in Belleville. He was a medalist, stamp cutter, and sculptor, and learned from his father, his uncle Fleury Montagny, and from Cartelliers.

421A PUTTO WITH A SEA MONSTER, 1834

A putto, nude except for a piece of drapery, holding a trident in his right hand and part of his drape in his left, lies upon a sea monster which swims to the left. Below, 1834 1 MONTAGNY FECIT. Raised border.

Bronze, 51 x 94 mm.

1967.31.1

Another specimen: (bronze) Belluno, Museo Civico.

421B PUTTO WITH A SEA MONSTER, 1834

A putto, nude except for a narrow piece of drapery, holding an oar in his right hand, lies upon a sea monster which swims to the right. Below, 1834 MONTAGNY FECIT. Raised border.

Bronze, 51 x 94 mm.

1967.31.2

Other specimens: (bronze) Berlin, Staatliche Museen; Belluno, Museo Civico.

Bibl.: Bange, no. 958, pl. 79 (as Italian, middle of the sixteenth century).

BOHEMIAN OR HUNGARIAN
Beginning of the Seventeenth Century

422 THE LAST SUPPER

Christ, with radiant halo and making a gesture of blessing, sits at the Passover table with six apostles ranged on each side. Several of the apostles wear damask robes. John, to the right of Christ, lays his head on the Saviour's breast; Peter, on the left, looks questioningly at the others; Judas, in the foreground, grasps the goblet. The floor is paved and the architecture hinted at by fluted lines, the walls and background enlivened by punching.

Bronze, gilt, chased, 79 x 159 mm.

1967.17.2

This representation varies slightly from a widespread type. The Bible passage represented is not clearly recognizable, namely that on the one hand Christ has blessed the bread and wine, and on the other hand, Judas is marked as the betrayer, since the latter at the same time grasps the goblet (I Cor. 11:23–26). This unclear reference and the slightly different conformation, for example, in the background, denote a provincial workshop. It is influenced by Augsburg works, for parts of the wall and surfaces are enlivened by punching. One may agree with the oral reference of P. Grotemeyer to a localization in Bohemia or Hungary.

Other specimens: New York, Coll. Michael Hall, Esq.; Washington, National Gallery of Art, Widener Collection.

Bibl.: Weber, no. 1050.

UNKNOWN
Seventeenth Century (?)

423 JOSEPH'S DREAM

A clothed angel with halo flies down from the left to Joseph, who sleeps at his workbench, his tools to the left, in a room with a cobbled floor. On the right, three steps lead up to another room in which Mary kneels at a prie-dieu.

Bronze, 48 x 66 mm.

1967.20.80

We are in doubt that this plaquette is a German work of the seventeenth century, as Middeldorf and Goetz think.

Other specimen: (bronze) Santa Barbara, University Art Gallery, Morgenroth Collection.

Bibl.: Morgenroth, no. 416, pl. 28; Weber, no. 903.

UNKNOWN
End of the Seventeenth Century or Later

424 THE REPENTANT MAGDALENE

Dressed in a belted robe and cape, a flower garland in her loosened hair, the Magdalene is seen beside a prayer stand. On an open book upon the stand is a skull which she holds with her left hand; in her right hand, a crucifix. Around her, a sort of cloud nimbus with blossoms. Narrow frame.

Copper, repoussé or molded, gilt, 110 x 95 mm. Holes at top right and bottom.

1967.17.6

It is unusual to see the Magdalene depicted with a flower garland in her hair and a cloud nimbus (gloriole) with blossoms. This iconography may be related to a local tradition, which, when determined, would assist in the proper attribution to the workshop, which by the quality of its work, must be provincial.

UNKNOWN
ca. 1800

425 THE RECRUITMENT—THEATER SCENE(?)

At left stands a young man by a Gothic-like church portal(?). His tricorne in his right hand, he raises his arms with a theatrical complaining gesture. Near him kneels a girl with clasped hands, supported by a man. A woman with half-exposed breast and a helmet with a plume approaches. At her right a soldier who points to a list (presumably at the signature of the plaintiff on the recruiting list), discusses with a man wearing a long wig (perhaps an advocate), in front of a classicistic building.

Bronze, 69 x 180 mm. Hole at top.

1967.20.99

UNKNOWN
Eighteenth Century or Later

426 CERES

Ceres, wearing a belted cloak and fluttering scapulary, strides to the right across a field. She carries a sheaf of wheat in her left hand and a bowl in her right. To the right, trees; to the left, a wheatfield and trees. Landscape with two small hills in the background.

Bronze, dia. 140 mm. Below, a narrow border, probably intended for placement in furniture or similar object.

1967.14.19

Ceres is copied from a figure from the two well-known Seasons plaquettes, Franco-Flemish works of about 1600 (Weber, no. 736). It is presumed that the four figures of the two plaquettes were used as four individual plaquettes in a series for the decoration of an object.

ILLUSTRATIONS OF THE

MEDALS AND PLAQUETTES

Except where noted, all illustrations are actual size.

1 John VIII Palaeologus, Emperor of Constantinople

2 *obv*. Jean d'Anjou, Duke of Calabria and Lorraine

2 *rev*. Figure of St. Michael atop a circular temple

PISANELLO (1) · FRANCESCO LAURANA (2)

3 *obv*. Borso d'Este, Duke of Modena and Reggio

3 *rev*. Unicorn in mountainous landscape

4 *obv*. Sigismondo Pandolfo Malatesta,
Lord of Rimini and Fano

4 *rev*. Casque, shield, elephant crest,
and mantling

5 *obv*. Sigismondo Pandolfo Malatesta,
Lord of Rimini and Fano

5 *rev*. The Castle at Rimini

JACOPO LIXIGNOLO (3) · MATTEO DE' PASTI (4, 5)

6 *obv.*
Sigismondo Pandolfo Malatesta
Lord of Rimini and Fano

7 *obv.* Francesco II Gonzaga, fourth Marquess of Mantua

6 *rev.*
San Francesco at Rimini

8 *obv.* Antonia del Balzo, wife of
Gianfrancesco Gonzaga di Rodigo

7 *rev.* Health standing between water and fire

8 *rev.* Hope on prow
of broken-masted vessel

9 *obv.* Francesco Sforza,
fourth Duke of Milan

9 *rev.* Galeazzo Maria Sforza,
fifth Duke of Milan

MATTEO DE' PASTI (6) · BARTOLOMMEO MELIOLI (7) · ANTICO (8) ·
GIANFRANCESCO ENZOLA (9)

10 Antonio Sarzanella De'Manfredi
of Faenza, diplomat

11 *obv*. Ludovico Carbone of Ferrara, poet

11 *rev*. Siren above waves holding tail in each hand

SPERANDIO OF MANTUA

12 Cornelio Castaldo, Jurisconsult,
poet and orator

13 *obv*. Isabella Sesso

13 *rev*. Fortune holding bridle

14 *obv*. Pope Julius II

14 *rev*. View of St. Peter's

CAMELIO (12) · GIOVANNI MARIA POMEDELLI (13) · CARADOSSO (14)

15 *obv*. Faustina I

15 *rev*. Faustina and Antoninus Pius with hands joined

MEDALIST OF THE ROMAN EMPERORS

16 *obv*. Pope Pius II

16 *rev*. Pelican in her piety

17 *obv*. Alfonso V of Aragon, King of Naples
and Sicily

17 *rev*. Alfonso crowned by Mars and Bellona

18 *obv*. Pope Paul II

18 *rev*. The Pope blessing
the faithful

ANDREA GUACIALOTI (16) · CRISTOFORO DI GEREMIA (17, 18)

19 *obv*. Pope Paul II

19 *rev*. Barbo coat of arms surmounted by papal tiara

20 *obv*. Pope Paul II

20 *rev*. Palazzo Venezia

21 *obv*. Maximilian of Austria

21 *rev*. Maria of Burgundy

22 *obv*. François de Valois

22 *rev*. Salamander in flames

23 *obv*. Marsilio Ficino, humanist

23 *rev*. Inscription

ROMAN SCHOOL UNDER PAUL II (19, 20) · GIOVANNI CANDIDA (21) ·
SCHOOL OF CANDIDA (22) · ATTRIBUTED TO NICCOLÒ FIORENTINO (23)

24 *obv*. Stefano Taverna, Secretary to the
Duke of Milan

24 *rev*. Virtue in armor, holding Love to left
and Fortune to right

25 *obv*. Francesco da Sangallo

25 *rev*. Helena Marsupina

27 *obv*.
Cosimo I de' Medici, first
Grand Duke of Tuscany

26 *obv*.
Alessandro I de' Medici,
Duke of Florence

26 *rev*.
Peace setting fire to the
weapons of war

27 *rev*.
Francesco de' Medici, second
Grand Duke of Tuscany

ATTRIBUTED TO NICCOLÒ FIORENTINO (24) · FRANCESCO DA SANGALLO (25) ·
DOMENICO DE' VETRI (26) · DOMENICO POGGINI (27)

28 *obv*. Cosimo I de' Medici,
Grand Duke of Tuscany

29 *obv*. Helen of Troy

28 *rev*. The Uffizi
and the Palazzo Vecchio

30 *obv*. Ferdinand I de' Medici,
third Grand Duke of Tuscany

29 *rev*. The Judgment of Paris

30 *rev*. Plan of the fortress
at Livorno

31 *obv*. Ferdinand I de' Medici,
third Grand Duke of Tuscany

32 *obv*. Giovanni Battista Grimaldi,
Genoese nobleman

31 *rev*. Grand Ducal crown and
scepter with Medici palle

33 *obv*. Gianfrancesco Trivulzio,
Marquess of Vigevano

32 *rev*. Prometheus chained to rocks
with eagle feeding on his liver

33 *rev*. Fortune on a dophin

DOMENICO POGGINI (28) · STYLE OF DOMENICO POGGINI (29) · MICHELE MAZZAFIRRI (30, 31) · PIER PAOLO GALEOTTI (32, 33)

34 *obv*. Pope Julius III

35 *obv*. Pope Martin V

34 *rev*. Prudence, right,
reaching for Fortune

36 *obv*. Pope Pius II

35 *rev*. Colonna shield,
papal tiara and keys

36 *rev*. Table with books

37 *obv*. Pope Clement VII

38 *obv*. Pierluigi Farnese,
Duke of Parma and Piacenza

37 *rev*. Medici coat of arms
surmounted by papal tiara and keys

39 *obv*.
Federico Cardinal Cesi

38 *rev*. Citadel of Parma

39 *rev*.
St. Caterina de' Funari

ALESSANDRO CESATI (34) · GIOVANNI PALADINO (35–37) ·
GIAN FEDERIGO BONZAGNI (38, 39)

40 *obv*. Pope Pius V

41 *obv*. Pope Pius V

40 *rev*.
Christ driving money changers
from the temple

42 *obv*. Pope Gregory XIII

41 *rev*. Battle of Lepanto

42 *rev*. Abraham with four soldiers

43 *obv*.
Pope Gregory XIII

44 *obv*. Pope Sixtus V

43 *rev*.
Roma seated on shield

45 *obv*. Pope Sixtus V

44 *rev*. The Pont Felice

45 *rev*. Obelisk

GIAN FEDERIGO BONZAGNI (40, 41) ·
BARTOLOMMEO ARGENTARIO AND BERNARDINO PASSERO (42) ·
LORENZO FRAGNI (43) · NICOLÒ DE BONIS (44, 45)

46 *obv*. St. Paul

46 *rev*. Inscription in wreath

47 *obv*. Pope Julius II

48 *obv*.
Giuliano II de' Medici

48 *rev*. Roma, seated,
holding Victory

47 *rev*.
Figure of Abundance

49 *obv*. Pope Pius V

50 *obv*.
Emperor Nero

50 *rev*.
Nero on horseback

49 *rev*.
Madonna and Child

ROMAN SCHOOL—UNATTRIBUTED (46–49) · GIOVANNI DEL CAVINO (50)

51 *obv*. Cosimo Scapti

51 *rev*. Salus and serpent

52 *obv*. Balduino del Monte,
brother of Pope Julius III

52 *rev*. Combat
between two horsemen

53 *obv*.
Giovanni Battaglini

53 *rev*.
Stork in her nest

54 *obv*.
Church of St. Giustina, Padua

54 *rev*. Inscription

55 *obv*. Tommaso Rangone
of Ravenna

55 *rev*. Jupiter as eagle
brings infant Hercules to Juno

56 *obv*. Andrea Gritti
Doge of Venice

56 *rev*. Facade of
St. Francesco della Vigna

57 *obv*. Marino Grimani,
Doge of Venice

58 Fountain of the Sciences

57 *rev*.
Lion of St. Mark

GIOVANNI DEL CAVINO (51, 52) · PADUAN SCHOOL (53, 54) · JACOPO TATTI (55) ·
ANDREA SPINELLI (56) · VENETIAN SCHOOL (57) · JACOPO NIZZOLA DA TREZZO (58)

59 *obv*. Ippolita di Ferdinando Gonzaga

59 *rev*. Aurora riding through the heavens

60 *obv*.
Alessandro Cardinal Farnese

62 Ercole II d'Este, fourth Duke of Ferrara

61 *obv*.
Alessandro Cardinal Farnese

60 *rev*.
Facade, Church of Il Gesù

61 *rev*.
Facade, Church of Il Gesù

JACOPO NIZZOLA DA TREZZO (59) · GIOVANNI V. MELON (60, 61) ·
ALFONSO DA TOMASO RUSPAGIARI (62)

63 *obv*. Unknown lady

63 *rev*. Unknown lady

65 *obv*. Pope Sixtus V

65 *rev*. Cityscape of Rome

64 Titian

66 *obv*.
Pope Urban VII

66 *rev*.
Candelabrum

ALFONSO DA TOMASO RUSPAGIARI (63) · AGOSTINO ARDENTI (64) ·
ITALIAN SCHOOL MEDALIST M. B. (65) · ATTRIBUTED TO MEDALIST M. B. (66)

67 *obv*. Antinous

68 *obv*.
Bishop Antonio Agostino
di Saragossa

68 *rev*.
Monogram of Christ

67 *rev*.
Antinous on griffin

69 *obv*. Pierio Valeriano Bolzanio

69 *rev*. Mercury

70 *obv*. Christ

70 *rev*. The crucifixion

ITALIAN—UNATTRIBUTED

71 Standing Christ

72 *obv*. Livia Colonna,
wife of Marzio Colonna

73 Vittoria Colonna

74 *obv*. Ercole II d'Este,
fourth Duke of Ferrara

72 *rev*. A cupid and bacchante

74 *rev*. Female draped figure
holding cornucopia

75 Innocenzo Francucci, painter

ITALIAN—UNATTRIBUTED

77 *obv*. Paolo Pellicani

76 *obv*. Gian Battista Malvezzi

76 *rev*. Palm tree

78 *obv*. Giacomo Cardinal Savelli

77 *rev*. Pelican nursing young

78 *rev*. Ship at sea

79 *obv*. General Gabriele Serbelloni

79 *rev*. Fortified city of Rome

ITALIAN—UNATTRIBUTED

80 *obv*. Subject unknown

81 *obv*.
Medal of Christ

82 *obv*. Pope Paul V

80 *rev*. Inscription

81 *rev*. Inscription

82 *rev*. St. Peter's

85 Maria Magdalena
of Austria

83 *obv*. Pope Paul V

84 *obv*. Pope Paul V

86 *obv*.
Pope Urban VIII

83 *rev*. St. Peter's

84 *rev*. Port of Fano

86 *rev*. Palace at
Castle Gandolfo

ITALIAN—UNATTRIBUTED (80, 81) · GIACOMO ANTONIO MORO (82) ·
PAOLO SANQUIRICO (83, 84) · GASPARE MOLA (85, 86)

87 Nicholas, Duke of Asinaglossi

88 *obv.*
Pope Urban VIII

88 *rev.*
Port of Civitavecchia

91 *obv.* Pope Alexander VII

89 *obv.* Vincenzo II Gonzaga,
seventh Duke of Mantua

89 *rev.* Hound

90 *obv.*
Pope Innocent X

90 *rev.* Inscription

91 *rev.* Church at Castle Gandolfo

92 *obv.* Count
Paolo Giordano II Orsini

92 *rev.* Minerva

ATTRIBUTED TO GASPARE MOLA (87) · ALESSANDRO ASTESANO (88) ·
GASPARE MORONI (89–91) · JOHANN JAKOB KORNMANN (92)

93 *obv*. Filippo Pirovani, jurisconsult

94 *obv*.
Christoph Cardinal Widman

94 *rev*. Two chamois

93 *rev*. Ship at sea

JOHANN JAKOB KORNMANN

96 *obv.* Pope Alexander VII

95 *obv.* Henri de Foix,
Duke of Candalle

95 *rev.* Stemma

96 *rev.* Androcles and the lion

ATTRIBUTED TO KORNMANN (95) · GIOACCHINO FRANCESCO TRAVANI (96)

97 *obv*. Pope Alexander VII

97 *rev*. Port of Civitavecchia

98 *obv*. Pope Alexander VII

98 *rev*. Santa Maria dell' Assunzione

99 *obv*. Pope Alexander VII

99 *rev*. Facade of church

GIOACCHINO FRANCESCO TRAVANI

100 *obv*. Ferdinand II de' Medici,
Grand Duke of Tuscany

100 *rev*. Rose branch with
three blooms

101 *obv*. Cosimo III de' Medici,
Grand Duke of Tuscany

101 *rev*. Three-masted ship
at sea

102 *obv*. Pope Clement IX

102 *rev*. Santa Maria Maggiore

GIOACCHINO FRANCESCO TRAVANI

103 *obv.*
Francesco Cardinal Barberini

103 *rev.*
Sunrise over sea

104 *obv.* Ippolito Fornasari,
Abbot of St. Michele del Poggio

104 *rev.* Horse's head above
burst of rays

105 Pope Innocent XI

GIOACCHINO FRANCESCO TRAVANI (103) · ANTONIO TRAVANI (104) ·
GIROLAMO LUCENTI (105)

106 *obv.*
Queen Christina of Sweden

107 *obv.*
Queen Christina of Sweden

108 *obv.* Cesare Ignazio d'Este,
Duke of Modena

106 *rev.* Sun

107 *rev.*
Celestial globe

108 *rev.* Heraldic eagle

109 *obv.*
Francesco Cardinal Nerli

110 *obv.*
Lodovico Cardinal Portocarrero

109 *rev.* Club and
slain animal on altar

111 *obv.*
Queen Christina of Sweden

110 *rev.*
Fame atop a tall pedestal

111 *rev.* Globe showing
Eastern Hemisphere

GIOVANNI BATTISTA GUGLIELMADA (106–108) · GIOVANNI HAMERANI (109–111)

112 *obv*. Francesco I Farnese,
Duke of Parma and Piacenza

114 *obv*. Livio Odescalchi,
Duke of Cera, Bracciano and Sirmia

113 *obv*. Nicolas Duodo,
Venetian Ambassador at Rome

112 *rev*. Faith and Justice

114 *rev*. Seaport

113 *rev*. Stairway flanked
by chapels

115 *obv*. Pope Alexander VIII

115 *rev*. Pope Alexander's tomb

GIOVANNI HAMERANI (112) · GIUSEPPE ORTOLANI (113) ·
FERDINAND DE SAINT-URBAIN (114–115)

116 *obv.*
Jacques de Sainte Marie

117 *obv.* Ulisse Giuseppe Gozzadini,
Cardinal

116 *rev.* Jean Philippe,
Prior of St. Étienne

118 *obv.* Jean II of Anjou,
Duke of Lorraine

117 *rev.* Minerva with dove of the
Holy Spirit on her head

118 *rev.* Marie of Bourbon,
Duchess of Lorraine

119 *obv.* Leopold I, Duke of Lorraine

119 *rev.* Hercules and Mercury

FERDINAND DE SAINT-URBAIN

121 *obv*. Philip V, King of Spain

120 *obv*. Leopold I, Duke of Lorraine

121 *rev*. Neptune

122 *obv*. Nicolas Duodo,
Venetian Ambassador at Rome

120 *rev*. Horseman crossing bridge

122 *rev*. Stairway
flanked by chapels

124 *obv*. James III Stuart

123 *obv*.
Pope Innocent XIII

123 *rev*. St. Michael

124 *rev*. Horse of Hanover tramples
Unicorn and Lion of England

FERDINAND DE SAINT-URBAIN (120, 121) · ERMENEGILDO HAMERANI (122, 123) ·
OTTONE HAMERANI (124)

125 *obv*. Cardinal Quirini
Archbishop of Brescia

125 *rev*. Inscription

126 *obv*. Pietro Leone Ghezzi, painter

126 *rev*. Winged caduceus

127 *obv*. Ferdinand, Infante of Spain

127 *rev*. Comedy and Tragedy receiving
wreaths from Genius

OTTONE HAMERANI (125) · GIOVANNI BATTISTA POZZO (126) ·
FILIPPO CROPANESE (127)

128 *obv.*
Pope Clement XIV

129 *obv.* Alessandro Antonio Barziza,
Governor of Bergamo

128 *rev.* Baptism of
the Infante of Spain

130 *obv.* Pietro Cardinal Serasi

129 *rev.* Inscription

130 *rev.* Woman holding book

131 *obv.* Giacomo Carrara and
Maria Anna Passi

133 *obv.* Giuseppe Ferreri,
Vicelegate of Avignon

131 *rev.* Palace facade

132 *obv.* Pope Paul V

133 *rev.* View of Avignon

132 *rev.* Chapel of Santa Maria Maggiore

FILIPPO CROPANESE (128) · FRANCESCO CORRAZZINI (129–131) ·
ROMAN SCHOOL—UNATTRIBUTED (132, 133)

134 *obv*. Church of St. Ignazio

134 *rev*. Inscription

135 *obv*. St. Ignatius

135 *rev*. Inscription

136 *obv*. Church of St. Gregorio

136 *rev*. Arms of
Prince Giovanni Battista Borghese

ROMAN SCHOOL—UNATTRIBUTED

137 Pope Alexander VIII

138 *obv*. Giovanni Ansano, tenor

138 *rev*. Inscription

ROMAN SCHOOL—UNATTRIBUTED

139 *obv.* Pope Pius VI

139 *rev.* Christ carrying cross

140 *obv.* Valentino Farinola

140 *rev.* A bridle

141 *obv.* Ludovico Caprara

141 *rev.* Peace and Mars

ROMAN SCHOOL—UNATTRIBUTED (139) · MASSIMILIANO SOLDANI-BENZI (140, 141)

142 *obv*. Flavio Cardinal Chigi

142 *rev*. Justice and Truth

143 *obv*. Pietro Matteo Maggi

143 *rev*. Justice and Peace

144 Ercole Ferrata, sculptor

MASSIMILIANO SOLDANI-BENZI

145 *obv*. Francesco Redi, doctor, poet, philosopher

145 *rev*. Bacchus and Silenus with maenads and satyrs

146 Cosimo III de' Medici, Grand Duke of Tuscany

MASSIMILIANO SOLDANI-BENZI

147 *obv*. Vittoria della Rovere,
wife of Ferdinand II de' Medici

147 *rev*. Winged figure of Fame

148 *obv*. Cosimo III de' Medici,
Grand Duke of Tuscany

148 *rev*. Plan of church and
monastery on scroll

MASSIMILIANO SOLDANI-BENZI (147) · CIRCLE OF SOLDANI (148)

149 *obv*. Lorenzo Magalotti,
Florentine scholar, philosopher, theologian, poet

149 rev. Apollo

150 *obv*. Francesco Riccardi

150 *rev*. View of the Medici-Riccardi palace

ANTONIO MONTAUTI (149) · GIOVACCHINO FORTINI (150)

151 *obv*. Cosimo III de' Medici,
Grand Duke of Tuscany

151 *rev*. St. Joseph offering lily to Christ Child

152 *obv*. Gian Gastone de' Medici,
seventh Duke of Tuscany

152 *rev*. Gian Gastone accepting crown
and scepter

GIOVACCHINO FORTINI (151) · FRANCESCO PIERI (152)

153 *obv*. Giovanni Lami, theologian and historian

153 *rev*. Pedestal with bust flanked by Minerva and Florence

154 *obv*. Bernardino Perfetti, Sienese poet

154 *rev*. Sibyl

GIOVANNI BATTISTA LAPI (153) · ANTONIO SELVI (154)

155 *obv*. Francesco del Teglia, jurisconsult

155 *rev*. Philosophy seated with book

156 *obv*. Ferdinand II de' Medici,
Grand Duke of Tuscany

156 *rev*. Rosebush with three blossoms

ANTONIO SELVI

157 *obv*. Emperor Francis I

157 *rev*. Jupiter holding lightning rods

158 *obv*. Giovanni Lami, theologian and historian

158 *rev*. Minerva

ANTONIO SELVI

159 *obv*. Pietro Cardinal Ottoboni

159 *rev*. Kneeling figure

160 *obv*. Francis III, Grand Duke of Tuscany

160 *rev*. Duke on horseback

BARTOLOMMEO GIOVANNI VAGGELLI (159) · LORENZO MARIA WEBER (160)

161 *obv*. Maria Maddalena Morelli Fernandez

161 *rev*. Indians shooting arrows at the sun

162 *obv*. Giovanni Bottari

162 *rev*. Woman leaning against column being broken by lightning bolt

GIOVANNI ZANOBIO WEBER

163 *obv*. The first Medici

163 *rev*. Inscription

164 *obv*. Eleanor of Toledo,
wife of Cosimo I de' Medici

164 *rev*. Table with medals on it

165 *obv*. Bianca Cappello, second wife
of Francesco I de' Medici

165 *rev*. Stork standing among flora

166 *obv*. Christina of Lorraine, wife
of Ferdinand I de' Medici

166 *rev*. Column with
Corinthian capital

GIOVANNI ZANOBIO WEBER

168 *obv.* Pietro Cardinal Aldobrandini

167 *obv.* Maria Magdalena,
wife of Cosimo II

167 *rev.* Bush

168 *rev.* Procession

GIOVANNI ZANOBIO WEBER (167) · FELICE ANTONIO CASONI (168)

169 *obv*. Alfonso Paleotti,
Archbishop of Bologna

169 *rev*. Stemma surmounted by cross

170 *obv*. Laura Maria Caterina Bassi,
professor of philosophy

170 *rev*. Minerva with lamp and shield

171 *obv*. Vincenzo Riccati, physician
and mathematician

171 *rev*. Two figures

FELICE ANTONIO CASONI (169) · ANTONIO LAZARI (170) ·
FILIPPO BALUGANI (171)

172 *obv*. Francesco Marchi,
military engineer and architect

172 *rev*. Figure seated on spears

173 *obv*. Guido Zanetti, numismatist

173 *rev*. Scales

174 *obv*. Giacomo Biancani Tazzi, classicist,
scientist, numismatist

174 *rev*. Inscription

FILIPPO BALUGANI (172) · BOLOGNESE SCHOOL—UNATTRIBUTED (173, 174)

175 *obv*. Giovanni Crisostomo Trombelli, Jesuit, classicist

175 *rev*. Inscription

176 *obv*. Pietro Paolo Molinelli, physician

176 *rev*. Inscription on shield

177 *obv*.
St. Catherine of Bologna

178 *obv*. Francisco Morosini
Doge of Venice

178 *rev*. Winged victory
blowing horn

177 *rev*. Stemma

BOLOGNESE SCHOOL—UNATTRIBUTED (175–177) · JOHANN FRANZ NEIDINGER (178)

179 *obv*. Flaminio Cornaro
Venetian Senator and author

180 Francesco Morosini

179 *rev*.
St. Nicolo Tolentino

181 Religion

182 *obv*. Man on a chariot

182 *rev*. Inscription

AGOSTINO FRANCHI (179) · VENETIAN SCHOOL—UNATTRIBUTED (180–182)

184 *obv*. St. Januarius

183 Portrait of a doge

184 *rev*. Inscription

186 *obv*. Antonio Magliabecchi,
librarian at Florence

185 *obv*. Philip V, King of Spain

186 *rev*. Magliabecchi reading

187 *obv*. Elizabeth de Montaperto

187 *rev*. Knight

185 *rev*. Minerva

188 *rev*. Woman handing boy
a palm branch

188 *obv*. Polissena Cristina

VENETIAN SCHOOL—UNATTRIBUTED (183) ·
GIOVANNI COSTANZI (184) · MARIA ANTONIO DI GENNARO (185, 186) ·
ARTIST UNKNOWN (187) · LORENZO LAVY (188)

189 *obv.* Mario Lupo

191 *obv.* Ermolao Pisani,
Prefect of Verona

189 *rev.* Lupo standing

190 *obv.* Niccolò Venier

191 *rev.* Meat market at Verona

190 *rev.* Eleanora Bentivoglio

192 *obv.* Gian Paolo Simone Bianchi

192 *rev.* Lynx

ANTON GUILLEMARD (189–191) · B. CIANTOGNI (192)

193 *obv*. Giovanni Battista
and Caterina F...

193 *rev*. Inscription

194 *obv*. Ottavio Tassone Estense

194 *rev*. Castle

195 *obv*. Enea Montecuccoli,
Governor of Carpi

195 *rev*. Pallas Athena

196 *obv*. Amico Sinibaldo

196 *rev*. Inscription

S. A. B. A. (193) · ITALIAN—UNATTRIBUTED (194–197)

197 *obv.* Three stemmae
surmounted by cardinal's hat

197 *rev.* Inscription

198 *obv.* Inscription

198 *rev.* Church of
St. Stefano

199 *obv.* St. Filippo Neri Oratory

199 *rev.* Inscription

200 *obv.* Lucrezia Capranica

200 *rev.* Prudence

ITALIAN—UNATTRIBUTED

201 *obv*. Niccolò Machiavelli

201 *rev*. Serpent

202 Girolamo da Carpi

203 Alexander Malegonnelle

204 *obv*. Giuseppe Compagniucci

204 *rev*. Two river gods and eagle

ITALIAN—UNATTRIBUTED

205 *obv*. Francesco I Farnese,
Duke of Parma and Piacenza

205 *rev*. Phaeton and Zeus
above Zodiac band

206 *obv*. Vincenzo Bellini,
Ferrarese antiquarian and numismatist

206 *rev*. Two palm trees, flowers,
bees and a beehive

207 *obv*. Francis Hyacinth of Savoy

207 *rev*. Boy protected by Minerva

ITALIAN—UNATTRIBUTED

208 *obv*. Pope Pius VII

209 *obv*. Pope Pius VII

210 *obv*. Pope Leo XII

208 *rev*. The Laocoon

209 *rev*. Christ washing
St. Peter's feet

210 *rev*. St. Maria Maggiore
baptistry and font

211 *obv*. Pope Pius IX

213 *obv*. Pope Gregory XVI

211 *rev*. Ruins of St. Paul's
Outside the Walls

212 *obv*. Pope Pius IX

213 *rev*. Pope kneels before a
vision of the Madonna

212 *rev*. Daniel

TOMMASO MERCANDETTI (208, 209) · GIUSEPPE GIROMETTI (210–212) ·
PIETRO GIROMETTI (213)

215 *obv*. Angelo Poliziano

214 Michelangelo

215 *rev*. Inscription

216 *obv*. Pope Pius IX

216 *rev*. Interior of St. Paul's Basilica

217 *obv*. Pope Pius IX

218 *obv*. Francis IV,
Duke of Modena

218 *rev*. Peace leading
male figure

217 *rev*. View of piazza

NICCOLÒ CERBARA (214, 215) · IGNAZIO BIANCHI (216, 217) ·
LUIGI MANFREDINI (218)

219 *obv*. Ferdinand I,
Emperor of Austria

221 *obv*.
Antonio Canova

220 *obv*. Giuseppe Cardinal Ugolini

219 *rev*. Ferdinand kneeling
before a bishop

221 *rev*.
Inscription

220 *rev*. Fama (?) kneeling and
Victory standing

222 *obv*.
Luigi Malaspina

223 *obv*.
Countess Giulia Samoyloff

223 *rev*. Inscription

222 *rev*.
Palace facade

LUIGI MANFREDINI (219) · LUIGI COSSA (220) · FRANCESCO PUTINATI (221, 222) ·
DEMETRIO CANZANI (223)

225 *obv*. Rebuilding of
Campanile, Venice

224 *obv*. Cesare Cantù, historian

225 *rev*. Loggetta
of Campanile

226 *obv*. Victor Emmanuel I

224 *rev*. Inscription

226 *rev*. City tyche of Turin
kneels before Victor Emmanuel

227 *obv*.
Vittorio Alfieri

227 *rev*.
Inscription

228 *obv*.
Lorenzo Cigna

228 *rev*.
Inscription

FRANCESCO BROGGI (224) · STEFANO JOHNSON (225) · AMADEO LAVY (226) ·
GASPARE GALEAZZI (227, 228)

229 *obv.*
Giovanni Battista Beccaria

230 *obv.* Lord Byron

232 *obv.*
Marie Louise

229 *rev.* Inscription

232 *rev.*
Inscription

231 *obv.*
Marie Louise

230 *rev.*
Winged young man playing lyre

233 *obv.* Dante

231 *rev.*
Inscription

233 *rev.* Female figure
holding book

GASPARE GALEAZZI (229, 230) · GIOVANNI ANTONIO SANTARELLI (231, 232) ·
DOMENICO TRENTACOSTE (233)

234 *obv*. Pope Pius IX

235 *obv*.
Gian Domenico Romagnosi

235 *rev*. Inscription

234 *rev*. Inscription

PICCIOLI (234) · DONNINO BENTELLI (235)

236 Marie Louise Bourbon del Monte S. Maria

LUIGI DE FEO

237 *obv*. Ludovico Pavoni

237 *rev*. Inscription

238 *obv*. Ludovico Antonio Muratori

238 *rev*. Statue on a pedestal

PIVETTI (237) · ARTIST UNKNOWN (238)

239 *obv.*
Henry II, King of France

239 *rev.*
Fame, Abundance and a third figure

240 *obv.*
Henry II, King of France

240 *rev.*
Fame, Abundance and Victory

241 *obv.*
Henry II, King of France

241 *rev.*
Inscription in laurel wreath

MARC BECHOT (239) · ÉTIENNE DELAUNE (240, 241)

242 obv.
Henry II, King of France

242 rev.
Fame, Abundance and Victory

243 obv. Henry II as Dauphin

243 rev. St. Michael killing a monster

244 obv.
Henry of Lorraine

244 rev. A man plowing

ÉTIENNE DELAUNE (242) · UNATTRIBUTED (243, 244)

246 Francesco de' Medici, brother of
Cosimo II

245 *obv*. Antoine de Bourbon,
King of Navarre

245 *rev*. Jeanne d'Albret,
consort of Antoine

247 Maria Magdalena of Austria, wife of
Cosimo II

UNATTRIBUTED (245) · GUILLAUME DUPRÉ (246, 247)

248 *obv*. Cardinal de Richelieu

248 *rev*. Hands binding laurel wreath

249 *obv*. Marshal d'Argencourt

249 *rev*. Sword, shield and ribbon

250 *obv*. Armand-Jean Duplessis, Cardinal de Richelieu

250 *rev*. France seated with Fortune and Fame in chariot

GUILLAUME DUPRÉ (248, 249) · JEAN VARIN (250)

251 *obv*. Cardinal de Richelieu

253 *obv*. Johann and Cornelius de Witt

251 *rev*. The globe and
the planets

252 *obv*. Louis XIV

253 *rev*. The brothers being consumed

252 *rev*. Anne of Austria

254 *obv*. Pietro da Cortona

254 *rev*. Fame

JEAN VARIN (251, 252) · PIERRE AURY (253) · CHARLES JEAN FRANÇOIS CHÉRON (254)

255 *obv*. Giovanni Paolo Oliva,
Jesuit Preceptor-General

255 *rev*. Saint being borne to
heaven by angels

256 *obv*. Cosimo III de' Medici,
Grand Duke of Tuscany

256 *rev*. Margaret d'Orleans

257 *obv*. Louis XIV

257 *rev*. Helios riding across heavens

CHARLES JEAN FRANÇOIS CHÉRON

258 Marie Descoraille, Duchess of Fontagnes

260 Louis XIII making vow

259 *obv*. Louis XIV

259 *rev*. Inscription

NICOLAS DELAHAYE (258) · ANTOINE BENOIST (259) · THOMAS BERNARD (260)

262 *obv*. Louis XIV

261 *obv*. Henri de la Tour of Auvergne

263 *obv*. Louis XIV

262 *rev*. Tyche of Paris

261 *rev*. Lightning striking tree

263 *rev*. War and France

264 *obv*. Louis XIV

265 *obv*. Louis XIV

266 *obv*. Louis XIV

264 *rev*. Louis receiving
Queen of Sweden

265 *rev*. Louis XIV and
Pontifical Legate

266 *rev*. Cross of the
Order of St. Louis

THOMAS BERNARD (261, 262) · JEAN MAUGER (263–266) · JEAN DUVIVIER (263) ·
JEAN DOLLIN (264, 265)

267 Louis XIV

268 *obv.* Louis XIV

268 *rev.* Justice and Mercury

269 *obv.* Louis XIV

269 *rev.* Versailles

270 *obv.* Louis XIV

273 Louis XIV (?)

270 *rev.* Louis receiving plan
for Citadel of Casale

271 *obv.* Louis XIV

271 *rev.* Institution of
Cadet Corps

272 *obv.* Louis XIV

272 *rev.* Institution of the
Military Order of St. Louis

JEAN MAUGER (267–272) · JEAN DOLLIN (269–272) · UNATTRIBUTED (273)

274 *obv*. Nicolas de Bailleul

274 *rev*. Nymph of the Seine

276 Church of Val de Grâce

275 *obv*. Woman seated among masks

275 *rev*. Prudence, Bellona and
Bona Fortuna

UNATTRIBUTED

277 *obv*. St. Louis

277 *rev*. Church of St. Louis

278 *obv*. Louis XIV

279 *obv*. Vincent Voiture,
writer and diplomat

279 *rev*. The Three Graces

278 *rev*. Justice, left,
and Louis

280 *obv*. René Rapin, Jesuit poet

280 *rev*. Fountain

UNATTRIBUTED (277, 278) · SIMONE CURÉ (279, 280)

282 *obv.* Louis XV

281 *obv.* Elizabeth, Duchess of Orleans,
Princess Palatine

282 *rev.* Louis receiving
Turkish Ambassador

283 *obv.* Louis XV

283 *rev.* Victory and Peace

281 *rev.* Tyche of Orleans

284 *obv.* Louis XV

284 *rev.* Mars receiving
supplicant tyche of Milan

285 *obv.*
Philip Stosch, archaeologist

285 *rev.*
Diogenes, seated, and Alexander

NORBERT AND JOSEPH CHARLES ROETTIERS (281) · JEAN LE BLANC (282) ·
JEAN DUVIVIER (283, 284) · MICHAEL ROEG (284) · FRANÇOIS JOSEPH MARTEAU (285)

286 *obv*. Louis XV

288 *obv*. Isaac Newton

287 *obv*. Louis XV

286 *rev*. Corsica kneeling
before Mars

288 *rev*. Woman holding shield
inscribed with solar system

287 *rev*. Louis on horseback

289 *obv*. Louis XV

290 *obv*. Marie Antoinette

291 *obv*. Louis XVI and
Marie Antoinette

289 *rev*. Pont de Neuilly

290 *rev*. France holding Marie's
daughter

291 *rev*.
France holding Dauphin

FRANÇOIS JOSEPH MARTEAU (286, 287) · JOSEPH CHARLES ROETTIERS (286) ·
JACQUES ROETTIERS (288) · BENJAMIN DUVIVIER (289–291) · LAURENT LÉONARD (289)

292 *obv*. Louis XVI

293 *obv*. Louis XVI

294 *obv*. Louis XVI

292 *rev*. Paris

293 *rev*. Inscription

294 *rev*. King, Queen, and Dauphin
led by tyche of Paris

295 *obv*. Charles-Michel,
Abbé de l'Épée

296 *obv*. Louis XVI

297 *obv*. Joseph Jerome
Lefrançois de Lalande

295 *rev*. Inscription

296 *rev*. Montgolfier, balloon
and Cybele

297 *rev*. Inscription

BENJAMIN DUVIVIER (292–295) · AUGUSTIN DUPRÉ (292) ·
NICOLAS MARIE GATTEAUX (296, 297)

298 *obv*. Louis XVII

299 *obv*. Pope Pius VII

300 *obv*. Emperor Alexander I

298 *rev*.
Lily with broken stem

299 *rev*. Notre Dame

300 *rev*. History

301 *obv*. Louis XVIII

301 *rev*. Church of St. Geneviève

NICHOLAS PIERRE TIOLIER (298) · JEAN PIERRE DROZ AND LOUIS JALEY (299) ·
BERTRAND ANDRIEU (300, 301) · JEAN JACQUES BARRE (301)

302 *obv.* Charles X, King of France

302 *rev.* Bishop anointing Charles

304 *obv.* Maria Christina,
Princess of Naples

303 *obv.* Marie Caroline
de Bourbon-Siciles

304 *rev.* Inscription

305 *obv.* Hyacinth Louis de Quelen,
Archbishop of Paris

303 *rev.* Inscription

305 *rev.* Notre Dame

JEAN JACQUES BARRE (302, 305) · JACQUES ÉDOUARD GATTEAUX (302) ·
JOSEPH EUGÈNE DUBOIS (303–305)

306 Dieudonné, Comte de Las-Cases

308 Abbé de la Mennais

PIERRE JEAN DAVID D'ANGERS

307 Jean Paul Marat

309 *obv*. Claude Joseph
Rouget de Lisle

309 *rev*. All six verses of
the *Marseillaise*

PIERRE JEAN DAVID D'ANGERS (307) · ÉMILE ROGAT (309)

310 *obv*. Louis Philippe I, King of France

310 *rev*. Mercury and Mars flank female figure

JEAN FRANÇOIS ANTOINE BOVY

311 *obv*. N. Th. Oliver,
Bishop of Évreux

311 *rev*. Cardinal's coat of arms

312 Jules Brame, Deputy de Nord

313 *obv*. Prize Medal,
Ministry of the Interior

313 *rev*. Inscription

VALENTIN MAURICE BORREL (311) · FRANÇOIS JOSEPH HUBERT PONSCARME (312) ·
LOUIS OSCAR ROTY (313)

314 *obv*. Albert Dumont, historian

314 *rev*. Draped female figure

JULES CLÉMENT CHAPLAIN

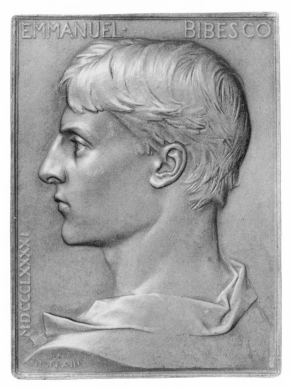

315 Emmanuel Bibesco

316 *obv*. Émile François Loubet,
President of France, 1899–1906

316 *rev*. Urn and spear on altar

JULES CLÉMENT CHAPLAIN

317 *obv.*
Universal Exhibition of 1900

318 *obv.* Redemption

317 *rev.*
Putto leaning on die press

319 *obv.* Amedeo Godard,
publisher of medals

318 *rev.* Young man holding crucifix

319 *rev.* Inscription

320 *obv.* Alessandro Farnese,
Governor of the Netherlands

320 *rev.* Alexander the Great

JEAN-BAPTISTE DANIEL DUPUIS (317) · GEORGES DUPRÉ (318) · OVIDE YENCESSE (319) ·
ATTRIBUTED TO JACOB JONGHELINCK (320)

322 *obv.* Emperor Charles V

321 *obv.* Anton Strale,
Duke of Merxem and Dambrugge

321 *rev.* Nude female figure

322 *rev.* The Infante Philip

ATTRIBUTED TO JONGHELINCK (321) · 16TH CENTURY NETHERLANDS? (322)

323 *obv.*
Johann and Cornelius de Witt

324 *obv.*
Johann and Cornelius de Witt

325 *obv.* King Charles I

323 *rev.* Inscription

324 *rev.* Two ships

325 *rev.* Arm from clouds holding
celestial crown

326 *obv.* Prince Albert

328 *obv.* Philippe, Duc d'Orleans

328 *rev.* Inscription

326 *rev.* Globe with laurel wreath

327 *obv.*
King Victor Amadeus II

327 *rev.* Justice, Fortitude and
Prudence

17TH CENTURY NETHERLANDS (323, 324) · JAN ROETTIERS (325) ·
WILLIAM WYON (326) · JEAN DASSIER (327, 328)

329 *obv*. Louis Lefort,
Chief Burgomaster of Geneva

330 *obv*. D. F. Count of Lautrec

329 *rev*. Geneva with cornucopia

331 *obv*.
King George II of England

330 *rev*. Prudence flanked by Fortitude
(Mars) and Justice

331 *rev*. Inscription

332 *obv*. Queen Maria Theresa

332 *rev*. Minerva

JEAN DASSIER (329–331) · JACQUES ANTOINE DASSIER (332)

333 *obv.* King Charles Emmanuel III

334 *obv.* Marchese Scipione Maffei,
scholar and poet

335 *obv.*
Count Giovanni Maria Mazzucchelli

333 *rev.*
Charles Emmanuel and Minerva

334 *rev.* Museum of Verona

335 *rev.* Lion of St. Mark

336 *obv.* Maurice, Comte de Saxe,
Marshal of France

336 *rev.* Victory seated on weapons

JACQUES ANTOINE DASSIER (333–336) · JEAN DASSIER (335, 336)

337 *obv*. Nicolaus Keder,
antiquarian

337 *rev*. Phoenix

338 *obv*. Anna Ivanowna,
Empress of Russia

338 *rev*. Eagle

339 *obv*. Religion holding chalice

339 *rev*. Fortitude, Faith and Peace

JOHANN KARL HEDLINGER (337, 338) · JOHANN HÖHN (339)

341 *obv*. Maximilian II,
Elector of Bavaria

340 *obv*. Allegory of a virtuous way of life

341 *rev*. Map showing recapture
of Belgrade

342 *obv*. Lion of St. Mark and
five chained Turkish prisoners

340 *rev*. Faith, Hope and Charity

342 *rev*. Map of Morea

343 *obv*. St. George and the Dragon

343 *rev*. Inscription

JOHANN KITTEL (340) · GEORG HAUTSCH (341, 342) · GERMAN—UNATTRIBUTED (343)

344 *obv*. Cardinals Paolucci (*r*.)
and Piazza (*l*.)

346 Peter Paul Werner, medalist

344 *rev*. Forli city square

345 *obv*. Church of St. Hedwig

345 *rev*. Inscription

348 Unknown female

347 *obv*. Voltaire

347 *rev*. Altar

GEORG WILHELM VESTNER (344) · PETER PAUL WERNER (345) ·
JOHANN PETER WERNER (346) · GEORGE CHRISTIAN WAECHTER (347) ·
LEONARD POSCH (348)

349 Unknown male

350 *obv*. Frederick Wilhelm III,
King of Prussia

350 *rev*. Hygeiea seated on cow

351 *obv*. John Scott, Earl of Eldon

351 *rev*. Inscription

LEONARD POSCH (349) · ABRAHAM ABRAMSON (350) · KARL FRIEDRICH VOIGT (351)

352 *obv*. J. W. von Schlatter,
director, St. Petersburg Mint

352 *rev*. Woman sitting among tools
used in minting coins

353 *obv*. Emperor Leopold I

353 *rev*. Battle scene

354 *obv*. King Charles X of Sweden

354 *rev*. Queen Hedvig

JOHANN GEORG WAECHTER AND JOHANN BALTHASAR GASS (352) ·
ANTON MEYBUSCH (353, 354)

355 *obv*. Charles II, King of Spain, Naples
and Sicily

355 *rev*. St. James

356 *obv*. King Charles III

356 *rev*. Charles IV, Infante of Spain,
and Maria Luisa de Bourbon

357 *obv*. King Ferdinand VII

357 *rev*. Woman holding shield

17TH CENTURY SPAIN (355) · TOMAS FRANCISCO PRIETO (356) ·
PEDRO JUAN MARIA DE GUERRERO (357)

PLAQUETTES

358 Hercules and the Nemean Lion

359 Madonna of Loreto

360 The Flagellation

VENETIAN: LATE 16TH CENTURY (359) · NORTH ITALIAN: LATE 16TH CENTURY (360)

362 St. Simon

361 St. John, the Madonna and Christ Child

ITALIAN: 16TH CENTURY

363 Pieta

ITALIAN: LATE 16TH CENTURY (?)

364 The Assumption of Mary

ITALIAN: LATE 16TH CENTURY

365 Venus and Putto (Cupid?)

367 St. John the Evangelist

366 The Virgin Immaculate

368 The Annunciation

NORTH ITALIAN?: LATE 16TH CENTURY (365) ·
NORTH ITALIAN 16TH OR 17TH CENTURY (366) ·
ITALIAN: 16TH OR 17TH CENTURY (367) · ITALIAN: LATE 17TH CENTURY (368)

369 Ascension of Christ

370 Christ and Samaritan woman

ITALIAN? (369) · PETER FLÖTNER (370)

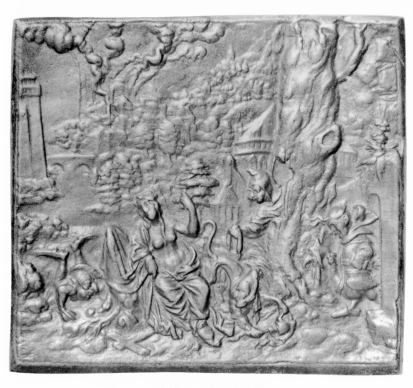

371 Temptation of Faith

372 Pagan King in a scroll ornament frame

373 Euterpe

PETER FLÖTNER (371) · AFTER FLÖTNER (372) · LABENWOLF WORKSHOP (373)

374 Rabbit hunt

GEORG LABENWOLF

375 Judgment of Paris

378 The Crucifixion

377 Allegory of unity

376 Dancing peasant
couple

379 Toilet of Venus

380A Pieta with angels

GERMAN: 16TH CENTURY (375–378) · ANTONIO ABONDIO (379, 380)

380B Pieta with angels

381 Pieta with angels

382 Christ surrounded by angels

383A Christ before Pilate

383B Pieta

ANTONIO ABONDIO (380, 381) · ATTRIBUTED TO JAKOB KROMER (382) ·
CIRCLE OF MATTHIAS WALLBAUM (383)

384A The Annunciation

384B Adoration of the Magi

384C The Last Supper

384D Christ on the Mount of Olives

CIRCLE OF MATTHIAS WALLBAUM

384E Crowning with thorns

384F Christ bearing the Cross

384G Entombment

384H The Resurrection

CIRCLE OF MATTHIAS WALLBAUM

385 Rape of the Sabine women

HANS JACOB BAIR?

386 Standing elder

SOUTH GERMAN?

388 Christ and Mary Magdalene

387 Alexander the Great

389A Pan and Syrinx

AFTER FRANÇOIS BRIOT (387) · SOUTH GERMAN: 17TH CENTURY (388, 389)

389B Fall of Phaeton

389C The Heliades

389D Jupiter seduces Callisto

389E Juno transforms Callisto into a bear

SOUTH GERMAN: 17TH CENTURY

389F Arkas killing Callisto and their apotheosis

389G Diana and Actaeon

SOUTH GERMAN: 17TH CENTURY

389H Thisbe at the grave of Ninus

389I Pyramus and Thisbe

SOUTH GERMAN: 17TH CENTURY

389J Perseus frees Andromeda

389K Rape of Prosperpina

SOUTH GERMAN: 17TH CENTURY

389L Abduction of Cephalus

389N Birth of Adonis

SOUTH GERMAN: 17TH CENTURY

389M Calydonian boar hunt

SOUTH GERMAN: 17TH CENTURY

389P The contest between Atalanta and Hippomenes (?)

SOUTH GERMAN: 17TH CENTURY

389O Venus and Adonis

389Q Death of Adonis

SOUTH GERMAN: 17TH CENTURY

389R King Midas receives Silenus

389S The contest between Apollo and Pan

SOUTH GERMAN: 17TH CENTURY

389T Battle of the Lapiths and Centaurs

389U Vulcan forging the weapons of Achilles

SOUTH GERMAN: 17TH CENTURY

389V Abduction of Helena (?)

389W Vertumnus and Pomona

SOUTH GERMAN: 17TH CENTURY

389X Venus anoints Aeneas a god

390 Adoration of the Christ Child

391A Gathering
of the manna

391B Christ appearing
to a saint

SOUTH GERMAN: 17TH CENTURY

392 Triumph of a princess

394B Joseph being pulled from the well

393 The repentant Magdalene

394A Cain killing Abel

SOUTH GERMAN OR AUSTRIAN (392) · GERMAN? (393) · FLEMISH OR GERMAN (394)

395 Triumph of Humility

396 St. Luke

397 Christ on Gethsemane

398 Scene at an inn

399 Scene on the road to Calvary (not illustrated)

NETHERLANDISH (395) · NETHERLANDISH OR SOUTH GERMAN? (396) ·
MONOGRAMMIST AVB (397) · NETHERLANDISH (398)

400 Bacchanal scene
(¾ actual size)

402 The repentant Magdalene
(¾ actual size)

FLEMISH?: 17TH CENTURY (400) · FLEMISH OR NETHERLANDISH?: 17TH CENTURY (402)

401 The repentant Magdalene

FLEMISH?: 17TH CENTURY

403 Moses and the serpent

404A The penitent St. Peter

NETHERLANDISH? (403) · FLEMISH OR SOUTH GERMAN (404)

404B The penitent St. Peter

FLEMISH OR SOUTH GERMAN

405 The mocking of Christ

406 Satyr and putti milking a goat

FLEMISH OR PRAGUE? (405) · FLEMISH (406)

407 Hercules and Omphale

408 Boar attacked by dogs

409 Putti with goats

410 Man of Sorrows

NETHERLANDISH, FLEMISH OR FRENCH (407) · FLEMISH? (408) · FLEMISH (409) ·
SPANISH (410)

411B The penitent St. Peter

412A St. Sebastian

411A The penitent St. Peter

SPANISH (411) · SPANISH? (412)

412B St. Jerome

412C Ss. Acisclus and Victoria (?)

412D The repentant Magdalene

412E St. Francis of Assisi

SPANISH?

414 The repentant Magdalene

413 Adoration of the Christ Child

415 Adoration of the Shepherds

SPANISH (413) · SPANISH? (414, 415)

416 The Flagellation

SPANISH?

417 The conversion of St. Paul

FRENCH?

419 Madonna and the Child
with the infant St. John

418 The education of Amor

420 Satyr unveiling a sleeping bacchante

FRENCH?

421A Putto with a sea monster

421B Putto with a sea monster

422 The Last Supper

JEAN PIERRE MONTAGNY (421) · BOHEMIAN OR HUNGARIAN (422)

423 Joseph's dream

424 The repentant Magdalene

UNKNOWN

425 The recruitment—theater scene (?)

426 Ceres

UNKNOWN

INDEXES TO THE CATALOGUES

INDEXES TO THE MEDALS CATALOGUE

The numbers are those of the medals. Page references are indicated in italics and are preceded by *p.*

I. Artists

Only those whose works appear in the catalogue are listed here. References to other artists are found in the general index.

II. Subjects of the Medals

III. General Index

Saint James 355
Saint Louis, Military Order of 272
Saint Michael 123, 243
Salamander 22
Salus 51
Salviati, Alamanno p. 46
Sangallo, Giuliano da p. 18
San Martino, Count Carlo Enrico di 115
Sansovino, Andrea p. 18, p. 25
Savoie, Louise de 22
Savoy, House of, medallic series p. 54; medals 207
Scales 28, 173, 317
Scarampi, Cardinal p. 16
Sciences, Fountain of 58
Sea 350
Seaport 114
Seminario Tridentino of Mexico to the Captive King of Spain 357
Serie iconografica numismatica dei piu famosi Italiani p. 59
Serpent 51, 201
Sforza, Costanzo p. 14
Sibyl 154
Sicily and southern Italy, aerial view 121
Siege of Guise 263
Silenus 145
Siren 11
Sixtus IV p. 19
Sheep 325
Shield 43, 185, 249, 288
Ship 78, 93, 101, 110, 162, 262, 324, 335
Skull 13
Snake 34, 38, 200, 221, 350
Sobieski, John p. 37
Soldani, *Bacco in Toscana* 145
Soldier 110
Spain, baptism of the Infante Carlo Clemente 128; personification of 128
Spear with banner 316
Spinola, Ugo p. 63
Stanislaus I 160
Stars 55, 101, 107, 109
Statue 238
Stemma 95, 130, 169, 177, 182, 197
Stork 53, 165
Stuckhardt, F. p. 54
Suhl p. 90
Sun 3, 106, 161
Sunrise 103
Swans 155
Swimmers 33
Sword 157, 249

Table 36, 164
Tasso, Torquato, biographer of 130
Temple 112
Temple of St. Michael 2
Thomas, J. G. p. 84
Thorwaldsen p. 81, p. 92
Three Graces 279
Tiolier, Pierre Joseph p. 78

Titian, portrait of his son Orazio 64
Titon du Tillet, Evrard 279
Tournon, François de 243
Town 113, 122, 168
Tragedy 127
Trains 310
Travani, Pietro p. 44
Tree 261, 300
Tree, dry 13
Trees, palm 206
Triangle 162, 193
Triumphal Arch at Naples 2
Trophies 79, 338
Truth 142
Tuileries palace 294
Turin, tyche of 226
Tyche of Paris 262
Tyche kneeling 160

Unicorn 3, 124
Uniform Series 264–266, 268–272
Urban VIII p. 34, 103
Urn 316

Vaccaro, Lorenzo 185
Valadier, Giuseppe 210
Val de Grâce 276
Valdor, Jean-Baptiste de p. 74
Valois, Charles de, duc d'Angoulême 22
Valois-Angoulême, Marguerite de 22
Vatican, Appartamenti Borgia 210
Vauthié p. 82
Venice 335; Loggetta of Campanile 225; S. Maria dei Frari 69; S. Nicolo Tolentino 179; St. Francesco della Vigna 56
Venus 321
Verona, meat market 191
Verona, Museum 334
Versailles, palace and gardens 269
Vesuvius 185
Victory 48, 79, 220, 240, 242, 250, 283, 287, 333, 353
Victory seated on weapons 336
Victory, winged 178
Virgin 344
Virtues 110
Virtus in armor 24
Vittoria, Alessandro 55
Vollgold p. 92

War 263
Weapons 26, 157, 263
Widemann, A. p. 48
Winds 78
Winged horse 59
William of Orange 253
Wolf 162
Wolrab, J. J. p. 90
Wreaths 261

Zeus 205
Zodiac 157
Zodiac band 205

IV. Inscriptions

CYRILLIC

АННА Б М ІМПЕ РАТРИЦАИСАМОΔЕР ЖИЦА ВСЕРОСС 338
МІР СТУРК ВОЗСТА 7 СЕНТ 1739 338
СЛАВА ІМПЕРИИ 338

GREEK

Ακαθαρτος γαριδοσκγισις 29
Αντ αυτουστιν εριστκιλερδ 68
Αντινοος ηρως 67
Αω 68
Γνωθι σαυτον και θεον 68
Εκ παλαιμοι μηνιζ ομενη 13
Ελενη λυδαια σγαρτης βασιλισσα 29
Ιππων 67
Ιωαννης ολαμιος 158
Ιωαννης βασιλευς και αυτοκρατωρ ρωμαιων ο παλαιολογος 1
Καδχαδονιοις 67
Κρατονμαι 34
Λυμζ 158
[Σ]ατyro[s] 320

HEBREW

חי דם עשוי לום ואדמא מלך באבש משיח 81
א ישו 81

LATIN ALPHABET

A bouy 310
A d ianuario f 186
A d f 334
A f 179
A franchi f 179
A g f 190
A gall perfid capto trident semin mdcccix 357
A guillemard f 189, 191
A ioue et sorore genita 55
A lavy f 226
A lodovico antonio muratori la patria 238
A s [f] 157
A teneris ad fata suprema 340
A travanus f 104
Abenoist eques ad vivum f 259
Abraham trecentos uernaculos expeditos numerat 42
Abramson 350
Academia philarmonica an mdcclv 334
Academiae reg scient paris astronomus acad londin berolin petrop holmi hafniens roter bruxel gotting dublin edimb bonon florent rom patav mant taurin bostoniensis monspel tolos & socius 1787 297
Accedo sed non sucedo oneri 76
Acquirit et seruat 167
Ad astra 187

INDEXES TO THE PLAQUETTES CATALOGUE

The numbers are those of the plaquettes. Page references are indicated in italics and are preceded by *p*.

III. General Index

IV. Inscriptions

267286

267286